Prentice Hall

Health

Teaching Resources

Boston, Massachusetts
Upper Saddle River, New Jersey

ISBN 0-13-181235-1

2 3 4 5 6 7 8 9 10 11 10 09 08 07

Contents

Contents (continued)

Contents (continued)

Contents *(continued)*

Name ______________________ Class ___________________ Date ______

Letter to Parents

Dear Parents:

In recent years, the term *health* has acquired a much greater significance. It no longer means simply an absence of sickness but refers to well-being of the body, of the mind, and of relationships among people. The word *wellness* is used for this comprehensive concept of health. From this concept comes Prentice Hall's new textbook, ***Prentice Hall Health.*** This is the text that your son or daughter will be using this school year.

Every day students are confronted with important decisions about how to maintain their health. They need to be well-informed enough to make decisions. They must also learn to act on this knowledge. To achieve this goal, ***Prentice Hall Health*** teaches and reinforces life skills students need to weigh options and to make responsible decisions that promote a healthy lifestyle.

Family involvement is a vital part of this health education process. While studying health, your son or daughter may come to you with questions or seek your help with community-related projects. These are opportunities for you to share in your teen's growth and development at a crucial time in his or her life. With your support, students can make the right choices to prepare for a healthy future.

To your good health,

____

Teacher

Name ______________________ Class __________________ Date ______

Carta a los Padres

Estimados padres:

En estos últimos años, el léxico *salud* ha adquirido un significado mucho más amplio. Ya no se refiere sólo a una ausencia de enfermedad, sino que alude al bienestar del cuerpo, de la mente y de las relaciones entre personas. Se usa la palabra *wellness* para describir este concepto comprensivo de la salud. De este concepto se crea el nuevo libro de texto de Prentice Hall, ***Prentice Hall Health.*** Éste es el texto que su hijo(a) usará durante este año escolar.

Cada día los alumnos se enfrentan a decisiones importantes de cómo pueden mantener la salud. Es necesario que estén lo suficientemente informados para tomar sus decisiones. También tienen que aprender a aplicar este conocimiento. Para alcanzar esta meta, ***Prentice Hall Health*** enseña y refuerza las habilidades de la vida que los alumnos necesitan para medir las alternativas y tomar unas decisiones responsables que promuevan un estilo de vida sano.

La participación de la familia es una parte integra de este proceso de la educación sobre la salud. Mientras estudie la salud, es posible que su hijo(a) vaya a hacerles preguntas o a pedirles ayuda con proyectos relacionados con la comunidad. Éstas son oportunidades para que ustedes puedan tomar parte en el crecimiento y el desarrollo de su hijo(a) en esta época decisiva de su vida. Con el apoyo de ustedes, los alumnos pueden tomar las decisiones apropiadas para prepararse para un futuro sano.

Que gocen de buena salud,

____

Maestro/a

Name ____________________ Class ____________________ Date ________

Chapter 1

Personal Inventory

Identifying Your Values

The decisions you make are influenced by your values—the things that really matter to you. This personal inventory will help you identify your values.

Place a check next to 9 of the following 18 items. Select the items that are most important to you or you think would make you the happiest.

_____ Being handsome or beautiful

_____ Being able to make your own decisions

_____ Having the talent to be a sucessful musician or artist

_____ Being guaranteed good health for the rest of your life

_____ Having the ability to eat as much as you like and never get fat

_____ Being considered a person that others can always rely on

_____ Being famous as a actor, politician, or other high-profile personality

_____ Having the skill to be the top athlete in the sport of your choice

_____ Having the chance for adventure, such as a trip into outer space

_____ Having close friends that you can always count on and trust

_____ Finding a cure for cancer or another deadly disease

_____ Having a warm, loving, and supportive family

_____ Inventing a device that would guarantee clean air and water forever

_____ Dying a peaceful, painless death at an old age

_____ Having friendships with famous, influential people

_____ Having a clear conscience and no regrets at the end of your life

_____ Being wealthy enough to buy anything you want

_____ Having the ability to end hunger and homelessness

Answer the following questions in the spaces provided.

1. Are there any items you would like to add to the list? If so, what are they?

____

____

____

2. Based on your choices, pick four words to describe what you care about most. Possible examples are fame, friendship, and the environment.

____

____

Name______________________ Class__________ Date__________ M T W T F

Section 1-1 What Is Health? Lesson Plan

Section Objectives

- **Describe** two factors that can be used to evaluate overall health.
- **List** three aspects of overall health.
- **Explain** how the choices that people make can affect their positions on the health continuum.

Vocabulary health • life expectancy • quality of life • goal • physical health • mental health • emotional health • social health • continuum • wellness

Time
1 period
1/2 block

Local Standards

1. FOCUS

Warm-Up: Health Stats Ask students to suggest possible reasons why life span increased during the 1900s.

Targeted Resources
- ❑ Transparency W1

2. TEACH

Addressing Misconceptions Explain why obesity may reverse the upward trend in life expectancy. L3

Class Discussion Use the example of older adults who are unable to renew a driver's license due to poor eyesight to discuss the concept of quality of life. L3

Visual Learning: Figure 1 Call on students to explain how the photos illustrate different aspects of health. L2

Differentiated Instruction Use concrete examples to make the aspects of health less abstract. L1

Teacher Demo Demonstrate a continuum by gradually increasing the volume of music. L2

Visual Learning: Figure 2 Ask students to identify where most people are on the health continuum and to explain why. L3

Targeted Resources
- ❑ RN Note Taking Guide 1-1 L3 EL
- ❑ ARN Note Taking Guide 1-1 L2
- ❑ Transparencies and Worksheets 1, 2
- ❑ TR Practice 1-1
- ❑ TR Enrich 1-1 L4
- ❑ Audio Summary 1-1 L1 L2 EL
- ❑ PHSchool.com: More on assessing your health

3. ASSESS

Evaluate Understanding The assignments listed in the Teacher's Edition can help you assess students' mastery of the section content.

Reteach Have students copy and label models of overall health and the health continuum. L2

Targeted Resources
- ❑ TR Section 1-1 Quiz
- ❑ CTB Chapter 1

KEY

L1 Special Needs	L4 Gifted and Talented
L2 Less Proficient Readers	EL English Language Learners
L3 All Students	

Name ______________________ Class ________________ Date ______

Section 1-1 **Practice**

Group Activity: Health Triangle

Overall health can be represented by a triangle. Each side of the triangle represents one aspect of health. Healthy behaviors can help you maintain your overall health.

Label each side of the triangle with one aspect of health. As a group, brainstorm healthy behaviors that can help maintain each aspect of health. Then record two healthy behaviors for each aspect of health.

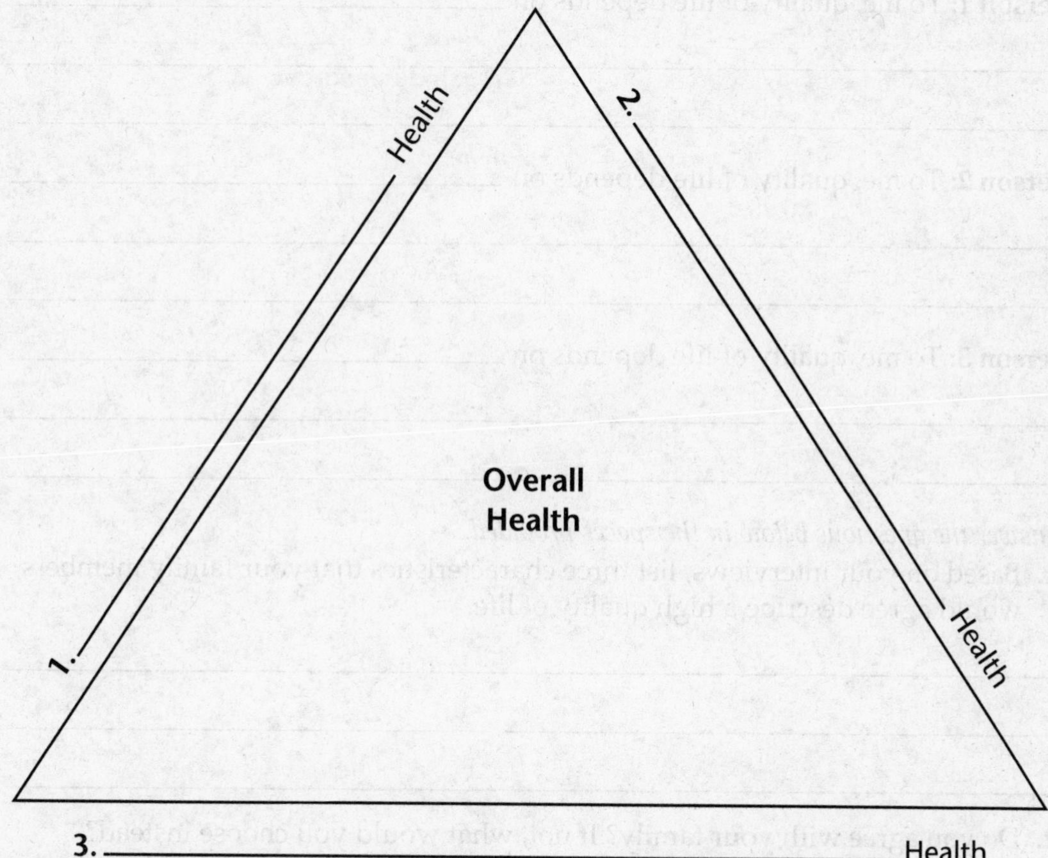

Healthy Behaviors:

1a. ______________________________

b. ______________________________

2a. ______________________________

b. ______________________________

3a. ______________________________

b. ______________________________

Name ______________________ Class __________________ Date ______

Section 1-1 **Enrich**

Family Involvement: Quality of Life

Quality of life is a subjective concept. It means different things to different people. One person might enjoy a life that is exciting and hectic, another person might want a life that is quiet and predictable. How do the members of your family define *quality of life*?

Interview family members about quality of life. What makes them feel happy and satisfied? Record their responses below. Use an extra sheet of paper if necessary.

Person 1: To me, quality of life depends on ______________________________

Person 2: To me, quality of life depends on ______________________________

Person 3: To me, quality of life depends on ______________________________

Answer the questions below in the spaces provided.

1. Based on your interviews, list three characteristics that your family members would agree describe a high quality of life.

2. Do you agree with your family? If not, what would you choose instead?

3. List two actions you could take throughout your life to help ensure a high quality of life for yourself.

Name ________________ Class ________________ Date ________

Section 1-1

Quiz

Write the letter of the correct answer in the space provided.

______ **1.** What is life expectancy?
a. the ability to find enjoyment in life
b. the only factor used to evaluate health
c. the average age of people in a population
d. the number of years a person is likely to live

______ **2.** The degree of overall satisfaction a person gets from life is called
a. quality of life.
b. quality of health.
c. life expectancy.
d. life satisfaction.

______ **3.** Which aspect of health refers to how you react to events in your life?
a. emotional health
b. physical health
c. mental health
d. social health

______ **4.** A trait associated with good social health is the ability to
a. learn from your mistakes.
b. get along well with others.
c. recognize your achievements.
d. do daily tasks without getting too tired.

______ **5.** A person at the midpoint of the health continuum is
a. very ill.
b. perfectly well.
c. neither ill nor perfectly well.
d. unable to move on the continuum.

Decide whether each statement is true or false. Write true *or* false *in the space provided.*

______ **6.** Health is the same as the absence of illness.

______ **7.** Life expectancy in the United States today is 90 years.

______ **8.** Physical health refers to how well your body functions.

______ **9.** Physical health is more important than mental and emotional health.

______ **10.** Your choices affect your position on the health continuum.

Name________________________ Class__________ Date__________ M T W T F

Section 1-2

Identifying Health Risks Lesson Plan

Section Objectives

- Identify factors that can influence a person's health.
- Describe three strategies you can use to evaluate risk factors.

Vocabulary heredity • gender • environment • culture • media • habit • risk factor

Time
2 periods
1 block

Local Standards

1. FOCUS

Warm-Up: Myth/Fact Ask students where they think people get information on health risks. Discuss the reliability of these sources.

Targeted Resources
- ❑ Transparency W2

2. TEACH

Cultural Connection Have students identify cultural differences that might affect health. EL

Building Health Skills Have students analyze what influence a medium other than television can have on health. L4

Building Media Literacy Have students develop a list of guidelines for evaluating health Web sites. L3

Class Discussion Invite the school nurse to class to discuss his or her role in providing healthcare to students. L1

Building Health Skills Ask students to think of excuses people might use for not breaking unhealthy habits. Then have them think of an argument to counter each excuse. L3

Cooperative Learning Have small groups of students brainstorm a list of risks and benefits for participating in a team sport. L2

Targeted Resources
- ❑ RN Note Taking Guide 1-2 L3 EL
- ❑ ARN Note Taking Guide 1-2 L2
- ❑ TR Practice 1-2
- ❑ TR Enrich 1-2 L4
- ❑ Audio Summary 1-2 L1 L2 EL
- ❑ PHSchool.com: More on risk factors

3. ASSESS

Evaluate Understanding The assignments listed in the Teacher's Edition can help you assess students' mastery of the section content.

Reteach Have students write paragraphs that address section objectives and use the vocabulary terms. L2

Targeted Resources
- ❑ TR Section 1-2 Quiz
- ❑ CTB Chapter 1

KEY

L1 Special Needs	L4 Gifted and Talented
L2 Less Proficient Readers	EL English Language Learners
L3 All Students	

Name ______________________ Class ____________________ Date ______

Section 1-2 **Practice**

Role-Playing: Influences on Health

Factors that influence health include heredity, environment, media, technology, healthcare, and behavior. Each factor can have a positive or negative influence on health. For example, television news programs can help you learn about health risks, but spending hours watching television can cause you to exercise less.

As a group, select one of the factors that influence health. Brainstorm a situation in which that factor could affect your health. Write a role-play about the situation. Use the spaces below to record your ideas. Then practice your role-play.

Factor: ____

Situation: ____

____

____

____

____

Overview of Role-Play:

____

____

____

____

____

____

____

____

____

____

____

____

____

____

Name ______________________ Class ____________________ Date ________

Section 1-2

Enrich

Family Involvement: Evaluating Health Risks

You make decisions every day that can have short- or long-term consequences for your health. In most cases, you probably make a decision without thinking about the risks involved in a given situation.

Read the situations below and identify the health risk for each situation, Also, decide what you could do to reduce the risk. After you record your answers, discuss the situations and your responses with a parent or other trusted adult.

1. You are going to a party where you know people will be drinking alcohol.

____

____

____

____

2. You have a bad cold, but you don't want to miss school.

____

____

____

____

3. You are out with friends who choose to have lunch in a fast-food restaurant.

____

____

____

____

4. A person at school has been spreading false rumors about you, which is making you very angry.

____

____

____

____

Name ______________________ Class ______________________ Date ________

Section 1-2

Quiz

Write the letter of the correct answer in the space provided.

______	**1.** all the traits that are passed biologically from parent to child	**a.** habit
______	**2.** all the physical and social conditions that surround a person	**b.** media
______	**3.** forms of communication that provide news and entertainment	**c.** heredity
______	**4.** behavior that is repeated so often it becomes almost automatic	**d.** gender
______	**5.** action or condition that increases the chances of illness or injury	**e.** risk factor
		f. environment

Write the letter of the correct answer in the space provided.

______ **6.** A person's culture is part of his or her
- **a.** heredity.
- **b.** indoor surroundings.
- **c.** social environment.
- **d.** physical environment.

______ **7.** People are more likely to take advantage of available healthcare if
- **a.** they need to take time off from work for a checkup.
- **b.** they must travel for over an hour to see a doctor.
- **c.** a clinic is open only during the day Monday through Friday.
- **d.** they have health insurance that pays for medications.

______ **8.** If you are tired because you stay up late watching television, the factor having a negative influence on your health is
- **a.** environment.
- **b.** technology.
- **c.** behavior.
- **d.** media.

______ **9.** You cannot control health risks that result from
- **a.** media.
- **b.** heredity.
- **c.** environment.
- **d.** behavior.

______ **10.** One way to evaluate health risks is to
- **a.** get enough sleep.
- **b.** break unhealthy habits.
- **c.** consider consequences.
- **d.** engage in risk-free behaviors.

Name__________________ Class__________ Date__________ M T W T F

Section 1-3

Taking Responsibility for Your Health

Lesson Plan

Section Objectives

- **Describe** the broad goals of *Healthy People 2010.*
- **Identify** three steps you can take to meet your personal goals.

Vocabulary prevention • values • action plan • advocacy • health literacy

Time
1 period
1/2 block

Local Standards

1. FOCUS

Warm-Up: Quick Quiz Have students use the quiz to evaluate how responsible they are about their own health.

Targeted Resources

- ❑ Transparency W3

2. TEACH

Building Vocabulary To help teach the important concept of prevention, explain that the word *prevention* comes from a Latin word meaning "to anticipate." EL

Visual Learning: Figure 7 Ask students to identify causes of death that are due to injury or violence and explain why these deaths can be prevented. L2

Building Media Literacy Have students compare the treatment of a current health topic in different print media. L3

Differentiated Instruction Ask students to identify teen-relevant target goals of *Healthy People 2010.* L4

Journal Writing Have students record one or two goals they would like to achieve in the next few months and write an action plan to achieve those goals. L3

Targeted Resources

- ❑ RN Note Taking Guide 1-3 L3 EL
- ❑ ARN Note Taking Guide 1-3 L2
- ❑ Transparency and Worksheet 3
- ❑ TR Practice 1-3
- ❑ TR Enrich 1-3 L4
- ❑ Audio Summary 1-3 L1 L2 EL
- ❑ Health Links: Updates on communication skills

3. ASSESS

Evaluate Understanding The assignments listed in the Teacher's Edition can help you assess students' mastery of the section content.

Reteach Call on students to name the seven health skills. Call on other students to give examples of the skills. L2

Targeted Resources

- ❑ TR Section 1-3 Quiz
- ❑ CTB Chapter 1

KEY

L1 Special Needs
L2 Less Proficient Readers
L3 All Students
L4 Gifted and Talented
EL English Language Learners

Name ____________________ Class ____________________ Date ________

Section 1-3 **Practice**

Class Activity: Healthful Behaviors

This exercise is designed to help your learn more about healthful behaviors (and get to know your classmates at the same time).

Obtain a signature for each behavior described below. You must get a different signature for each behavior.

Description	Signature
1. Someone who always wears a seat belt in a car.	________
2. Someone who exercises at least three times a week.	________
3. Someone who recycles paper and bottles.	________
4. Someone who has a dental checkup every six months.	________
5. Someone who recently made an important decision.	________
6. Someone who usually reads food labels.	________
7. Someone who has refused an alcoholic beverage.	________
8. Someone who adds little or no salt to food.	________
9. Someone who had an eye test within the last year.	________
10. Someone who had a physical examination in the past year.	________
11. Someone who eats fresh vegetables every day.	________
12. Someone who warms up for 10 minutes before exercising.	________
13. Someone who goes to sleep at a regular time each night.	________
14. Someone who brushes his or her teeth after every meal.	________
15. Someone who does volunteer work.	________
16. Someone who can discuss problems with a trusted adult.	________
17. Someone who is good at managing his or her time.	________
18. Someone who wears a helmet while riding a bicycle.	________

Name ______________ Class ______________ Date ______

Section 1-3 **Enrich**

Community Involvement: Healthy Behaviors

Behavior can have a major impact on health. How healthy are the behaviors of people in your community? Do community members practice behaviors that improve their health or behaviors that put their health at risk?

Ask five people of different ages from your community to respond to the questions below. Use the following scale for responses: 1 = always, 2 = sometimes, and 3 = never.

Community Health Survey					
Questions	**Person 1**	**Person 2**	**Person 3**	**Person 4**	**Person 5**
Do you exercise at least three times a week?					
Do you wear a seat belt when in a motor vehicle?					
Do you avoid smoking or chewing tobacco?					
Do you avoid foods that are high in fat?					
Do you make time to rest and relax each day?					
Do you share your feelings with family or friends?					

Answer the following questions in the spaces provided.

1. In which areas could the people surveyed practice healthier behaviors?

____

____

2. Based on your answer to Question 1, what services or programs might your community offer to help community members improve their health?

____

____

____

Name ______________________ Class ______________________ Date ________

Section 1-3

Quiz

Decide whether each statement is true or false. Write true *or* false *in the space provided.*

______ **1.** A specific goal of *Healthy People 2010* is to increase seat belt use.

______ **2.** The leading causes of death for young people are related to behaviors.

______ **3.** Knowing how to locate a doctor is an example of making decisions.

______ **4.** One of the steps in analyzing influences is to make an action plan.

______ **5.** Health literacy is the ability to gather, understand, and use health knowledge.

Write the letter of the correct answer in the space provided.

______ **6.** What does the term *prevention* mean?
a. increasing years of healthy life
b. eliminating differences in health
c. being productive at school and work
d. acting to avoid negative health outcomes

______ **7.** What is an example of gaining awareness about a health problem?
a. having your blood pressure measured during a medical checkup
b. reading about the effects of high blood pressure
c. taking medication to lower blood pressure
d. communicating the dangers of high blood pressure to others

______ **8.** Figuring out why you choose to eat certain foods is an example of
a. accessing information.
b. analyzing influences.
c. making decisions.
d. communicating.

______ **9.** In the DECIDE process, the letter I stands for Identify your
a. values.
b. results.
c. actions.
d. decisions.

______ **10.** How is communication generally used in advocacy?
a. to gather and understand health information
b. to make a plan for breaking an unhealthy habit
c. to practice new behaviors until they become habits
d. to influence others in making positive health decisions

Name______________________ Class__________ Date__________ M T W T F

Section 1-4

Being a Wise Health Consumer Lesson Plan

Section Objectives

- **Describe** how to evaluate health products, services, and information.
- **Evaluate** what advertising does and does not do for a consumer.
- **Explain** how a person can avoid health fraud.
- **Identify** your rights as a consumer.

Time
2 periods
1 block

Local Standards

Vocabulary consumer • warranty • advertising • fraud • quackery

1. FOCUS

Warm-Up: Advice Line Call on students to explain which of two shampoos they would buy and how they could learn more about the products.

Targeted Resources

- ❑ Transparency W4

2. TEACH

Cooperative Learning Have pairs of students identify items in advertising flyers as *consumable* and *durable*. EL

Differentiated Instruction Have students use empty product packages or inserts to find information about products. L1

Addressing Misconceptions Discuss the use of infomercials to convince viewers that the information presented is reliable. L3

Journal Writing Have students write a journal entry analyzing a consumer decision they made based on advertising. L3

Class Discussion Discuss factors that make people susceptible to health fraud. L2

Differentiated Instruction Have students prepare a graphic roadmap for services and data available on the Web site for your state's office of the attorney general. L4

Targeted Resources

- ❑ RN Note Taking Guide 1-4 L3 EL
- ❑ ARN Note Taking Guide 1-4 L2
- ❑ Transparency and Worksheet 4
- ❑ TR Practice 1-4
- ❑ TR Enrich 1-4 L4
- ❑ Audio Summary 1-4 L1 L2 EL
- ❑ Health Links: Updates on fraud, quackery, and health

3. ASSESS

Evaluate Understanding The assignments listed in the Teacher's Edition can help you assess students' mastery of the section content.

Reteach Have students write questions based on the figures. Have pairs of students exchange and answer each other's questions. L2

Targeted Resources

- ❑ TR Section 1-4 Quiz
- ❑ CTB Chapter 1

KEY

L1 Special Needs	L4 Gifted and Talented
L2 Less Proficient Readers	EL English Language Learners
L3 All Students	

Name ______________________ Class __________________ Date ______

Section 1-4

Practice

Skill-Building Activity: Advertising Methods

Assume you work for a company that produces advertising. You have been asked to write an advertisement for a new athletic shoe. The ad is being targeted to teens. The manufacturer wants to see a few different approaches.

Write six different messages to advertise the shoe, one for each advertising method listed below. Refer to Figure 12 on page 21 of your textbook for a description of each method.

Scientific studies:

____

____

____

Bandwagon approach:

____

____

____

Testimonial:

____

____

____

Comparison to other products:

____

____

____

Emotional appeal:

____

____

____

Price appeal:

____

____

____

Name ______________________ Class ______________________ Date __________

Section 1-4 **Enrich**

Consumer Skills: DECIDE Which Bicycle to Buy

Assume that you want to buy a bicycle so you can increase the amount of exercise you get. For about the same amount of money, you can buy a bicycle that is meant to be used outdoors or a stationary exercise bicycle that you can use indoors.

Use the table below to apply DECIDE to this decision. For the last step of the process, explain how you would evaluate the results if you actually bought one of the bicycles.

Applying the DECIDE Process	
Define the problem	
Explore the alternatives	
Consider the consequences	
Identify your values	
Decide and act	
Evaluate the results	

Answer the questions below in the spaces provided.

1. Did using DECIDE make it easier to choose a bicycle? Why or why not?

____

____

____

2. What are some other consumer decisions you could use DECIDE to make?

____

____

Name ______________________ Class ______________________ Date __________

Section 1-4

Quiz

Write the letter of the correct answer in the space provided.

______ **1.** Which is a consumable product?
a. soap
b. helmet
c. bicycle
d. CD player

______ **2.** An example of a service is a(an)
a. hair cut.
b. new pair of shoes.
c. battery-powered radio.
d. reconditioned video game.

______ **3.** To evaluate health information, you need to consider
a. safety.
b. the source.
c. the warranty.
d. consumer testing.

______ **4.** What is the message of the bandwagon approach in advertising?
a. The product is more effective than others.
b. The product is safest for you and your family.
c. The product gives you more for your money.
d. Everyone is using the product, and so should you.

______ **5.** Which is a consumer right?
a. right to information
b. right to a lower price
c. right to pay sales tax
d. right to free shipping

Write the letter of the correct answer in the space provided.

______ **6.** someone who buys products or services for personal use

______ **7.** offer to repair or replace a product if there is a problem

______ **8.** public promotion of a product or service

______ **9.** lying to obtain money or property

______ **10.** selling useless medical treatments or products

a. fraud
b. warranty
c. quackery
d. consumer
e. advertising
f. certification

Name ____________________ Class ____________________ Date ____________

Chapter 1 Test

Write the letter of the correct answer in the space provided.

_____ **1.** If you have good mental health,
a. your mind is alert.
b. you never make a mistake.
c. your body functions well.
d. your feelings are appropriate to events.

_____ **2.** Which is part of your social environment?
a. air quality
b. noise levels
c. video games
d. family members

_____ **3.** An often-repeated behavior that becomes almost automatic is a(an)
a. action plan.
b. value.
c. habit.
d. goal.

_____ **4.** Janine is gaining knowledge about a health problem when she
a. is told that her upper teeth stick out too far.
b. learns that braces can be used to move teeth.
c. has braces placed on her upper teeth.
d. has the braces removed from her teeth.

_____ **5.** Which is a warning sign of quackery?
a. A product costs less than similar products.
b. A product is said to contain common ingredients.
c. Claims for a product seem too good to be true.
d. A product is recommended by a doctor.

Write the letter of the correct answer in the space provided.

_____ **6.** overall well-being of body, mind, and relationships
_____ **7.** result a person aims for and works hard to reach
_____ **8.** beliefs and behaviors shared by a group of people
_____ **9.** standards and beliefs that are most important to you
_____ **10.** advertising method involving trustworthy people

a. goal
b. values
c. culture
d. health
e. action plan
f. testimonial

Name ______________________ Class ____________________ Date ________

Chapter 1: Test *(continued)*

Decide whether each statement is true or false. Write true *or* false *in the space provided.*

______ **11.** Your location on the health continuum never changes.

______ **12.** Your gender has no influence on your health.

______ **13.** "Decide and act" is the first step in the DECIDE process.

______ **14.** Ads rarely provide information needed to make wise choices.

______ **15.** Consumers have the right to be protected by government agencies.

Write the word that best completes each sentence in the space provided.

16. A gradual progression through many stages between two extremes is a(an) ________________.

17. Trying to influence someone to make healthy decisions describes the health skill of ________________.

18. Someone who buys products or services for personal use is called a(an) ________________.

Use complete sentences to answer the following questions.

19. Describe three strategies you can use to evaluate health risk factors.

____

____

____

____

____

____

20. Identify three steps you can take to meet your personal health goals.

____

____

____

____

____

____

Name ______________________ Class ______________________ Date __________

Chapter 2

Personal Inventory

Describing Yourself

This survey will help you understand how you tend to think, feel, and behave. Read each statement and decide how it applies to you. Put a checkmark in the appropriate column.

Statements	Always	Usually	Sometimes	Seldom/ Never
I like myself.				
I trust my own opinions.				
I appreciate my strengths.				
I am proud of my accomplishments.				
I can accept compliments.				
I avoid putting myself down.				
I can accept criticism.				
I don't have to be perfect.				
I can cope effectively with most situations.				
I like to set goals for myself and then accomplish them.				
I get along well with people.				
I have some good friends.				
I like meeting different people.				
I accept things about myself that I can't change.				
I learn from my mistakes.				
I am aware of my feelings.				
I share my feelings with others.				
When I am angry, I express my anger in an appropriate way.				

Look over your responses. Are there ways you typically think, feel, or behave that you would like to change? Why?

____

____

Name________________________ Class__________ Date__________ M T W T F

Section 2-1

Personality — Lesson Plan

Section Objectives

- **Name** five traits that are used to define personality.
- **Identify** two factors that determine how your personality develops.
- **Describe** what happens to personality over a lifetime.

Vocabulary personality • psychologist • modeling • peer group • identity

Time
2 periods
1 block

Local Standards

1. FOCUS

Warm-Up: Quick Quiz Ask students to identify behaviors that would support different ratings. Have them predict whether their answers might change in the future.

Targeted Resources

- ❑ Transparency W5

2. TEACH

Building Vocabulary Have students use the word parts *intro-* and *extro-* to determine the meaning of *introvert* and *extrovert*. L2

Cooperative Learning Have students work with a partner to make a list of adjectives that can describe personality traits. EL

Building Health Skills Ask students to identify specific actions they could take to model agreeableness. Have them make posters to encourage others to use these actions. L2

Cultural Connection Discuss the tendency of some people to assign positive or negative personality traits to individuals based on their culture. L3

Differentiated Instruction Have students debate the usefulness of personality tests. L4

Visual Learning: Figure 4 Help students relate the content of a photograph to the challenge faced at the related life stage. L1

Targeted Resources

- ❑ RN Note Taking Guide 2-1 L3 EL
- ❑ ARN Note Taking Guide 2-1 L2
- ❑ TR Practice 2-1
- ❑ TR Enrich 2-1 L4
- ❑ Audio Summary 2-1 L1 L2 EL
- ❑ PHSchool.com: More on personality

3. ASSESS

Evaluate Understanding The assignments listed in the Teacher's Edition can help you assess students' mastery of the section content.

Reteach Have students analyze and describe the personality traits of a character from a book, movie, or television program. L2

Targeted Resources

- ❑ TR Section 2-1 Quiz
- ❑ CTB Chapter 2

KEY

L1 Special Needs	L4 Gifted and Talented
L2 Less Proficient Readers	EL English Language Learners
L3 All Students	

Name ______________________ Class ______________________ Date __________

Section 2-1 **Practice**

Skill-Building Activity: Personality Traits

A good test of your understanding of a concept is to try explaining the concept to another person. Find a person who is willing to talk with you about his or her personality. Use your communication skills to interview the person. Tell the person that you will keep his or her identity private.

Describe each central personality trait. After you describe a trait, ask the person to select a rating on a scale of 1 to 5 for the trait. Circle the appropriate number on the worksheet. Then ask the person to provide a reason for the rating.

Extroversion

Rating: 1 2 3 4 5

Reason:

____

____

Agreeableness

Rating: 1 2 3 4 5

Reason:

____

____

Conscientiousness

Rating: 1 2 3 4 5

Reason:

____

____

Emotional Stability

Rating: 1 2 3 4 5

Reason:

____

____

Openness to Experience

Rating: 1 2 3 4 5

Reason:

____

____

Name ______________________ Class ______________________ Date ________

Section 2-1

Enrich

Family Involvement: Different Views

How would you describe yourself? Do you think others see you in the same way? Complete this activity to find out.

On the lines provided in the first box, fill in adjectives that you would use to describe yourself. Then share your responses with two family members to see if they agree or disagree with your responses. Record their responses in the appropriate boxes.

Adjective	Parent/Guardian	Sibling/Other

1. With which responses did your family members agree?

____

____

2. With which responses did your family members disagree?

____

____

3. How would you explain any differences in the responses?

____

____

____

____

____

Name ______________________ Class ____________________ Date ______

Section 2-1

Quiz

Write the letter of the correct answer in the space provided.

______	**1.** copying the behavior of others	**a.**	peer group
______	**2.** a person who studies how people think, feel, and behave	**b.**	identity
		c.	modeling
______	**3.** people whose ages and interests are similar	**d.**	psychologist
______	**4.** behaviors, attitudes, feelings, and ways of thinking	**e.**	personality
		f.	introvert
______	**5.** the sense of self		

Decide whether each statement is true or false. Write true *or* false *in the space provided.*

______ **6.** An extrovert is shy, quiet, and reserved.

______ **7.** Conscientious people tend to be dependable and usually make good decisions.

______ **8.** Personality traits are influenced by a combination of heredity and environment.

______ **9.** The main challenge of infancy is to develop trust in others.

______**10.** Nurturing is the main task of young adults.

Name_______________________ Class__________ Date__________ M T W T F

Section 2-2

Self-Esteem — Lesson Plan

Section Objectives

- **Compare** the effects of high and low self-esteem on health.
- **Describe** the changes in self-esteem that can occur as people age.
- **Identify** ways to achieve and maintain high self-esteem.
- **Summarize** Maslow's theory of self-actualization.

Vocabulary self-esteem • self-actualization • hierarchy of needs

Time
2 periods
1 block

Local Standards

1. FOCUS

Warm-Up: Health Stats Ask students to identify responses to a survey about self-esteem that surprised them and explain why.

Targeted Resources
- ❑ Transparency W6

2. TEACH

Building Health Skills Have students describe the possible responses of people with high and low self-esteem to common challenges. L2

Active Learning Have the class make a bulletin board that celebrates one strength or ability of each student in the class. Challenge students to think beyond typical examples of talents. L3

Differentiated Instruction Have students make a poster of actions and activities that make them feel good about themselves. L1

Focus on Issues Use the graph in Figure 6 to discuss gender differences in self-esteem. L3

Cooperative Learning Have students practice giving and receiving compliments that do not focus on personal appearance. EL

Visual Learning: Figure 8 Have students relate the content of the photographs to the levels in Maslow's hierarchy of needs. L2

Targeted Resources
- ❑ RN Note Taking Guide 2-2 L3 EL
- ❑ ARN Note Taking Guide 2-2 L2
- ❑ Transparency and Worksheet 6
- ❑ TR Practice 2-2
- ❑ TR Enrich 2-2 L4
- ❑ Audio Summary 2-2 L1 L2 EL
- ❑ Health Links: Updates on building healthy self-esteem

3. ASSESS

Evaluate Understanding The assignments listed in the Teacher's Edition can help you assess students' mastery of the section content.

Reteach Have students make posters that show actions or activities that could be used to improve self-esteem. L2

Targeted Resources
- ❑ TR Section 2-2 Quiz
- ❑ CTB Chapter 2

KEY

L1 Special Needs	L4 Gifted and Talented
L2 Less Proficient Readers	EL English Language Learners
L3 All Students	

Name ______________ Class ______________ Date ______

Section 2-2 **Practice**

Role-Playing: Self-Esteem

A person's level of self-esteem may affect his or her responses to the everyday challenges of life. You can demonstrate your understanding of this impact by working with a partner to write a role-play. After you perform your role-play, the audience should be able to tell which character has a higher level of self-esteem.

Identify a challenge that is commonly faced by teens. Then, write a role-play that shows how two teens with different levels of self-esteem might respond to that challenge.

Challenge: ______________

Characters: ______________

Setting: ______________

Student 1: ______________

Student 2: ______________

Student 1: ______________

Student 2: ______________

Student 1: ______________

Student 2: ______________

Student 1: ______________

Student 2: ______________

Student 1: ______________

Student 2: ______________

Name ______________________ Class ________________ Date ______

Section 2-2 **Enrich**

Community Involvement: Developing Self-Esteem

Some people seem to be born with high self-esteem. Some acquire it, or lose it, at various times during their lives. Learning about the traits of people with high self-esteem may help you boost your own self-esteem.

Interview a person whom you think has high self-esteem. Ask these questions.

1. Name of person interviewed ______________________
2. What three adjectives would you use to describe yourself?
____
3. What events or people have influenced your level of self-esteem?
____
4. Have you always had a high level of self-esteem, or has your level of self-esteem changed during your life? ______________________
5. What factors do you think contribute to high self-esteem?
____
6. What tips do you have for teens who want to improve their self-esteem?
____

After the interview, work with another student. Compare the responses you received to your questions and your impressions of the person you interviewed.

7. What traits, if any, did the people you interviewed have in common?
____
8. Identify two key factors that can influence a person's self-esteem.
____

Name ______________________ Class ____________________ Date ______

Section 2-2

Quiz

Write the letter of the correct answer in the space provided.

______ **1.** What might a person with high self-esteem say to explain a poor grade on a test?
a. I'm not smart enough.
b. I didn't study enough.
c. I never do well on tests.
d. The teacher doesn't like me.

______ **2.** On average, which person is most likely to have the highest self-esteem?
a. a male who is 15
b. a female who is 15
c. a male who is 50
d. a female who is 50

______ **3.** What term refers to how much a person respects and likes himself or herself?
a. self-actualized
b. identity
c. personality
d. self-esteem

______ **4.** According to Maslow, which human needs are the *most* basic?
a. safety needs
b. belonging needs
c. esteem needs
d. physical needs

______ **5.** Which of the following is a personality trait of a self-actualized person?
a. unrealistic
b. afraid to be different
c. unprejudiced
d. dependent

Decide whether each statement is true or false. Write true or false in the space provided.

______ **6.** Some psychologists think high self-esteem has a positive impact on health.

______ **7.** Focusing on your appearance may lower your self-esteem.

______ **8.** During adolescence most people have very high levels of self-esteem.

______ **9.** Physical needs include the need for food, water, and sleep.

______ **10.** Maslow thought that the approval of others was more important than self-esteem.

Name____________________ Class________ Date________ M T W T F

Section 2-3 Expressing Your Emotions Lesson Plan

Section Objectives

- **Identify** four primary emotions and three learned emotions.
- **Explain** why it is important to recognize your emotions.
- **Distinguish** helpful from harmful coping strategies.

Time
2 periods
1 block

Local Standards

Vocabulary emotion • primary emotion • grief • learned emotion • coping strategy • defense mechanism

1. FOCUS

Warm-Up: Myth/Fact After students have completed their writing, discuss examples of situations in which it might not be healthy to "let your feelings out."

Targeted Resources
- ❑ Transparency W7

2. TEACH

Differentiated Instruction Ask students to use symbols, words, or sentences to define and describe four primary emotions. **EL**

Cultural Connection Discuss strategies for avoiding misunderstandings caused by cultural differences in the way emotions are expressed. **L3**

Building Health Skills Have students analyze how drawings in graphic novels are used to express emotions and the influence these novels may have on how students express emotions. **L2**

Addressing Misconceptions Address the misconception that coping strategies are always positive. **L2**

Visual Learning: Figure 12 Have students suggest alternate strategies for dealing with the situations described. **L2**

Targeted Resources
- ❑ RN Note Taking Guide 2-3 **L3** **EL**
- ❑ ARN Note Taking Guide 2-3 **L2**
- ❑ Transparency and Worksheet 7
- ❑ TR Practice 2-3
- ❑ TR Enrich 2-3 **L4**
- ❑ Audio Summary 2-3 **L1** **L2** **EL**
- ❑ Health Links: Updates on emotions

3. ASSESS

Evaluate Understanding The assignments listed in the Teacher's Edition can help you assess students' mastery of the section content.

Reteach Have students pantomime the primary emotions and identify healthy ways to deal with each emotion. **L2**

Targeted Resources
- ❑ TR Section 2-3 Quiz
- ❑ CTB Chapter 2

KEY

L1 Special Needs
L2 Less Proficient Readers
L3 All Students
L4 Gifted and Talented
EL English Language Learners

Name ______________________ Class ______________________ Date ________

Section 2-3

Practice

Group Activity: Defense Mechanisms

The use of defense mechanisms can keep you from recognizing and dealing with your true feelings. If you understand defense mechanisms you can make sure that you do not overuse these coping strategies.

For each situation, discuss as a group how a person using the given defense mechanism might respond to the situation. Record a sentence that summarizes the group's response. Then identify and record a healthier way to cope with the situation.

Situation 1: Your sister stepped on and broke your radio, which was lying on the floor.

Projection: ____

____

Healthier Strategy: ____

____

Situation 2: You forgot about a major homework assignment until the day it was due.

Reaction Formation: ____

____

Healthier Strategy: ____

____

Situation 3: You got caught copying from a friend on a test.

Rationalization: ____

____

Healthier Strategy: ____

____

Situation 4: You are grounded because you stayed out later than your curfew without calling home.

Regression: ____

____

Healthier Strategy: ____

____

Name ______________________ Class ______________________ Date ________

Section 2-3 **Enrich**

Consumer Skills: Analyzing Advertisements

You have probably seen an advertisement that made you feel like you needed a particular product. After careful thought, you might have realized that you did not need that product at all! What was it about the advertisement that made you want something you didn't need? Many advertisements are designed to appeal to your emotions, rather than your logic.

Advertisements often use happiness, guilt, and fear. For each emotion, identify and describe one specific example of a print, radio, or television advertisement that appeals to that emotion. Provide evidence to support your choice.

Emotion: Happiness

Example: ______________________

Description: ______________________

Emotion: Guilt

Example: ______________________

Description: ______________________

Emotion: Fear

Example: ______________________

Description: ______________________

Name ______________________ Class ______________________ Date ______

Section 2-3

Quiz

Write the letter of the correct answer in the space provided.

______	**1.** refusing to recognize an emotion	**a.** denial
______	**2.** excelling in one area to make up for a weakness in another area	**b.** regression
______	**3.** making excuses for an action	**c.** projection
______	**4.** acting opposite of the way you feel	**d.** compensation
______	**5.** blaming another person for your faults	**e.** rationalization
		f. reaction formation

Write the letter of the correct answer in the space provided.

______ **6.** Emotions that are expressed by people in all cultures are called
a. social emotions.
b. primary emotions.
c. learned emotions.
d. coping emotions.

______ **7.** Which of these is a learned emotion?
a. happiness
b. sadness
c. guilt
d. anger

______ **8.** Shame is a feeling
a. of affection and concern.
b. of intense rage.
c. that you did something wrong.
d. that you are a bad person.

______ **9.** What is the first step toward dealing with emotions in healthy ways?
a. recognizing your emotions
b. recognizing your use of defense mechanisms
c. recognizing your coping strategies
d. recognizing your cultural values

______ **10.** Which defense mechanism involves using immature behaviors to express emotions?
a. regression
b. projection
c. rationalization
d. compensation

Name ______________________ Class ____________________ Date ________

Chapter 2 **Test**

Write the letter of the correct answer in the space provided.

_____ **1.** Which personality trait describes how responsible and self-disciplined you are?
a. extroversion
b. agreeableness
c. conscientiousness
d. emotional stability

_____ **2.** Why is the self-esteem of adults usually higher than that of teens?
a. Adults are very critical of their appearance.
b. Adults are better able to keep things in the proper perspective.
c. Adults tend to set unrealistic standards for themselves.
d. Adults often judge themselves harshly.

_____ **3.** Which of these is a safety need of humans?
a. food **b.** shelter
c. water **d.** sleep

_____ **4.** Which of the following emotions can be helpful in stopping people from doing something they know is wrong?
a. anger **b.** grief
c. sadness **d.** guilt

_____ **5.** What is another term for your sense of self?
a. identity
b. introvert
c. environment
d. personality

Write the letter of the correct answer in the space provided.

_____ **6.** the challenge for infants — **a.** developing trust
_____ **7.** the challenge for teens — **b.** taking initiative
_____ **8.** the challenge for young adults — **c.** looking back with acceptance
_____ **9.** the challenge of middle adulthood — **d.** establishing intimacy
_____ **10.** the challenge of older adulthood — **e.** searching for identity
f. creating and nurturing

Name ______________________ Class ____________________ Date ________

Chapter 2: **Test** *(continued)*

Decide whether each statement is true or false. Write true *or* false *in the space provided.*

______ **11.** Self-esteem is usually low during adolescence.

______ **12.** A self-actualized person usually is realistic, fair, and creative.

______ **13.** Guilt is a primary emotion.

______ **14.** Coping strategies are always helpful in dealing with problems.

______ **15.** The experiences you have influence your personality.

Write the word that best completes each sentence in the space provided.

16. Personality traits are influenced by __________ and environment.

17. How much you like and respect yourself is ____________________.

18. Emotions that are not expressed in the same way by all people are

____________________ emotions.

Use complete sentences to answer the following questions.

19. Identify and describe two steps you can take to boost your self-esteem.

____

____

____

____

____

____

20. Why is it important to recognize your emotions? What are three steps you can take to help you recognize your emotions?

____

____

____

____

____

____

____

Name ____________________ Class ____________________ Date ________

Chapter 3

Personal Inventory

Skills for Managing Stress

Imagine the following potentially stressful situations. How do you usually respond to each of them?

1. When I have too much to do and not enough time to do it,

   I usually ____________________

2. When I make a big mistake,

   I usually ____________________

3. When I am very late for something important,

   I usually ____________________

4. When I am really angry with someone I care about,

   I usually ____________________

5. When I cannot do something I want to do,

   I usually ____________________

6. When I lose something that is important to me,

   I usually ____________________

Look over your responses. What two techniques do you use most often to deal with stress? ____________________

____

How often do you use each of these skills? Put checks in the appropriate columns.

Stress Management Skills	Always	Usually	Sometimes	Seldom/ Never
Confronting the problem				
Time management				
Physical activity				
Relaxation				
Mental rehearsal				
Biofeedback				
Avoiding negative thinking				
Humor				
Reaching out for support				

Name______________________ Class__________ Date__________ M T W T F

Section 3-1 **What Causes Stress?** **Lesson Plan**

Section Objectives

- **Describe** what causes a person to experience stress.
- **Identify** four general types of stressors.

Vocabulary stress • eustress • distress • stressor • catastrophe

Time
1 period
1/2 block

Local Standards

1. FOCUS

Warm-Up: Myth/Fact Ask students to write and share reasons a certain situation might cause stress. Then discuss a myth about stress to assess students' understanding of stress.

Targeted Resources
- ❑ Transparency W8

2. TEACH

Building Vocabulary Have students use the meanings of *eu-*, and *dis-* to define the terms *eustress* and *distress*. L2

Cooperative Learning Ask students to take a school survey about stressors, rank the stressors identified by frequency, and classify them as major life changes or everyday problems. L3

Differentiated Instruction Give students a simple example to explain the terms *stress* and *stressor*. L1

Cultural Connection Discuss reasons why acculturation can be stressful. EL

Building Media Literacy Ask students to find three different articles about the same catastrophe and analyze the coverage. L3

Targeted Resources
- ❑ RN Note Taking Guide 3-1 L3 EL
- ❑ ARN Note Taking Guide 3-1 L2
- ❑ TR Practice 3-1
- ❑ TR Enrich 3-1 L4
- ❑ Audio Summary 3-1 L1 L2 EL
- ❑ Health Links: Updates on stress

3. ASSESS

Evaluate Understanding The assignments listed in the Teacher's Edition can help you assess students' mastery of the section content.

Reteach Work with students to make a concept map of major types of stressors, including examples of each type. L2

Targeted Resources
- ❑ TR Section 3-1 Quiz
- ❑ CTB Chapter 3

KEY

L1 Special Needs	L4 Gifted and Talented
L2 Less Proficient Readers	EL English Language Learners
L3 All Students	

Name ______________________ Class ____________________ Date ______

Section 3-1

Practice

Concept Check: Classifying Stressors

Stress is how your mind and body respond to a threat or challenge. Something that causes stress is called a *stressor.* Stressors can cause positive stress, or *eustress,* and negative stress, or *distress.*

Read the story, and underline situations and events that might be stressors.

At 7:30 on a snowy evening, Vince and the other members of his band are setting up for their first big performance. They are the opening band at a concert to raise money for hurricane relief. The hurricane destroyed hundreds of homes.

Vince feels good about helping the relief effort, but so far nothing has gone right. Before he could leave for the concert hall, he had to spend 20 minutes shoveling his car out of the snow. Kenji couldn't find his favorite drumsticks, and Vince is worried that the hall is too cold for him to keep his guitar in tune. Rashinda is distracted because she just found out that her sister is getting married.

After tuning his guitar, Vince looks up and sees the first members of the audience arriving. Rashinda gives him a thumbs-up sign, and he starts to grin. It's time to go to work.

Answer the following questions in the spaces provided.

1. Identify one example of each general type of stressor.

   Major life change: ______________________

   Catastrophe: ______________________

   Everyday problem: ______________________

   Environmental problem: ______________________

2. Select a stressor you underlined that you think might cause distress, and explain why.

   ____

   ____

   ____

3. Select a stressor you underlined that you think might cause eustress, and explain why.

   ____

   ____

   ____

Name ______________________ Class ______________________ Date ________

Section 3-1 **Enrich**

Family Involvement: Ranking Major Life Changes

Experts have created stress scales for many major life changes. The scales rank the changes based on how stressful they are to most people. The chart below lists ten major life changes in order from most stressful (10) to least stressful (1).

Stress Rankings of Ten Major Life Changes

Life Change	Ranking
Death of parent or spouse	10
Serious personal illness or injury	9
Change in health of family member	8
New baby in family	7
Death of close friend	6
Important personal achievement	5
Parent loses job	4
Move to new house or apartment	3
Change to different school	2
Older brother or sister leaves home	1

Write each life change on an index card, shuffle the cards, and ask one or more members of your family to place the cards in order from most to least stressful. Use the chart below to record how family members ranked the changes, with 10 being most stressful and 1 being least stressful.

Family Stress Rankings of Ten Major Life Changes

Life Change	Ranking
	10
	9
	8
	7
	6
	5
	4
	3
	2
	1

Name ______________________ Class ______________________ Date ______

Section 3-1: **Enrich** *(continued)*

Answer the following questions in the spaces provided.

1. What differences are there between your family chart and the first chart?

____

____

____

____

2. If the charts differ, what are possible reasons for the differences?

____

____

____

____

3. Pick one of the changes ranked 1, 2, or 3 on the first list. Explain what could be stressful about the change.

____

____

____

____

Name ______________________ Class ________________ Date ______

Section 3-1

Quiz

Write the letter of the correct answer in the space provided.

______ **1.** What is stress?
a. the response of the body and mind to being challenged or threatened
b. an event that threatens lives and property
c. an everyday problem
d. any upsetting experience

______ **2.** When stress helps you accomplish your goals, it can be called
a. negative stress.
b. distress.
c. eustress.
d. goal-related stress.

______ **3.** What is another term for negative stress?
a. distress
b. eustress
c. stressor
d. catastrophe

______ **4.** Which choice is an example of a major life change?
a. failing a quiz
b. losing your keys
c. failing a grade
d. experiencing an unusually cold winter

______ **5.** What type of stressor is a tornado?
a. major life change
b. catastrophe
c. everyday problem
d. environmental problem

Decide whether each statement is true or false. Write true *or* false *in the space provided.*

______ **6.** Stress is always negative.

______ **7.** Moderate levels of stress can increase concentration.

______ **8.** Everyday problems are too minor to cause stress.

______ **9.** Moving to a new school district is an example of an environmental stressor.

______ **10.** The more major life changes you experience, the less stress you are likely to feel.

Name____________________ Class__________ Date__________ M T W T F

Section 3-2

How Stress Affects Your Body Lesson Plan

Section Objectives

- **List** in order the three stages of the body's response to stress.
- **Identify** four types of early warning signs for stress.
- **Describe** the relationship between stress and illness.

Vocabulary fight-or-flight response

Time
1 period
1/2 block

Local Standards

1. FOCUS

Warm-Up: Health Stats Ask students to predict why prolonged stress increases the risk of developing a cold. Have students check their predictions when they read about stress and illness in the section.

Targeted Resources
- ❑ Transparency W9

2. TEACH

Cooperative Learning Ask groups of students to identify which changes take place in each of six major body systems during the alarm stage of stress. L3

Building Health Skills Ask students to write a private diary entry describing signs of stress that they experience and the stressors that cause them. L3

Building Media Literacy Have students find reliable Web sites about stress and illness and explain why the sites are reliable. Then have the class evaluate the criteria students used. L3

Addressing Misconceptions Explain why stress-related symptoms are just as "real" as symptoms caused by viruses, bacteria, and injuries. L2

Differentiated Instruction Describe or act out examples of warning signs of stress. EL

Targeted Resources
- ❑ RN Note Taking Guide 3-2 L3 EL
- ❑ ARN Note Taking Guide 3-2 L2
- ❑ Transparencies and Worksheets 8, 9
- ❑ TR Practice 3-2
- ❑ TR Enrich 3-2 L4
- ❑ Audio Summary 3-2 L1 L2 EL
- ❑ PHSchool.com: More on how to recognize stress

3. ASSESS

Evaluate Understanding The assignments listed in the Teacher's Edition can help you assess students' mastery of the section content.

Reteach Work with the class to create a bulletin board that illustrates the stages of stress, signs of stress, and the relationship between stress and illness. L2

Targeted Resources
- ❑ TR Section 3-2 Quiz
- ❑ CTB Chapter 3

KEY

L1 Special Needs	L4 Gifted and Talented
L2 Less Proficient Readers	EL English Language Learners
L3 All Students	

Name ______________________ Class ________________ Date ________

Section 3-2 **Practice**

Skill-Building Activity: Warning Signs of Stress

To deal with stress, you must be able to identify its warning signs. The signs can be behavioral, physical, mental, or emotional. Identifying warning signs of stress is a healthful behavior you can practice.

Underline each sentence in the following passage that contains a warning sign. In the table below, copy the sentences in which the warning signs occur. Identify the signs and classify them by type. The first one has been done to show you how. Look at Figure 5 on page 62 of your textbook if you need more help.

Deirdre rarely missed the bus. That's why she was so angry when it happened. Well, that and the fact that her little brother was the reason. He was always too slow getting ready in the morning! Now she had to ask her mom to drive her to school.

As they backed out of the driveway, Deirdre thought "There's no way I'll get to school on time." Then Deirdre's mom asked her what she planned to do after school. That made Deirdre even more irritable. She didn't want to talk about her plans with her mother.

By the time they got to school, Deirdre had a headache. It seemed like she had a lot of headaches lately. Maybe it was because she wasn't sleeping very well. She wasn't eating all that much, either. She just didn't feel very hungry most of the time.

Warning Signs of Stress

Sentence	Warning Sign	Type of Sign
That's why she was so angry when it happened.	Angry	Emotional

Name ______________ Class ______________ Date ______________

Section 3-2 **Enrich**

Community Involvement: Observing Signs of Stress

Stress is a fact of daily life for everyone. Public officials must face the stress of responding to a variety of conflicting viewpoints and demands. Their stress may be apparent at public meetings, if you know what to look for.

Attend a public meeting in your community, such as a school board meeting, town hall meeting, or meeting with a candidate for local office. Record the following information.

1. Type of meeting: ______________

2. Topic or topics discussed: ______________

____

3. Public officials present: ______________

____

____

4. Put a check by any of the following signs of stress you observed at the meeting:

_____ angry	_____ impatient	_____ nervous
_____ fidgeting	_____ critical of others	_____ forgetful

5. List any other signs of stress you noticed.

____

____

____

6. Who seemed to be under the most stress? Give reasons for your choice.

____

____

____

____

7. Can you think of any way stress might have been minimized at the meeting?

____

____

____

____

Name ______________________ Class __________________ Date ______

Section 3-2

Quiz

Write the letter of the correct answer in the space provided.

______ **1.** first stage of stress

______ **2.** increases when adrenaline is released

______ **3.** second stage of stress

______ **4.** behavioral warning sign of stress

______ **5.** respiratory illness triggered by stress

a. alarm stage

b. overeating

c. ulcer

d. asthma

e. heart rate

f. resistance stage

Decide whether each statement is true or false. Write true *or* false *in the space provided.*

______ **6.** The fight-or-flight response occurs during the resistance stage of stress.

______ **7.** The exhaustion stage occurs with every stress response.

______ **8.** Stress can cause problems with concentration.

______ **9.** Some headaches are triggered by stress.

______ **10.** Prolonged stress weakens the digestive system.

Name______________ Class__________ Date__________ M T W T F

Section 3-3

Stress and Individuals Lesson Plan

Section Objectives

- **Explain** how individuals can have different responses to the same stressor.
- **Describe** two ways that personality affects stress.
- **Identify** the key factor in resilience.

Vocabulary optimism • pessimism • perfectionist • resilience

Time
1 period
1/2 block

Local Standards

1. FOCUS

Warm-Up: Quick Quiz Discuss how different ways of thinking might influence how much stress different people feel.

Targeted Resources
- ❑ Transparency W10

2. TEACH

Teacher Demo Announce a surprise quiz, and discuss how students' responses to this potential stressor vary. L2

Differentiated Instruction Provide students with a concrete example to illustrate how a person's assessment of a situation affects the level of stress. L1

Visual Learning: Figure 8 Ask students to use the traits listed to classify the athletes as optimistic or pessimistic. L2

Class Discussion Discuss how procrastination causes stress and how time management can help people deal with procrastination. L3

Active Learning Have students find references to traits of resilience in articles about people who faced extreme challenges. Discuss how the traits helped the people tolerate high levels of stress. L4

Targeted Resources
- ❑ RN Note Taking Guide 3-3 L3 EL
- ❑ ARN Note Taking Guide 3-3 L2
- ❑ TR Practice 3-3
- ❑ TR Enrich 3-3 L4
- ❑ Audio Summary 3-3 L1 L2 EL
- ❑ Health Links: Updates on stress and personality

3. ASSESS

Evaluate Understanding The assignments listed in the Teacher's Edition can help you assess students' mastery of the section content.

Reteach Make a general outline of the section, and have pairs of students add details to the outline and use it to quiz each other on section content. L2

Targeted Resources
- ❑ TR Section 3-3 Quiz
- ❑ CTB Chapter 3

KEY

L1 Special Needs	L4 Gifted and Talented
L2 Less Proficient Readers	EL English Language Learners
L3 All Students	

Name ______________ Class ______________ Date ______

Section 3-3

Practice

Group Activity: Positive and Negative Thinking

How you think about situations makes a big difference in how much stress they cause you. You can think either positively or negatively about most situations. For example, as your teacher shows you how to do a difficult problem, you might think "I can learn how to do this if I try" (positive thinking) or "I'll never be able to do this, so I might as well not try" (negative thinking). Positive thinking can help you solve problems and decrease stress. Negative thinking can make problems worse and increase stress.

As a group, brainstorm and record negative thoughts about each situation below. For each negative thought, brainstorm and record a positive thought. Discuss how the different thoughts would make you feel if you were in each situation.

1. A basketball player is about to take a foul shot.

Negative Thoughts:	Positive Thoughts:
______________	______________
______________	______________
______________	______________

2. A student walks out on a stage to give a speech.

Negative Thoughts:	Positive Thoughts:
______________	______________
______________	______________
______________	______________

3. Your teacher hands you a test and tells you to finish it in 30 minutes.

Negative Thoughts:	Positive Thoughts:
______________	______________
______________	______________
______________	______________

4. You suddenly remember that you left your wallet on a park bench.

Negative Thoughts:	Positive Thoughts:
______________	______________
______________	______________
______________	______________

Name ______________________ Class ______________________ Date ________

Section 3-3

Enrich

Class Debate: Who Is More Resilient?

Who do you think tends to be more resilient in the face of extreme or prolonged stress: teens or older adults (age 80 and older)? Prepare to debate this topic by interviewing a few people aged 80 or older. Find out what traits of resilience they have by asking them how they coped with major challenges in their lives. If you are unable to interview any older adults, look for interviews that have appeared in magazines or newspapers.

With a group of students, discuss your findings and answer Questions 1 and 2. Then debate a group that has an opposing position. After the debate, answer Question 3.

1. Do you think teens or elderly people are more resilient?

____

2. List reasons or evidence that support your position.

____

____

____

____

____

____

____

____

____

3. List three reasons or evidence presented by the opposing team that you think best support their position.

____

____

____

Name ______________ Class ______________ Date ______

Section 3-3 Quiz

Write the letter of the correct answer in the space provided.

_____ **1.** ability to bounce back from stress	**a.** optimism
_____ **2.** key factor in resilience	**b.** perfectionist
_____ **3.** tendency to focus on the positive	**c.** resilience
_____ **4.** someone who accepts nothing less than excellence	**d.** pride
	e. pessimism
_____ **5.** tendency to focus on the negative	**f.** support of others

Write the letter of the correct answer in the space provided.

_____ **6.** Which statement about how people respond to a given stressor is most accurate?
a. Everybody responds exactly the same way.
b. How they respond depends on how they assess the stressor.
c. How they respond depends only on the type of stressor.
d. How they respond depends only on their past experiences.

_____ **7.** Which statement would an optimist be most likely to say?
a. I know I won't do well on the test.
b. I think the test will be really hard.
c. I think I will do well on the test.
d. I know I will fail the test.

_____ **8.** What do perfectionists tend to do?
a. set goals that are easy to attain
b. feel satisfied with their accomplishments
c. focus on their mistakes
d. accept that they cannot be perfect

_____ **9.** Which trait helps people tolerate high levels of stress?
a. pessimism
b. resilience
c. perfectionism
d. impatience

_____ **10.** What characteristic do people with resilience share?
a. lack of confidence
b. poor problem-solving skills
c. fear of change
d. ability to recognize and control their feelings

Name______________________ Class__________ Date__________ M T W T F

Section 3-4

Coping With Stress — Lesson Plan

Section Objectives

Time
2 periods
1 block

- **Identify** ways to control stress, reduce tension, and change the way you think about stressors.
- **Explain** why building resilience is important.
- **Describe** the value of seeking support from others when you are under stress.

Local Standards

Vocabulary mental rehearsal • biofeedback

1. FOCUS

Warm-Up: Advice Line Have students share ideas for making public speaking less stressful to make the point that there are many ways to cope with stress.

Targeted Resources
- ❑ Transparency W11

2. TEACH

Journal Writing Have students write in their journals about stressors in their lives and ways to reduce or eliminate stressors under their control. L3

Building Health Skills Have students create infomercials advocating the use of physical activity to reduce tension. L3

Cooperative Learning Have students work with partners to practice deep breathing. L2

Building Health Skills Describe stressful events, and call on students to state positive ways of thinking about the events. L2

Active Learning Have students interview a person with a highly stressful job to learn how the person builds resilience. L4

Teacher Demo Role-play how to reach out for support from another person. L2

Targeted Resources
- ❑ RN Note Taking Guide 3-4 L3 EL
- ❑ ARN Note Taking Guide 3-4 L2
- ❑ TR Practice 3-4
- ❑ TR Enrich 3-4 L4
- ❑ Audio Summary 3-4 L1 L2 EL
- ❑ PHSchool.com: More on coping with stress

3. ASSESS

Evaluate Understanding The assignments listed in the Teacher's Edition can help you assess students' mastery of the section content.

Reteach Ask students to describe or demonstrate methods for coping with stress. L2

Targeted Resources
- ❑ TR Section 3-4 Quiz
- ❑ CTB Chapter 3

KEY

L1 Special Needs	L4 Gifted and Talented
L2 Less Proficient Readers	EL English Language Learners
L3 All Students	

Name ______________________ Class __________________ Date ______

Section 3-4 **Practice**

Role-Playing: Coping With Stress

There are many different techniques for coping with stress—physical activity, relaxation, time management, mental rehearsal, avoiding negative thinking, humor, and reaching out for support. The technique you choose is likely to vary depending on the situation and what you feel comfortable doing.

With a partner, think of a stressful situation. Choose a technique for coping with the stress caused by the situation. Then write a dialogue about the situation and the coping technique. The dialogue should explain how to use the technique and why this technique will help to reduce the stress.

1. Stressful situation: ______________________

____

____

2. Dialogue between Student 1 and Student 2:

Student 1: ______________________

____

Student 2: ______________________

____

Student 1: ______________________

____

Student 2: ______________________

____

Student 1: ______________________

____

Student 2: ______________________

____

Student 1: ______________________

____

Student 2: ______________________

____

Name ______________________ Class __________________ Date ______

Section 3-4

Enrich

Consumer Skills: Help for Stress-Related Problems

Problems cause more stress when people do not have the resources to deal with them. Outside help can be an important resource for dealing with some problems. Sources of outside help include the following:

- psychologists, who may help people deal with emotional problems
- family or social services, which help families deal with financial, healthcare, and housing problems
- school guidance counselors, who help students deal with school-related problems
- doctors who help people with serious stress-related health problems

Below are descriptions of three stressful situations. Decide which source of help listed above would be most suitable for each situation, and explain your decision.

1. Your brother was in a serious car crash and suffered injuries that will keep him out of school for several months. He is concerned about how this will affect his grades and his ability to graduate with his class.

____

____

____

____

2. One of your teammates has been depressed for several weeks. Her father is remarrying, and she feels jealous, and angry.

____

____

____

____

3. Your friend's mom lost her job, and there isn't enough money to pay the bills. Your friend is thinking about quitting school and going to work to help out. He doesn't know what else the family can do.

____

____

____

____

Name ______________________ Class ____________________ Date ________

Section 3-4

Quiz

Decide whether each statement is true or false. Write true *or* false *in the space provided.*

______ **1.** Mental rehearsal helps you learn to use your time more efficiently.

______ **2.** You have to be an athlete to use physical activity to reduce tension.

______ **3.** Biofeedback may be able to help people with asthma.

______ **4.** Humor is an effective way to deal with stress.

______ **5.** Resilient people never experience stress.

Write the letter of the correct answer in the space provided.

______ **6.** What technique reduces stress by helping you get more done each day?

a. mental performance
b. biofeedback
c. time management
d. relaxation

______ **7.** What is the purpose of mental rehearsal?

a. It replaces the need to actually practice an activity.
b. It helps you feel confident you can perform an event.
c. It increases your ability to do mental activities.
d. It increases your stress level so you will try harder.

______ **8.** Why is physical activity a good way to reduce tension?

a. It helps take your mind off your problems.
b. It tightens and strengthens your muscles.
c. It makes you so tired you can't think about your problems.
d. It helps you identify thoughts that cause tension.

______ **9.** Which choice is an example of positive thinking?

a. I know I can't do this.
b. I've done things like this before.
c. Everyone will think I'm stupid.
d. I'm not as good at this as the others.

______ **10.** What is one way to build resilience?

a. Avoid acting on decisions.
b. Be critical of yourself.
c. Confide in yourself.
d. Don't waste time on other people's problems.

Name ____________________ Class ____________________ Date ________

Chapter 3 Test

Write the letter of the correct answer in the space provided.

______ **1.** Why are major life changes stressful?
- **a.** They are unexpected.
- **b.** They are always negative.
- **c.** They are everyday events.
- **d.** They threaten a person's feelings of security.

______ **2.** What is one way that adrenaline prepares the body for fight or flight?
- **a.** It increases blood flow to the brain.
- **b.** It decreases the rate of breathing.
- **c.** It increases the rate of digestion.
- **d.** It decreases blood pressure.

______ **3.** One way that prolonged stress can increase the risk of heart disease is by
- **a.** causing muscles to tense.
- **b.** lowering the heart rate.
- **c.** lowering blood pressure.
- **d.** damaging blood vessels.

______ **4.** Which choice reflects pessimism?
- **a.** I think I can win this race.
- **b.** I trained very hard for this race.
- **c.** I know I will not win this race.
- **d.** I will try my best to win this race.

______ **5.** What can you learn from biofeedback?
- **a.** how to control physical responses to stress
- **b.** how to use time efficiently
- **c.** how to think positively
- **d.** how to build a support system

Decide whether each statement is true or false. Write true *or* false *in the space provided.*

______ **6.** Moderate stress can improve your ability to perform well.

______ **7.** Stress can cause increased crying.

______ **8.** Everyone responds to a particular stressor in the same way.

______ **9.** The key factor in resilience is having the support of family and friends.

Name ______________ Class ______________ Date ______

Chapter 3: Test *(continued)*

Write the letter of the correct answer in the space provided.

______ **10.** positive stress

______ **11.** stressful event that threatens lives and may destroy property

______ **12.** initial reaction of the body to stress

______ **13.** emotional warning sign of stress

______ **14.** technique for controlling stress

a. anger

b. mental rehearsal

c. catastrophe

d. distress

e. eustress

f. fight-or-flight response

Write the word that best completes each sentence in the space provided.

15. An event or situation that causes stress is called a(an) ______________.

16. The third stage of the stress response is the ______________ stage.

17. How you react to a stressful event depends on how you ______________ the situation.

18. Progressive relaxation can help release muscle ______________.

Use complete sentences to answer the following questions.

19. What is the relationship between stress and illness? Give an example.

____

____

____

____

____

____

20. Why is building resilience important? Describe two ways a person could build resilience.

____

____

____

____

____

____

____

Name ____________________ Class ____________________ Date ________

Chapter 4

Personal Inventory

Depression and Anxiety

It is completely normal to feel anxious or depressed at times. Usually, these feelings are short-lived and related to a specific situation, such as a move to a new school or a disagreement with a friend.

Use the following questions to assess how you cope with feelings of anxiety or depression. Consider each statement below. Write Always, Often, Sometimes, or Never to describe how often the statement describes your thoughts or behaviors.

1. Once I get depressed, I cannot seem to get out of it. ____________

2. I feel sad more often than I feel happy or content. ____________

3. I cannot figure out exactly what is bothering me. ____________

4. Things I used to enjoy do not interest me anymore. ____________

5. Getting to sleep at night is a problem for me. ____________

6. I wake up feeling sad or anxious. ____________

7. I have trouble concentrating on my work. ____________

8. I feel tired most of the time. ____________

9. I worry about bad things happening to me. ____________

10. I have a lot of trouble making up my mind. ____________

11. I do not want to be around other people. ____________

12. I feel isolated from other people. ____________

13. I find it hard to keep appointments and make plans. ____________

14. It is difficult for me to express how I feel. ____________

15. Other people seem to enjoy life more than I do. ____________

16. I withdraw from others when I feel sad. ____________

17. I eat far too much or far too little. ____________

Most people will answer *Sometimes* to many of these questions and *Often* or *Always* to only a few of the questions. If you answered *Often* or *Always* to many of these questions, talk to a parent, guardian, or other trusted adult about getting help.

Name_________________________ Class__________ Date__________ M T W T F

Section 4-1

Mental Disorders Lesson Plan

Section Objectives

- **Explain** how mental disorders are recognized.
- **Identify** four causes of mental disorders.
- **Describe** five types of anxiety disorders and four other types of mental disorders.

Time
3 periods
1 1/2 blocks

Local Standards

Vocabulary mental disorder • anxiety • anxiety disorder • phobia • obsession • compulsion • mood disorder • depression • schizophrenia • personality disorder

1. FOCUS

Warm-Up: Quick Quiz Use the Quick Quiz to assess students' knowledge of and attitudes toward mental disorders.

Targeted Resources
- ❑ Transparency W12

2. TEACH

Addressing Misconceptions Explain that mental disorders are not a sign of weakness or bad character. L3

Class Discussion Have students differentiate between normal mood shifts and those associated with bipolar disorder. L2

Building Media Literacy Ask students to analyze the depiction of characters with mental disorders in books and movies. L4

Building Health Skills Have students locate resources, such as support groups, for people with impulse-control disorders. L3

Differentiated Instruction Help students focus on a general definition of mental disorders rather than specific examples. L1

Targeted Resources
- ❑ RN Note Taking Guide 4-1 L3 EL
- ❑ ARN Note Taking Guide 4-1 L2
- ❑ TR Practice 4-1
- ❑ TR Enrich 4-1 L4
- ❑ Audio Summary 4-1 L1 L2 EL
- ❑ PHSchool.com: More on bipolar disorder

3. ASSESS

Evaluate Understanding The assignments listed in the Teacher's Edition can help you assess students' mastery of the section content.

Reteach Have students summarize characteristics of each mental disorder described in the section. L2

Targeted Resources
- ❑ TR Section 4-1 Quiz
- ❑ CTB Chapter 4

KEY

L1	Special Needs	L4	Gifted and Talented
L2	Less Proficient Readers	EL	English Language Learners
L3	All Students		

Name ______________________ Class ____________________ Date ________

Section 4-1

Practice

Vocabulary Activity: Mental Disorders

Mental disorders are illnesses that affect the mind and reduce an individual's ability to function in everyday life. Understanding mental disorders can help you distinguish normal behavior from behavior that requires professional help.

Use vocabulary from the section to complete the crossword puzzle about mental disorders.

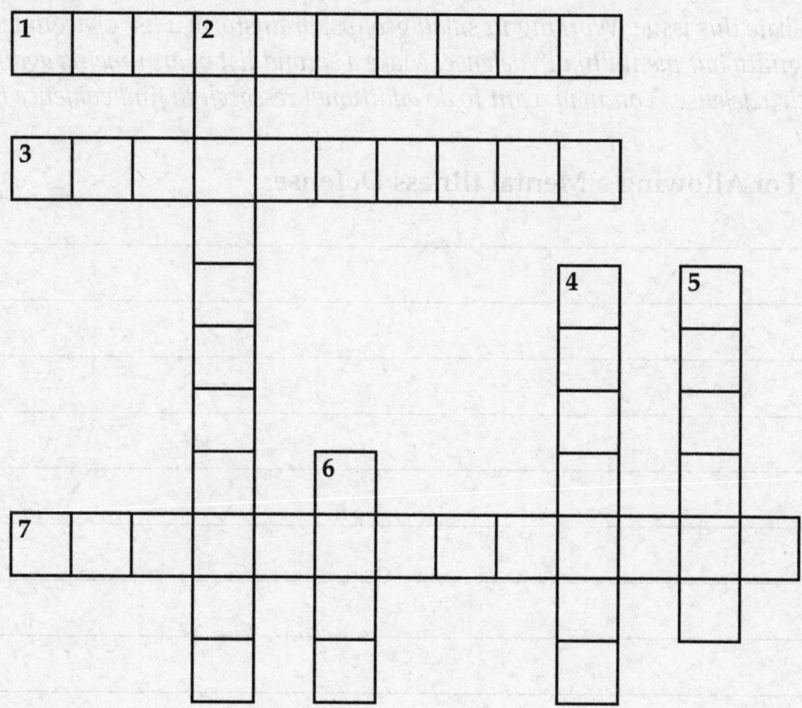

Clues Across

1. an unreasonable need to behave in a certain way
3. an emotional state in which a person feels extremely sad or hopeless
7. a mental disorder identified by severe disturbances in thinking, mood, awareness, and behavior

Clues Down

2. a type of disorder in which a person displays rigid patterns of behavior
4. fear caused by a source that cannot be identified
5. fear that is related to a specific situation or object
6. a type of disorder in which people experience extreme emotion

Name ______________________ Class ________________ Date ________

Section 4-1 **Enrich**

Class Debate: Mental Disorders and the Legal System

In some criminal trials, the defendant pleads "guilty by reason of insanity," or "guilty but mentally ill." This defense has been used since 1843, but in recent years some states have eliminated or greatly limited its use. Advocates of this defense say it helps protect those with mental disorders. Others say all individuals who commit crimes should be treated in the same way.

Prepare to debate this issue. Working in small groups, brainstorm a list of arguments for allowing a "guilty but mentally ill" defense. Make a second list of arguments against allowing such a defense. You may want to do additional research to find evidence to support each position.

Argument For Allowing a Mental Illness Defense:

____

____

____

____

____

____

____

____

____

Argument Against Allowing a Mental Illness Defense:

____

____

____

____

____

____

____

____

____

Name ______________ Class ______________ Date ______

Section 4-1

Quiz

Write the letter of the correct answer in the space provided.

______ 1. Which is a symptom of a mental disorder?
  - **a.** feeling sad when a friend moves away
  - **b.** feeling angry when you are cut from the soccer team
  - **c.** feeling upset if you cannot repeatedly wash your hands
  - **d.** feeling anxious before taking a college entrance exam

______ 2. Which is a physical factor that can lead to a mental disorder?
  - **a.** death of a loved one
  - **b.** emotional abuse
  - **c.** witnessing violence
  - **d.** exposure to lead

______ 3. During a manic episode, people usually
  - **a.** feel extremely sad.
  - **b.** feel hopeless.
  - **c.** make excellent decisions.
  - **d.** are overly excited and restless.

______ 4. A person who steals items that he or she does not need or want has
  - **a.** an impulse-control disorder.
  - **b.** generalized anxiety disorder.
  - **c.** a mood disorder.
  - **d.** a personality disorder.

______ 5. All personality disorders are characterized by
  - **a.** difficulty getting along with others.
  - **b.** inability to make decisions.
  - **c.** an overwhelming fear of rejection.
  - **d.** demanding and selfish behavior.

Write the letter of the correct answer in the space provided.

______ 6. extreme anxiety related to a specific situation or object

______ 7. unwanted thoughts or images that take control of the mind

______ 8. symptoms include flashbacks and nightmares that produce intense fear or horror

______ 9. a sudden period of intense fear with physical symptoms

______ 10. intense worry or fear without a specific source

a. panic attack
b. generalized anxiety disorder
c. phobia
d. obsession
e. post-traumatic stress disorder
f. ADHD

Name____________________ Class__________ Date__________ M T W T F

Section 4-2

Eating Disorders Lesson Plan

Section Objectives

- **Identify** health risks associated with anorexia.
- **Explain** the relationship between bulimia and dieting.
- **List** the main health risks of binge eating disorder.

Vocabulary eating disorder • anorexia nervosa • bulimia • binge eating disorder

Time
1 period
½ block

Local Standards

1. FOCUS

Warm-Up: Myth/Fact Make a class list of factors that might keep people from seeking help for an eating disorder. Refer to the list as you discuss each eating disorder.

Targeted Resources

- ❑ Transparency W13

2. TEACH

Addressing Misconceptions If students think anorexia is mainly a physical problem, point out that anorexia involves changes in brain chemistry similar to those that occur with anxiety disorders. L3

Building Vocabulary After providing the literal meaning of the term *anorexia*, have students explain why this meaning is an inaccurate description of the disorder. L2

Building Health Skills Have students create a pamphlet or poster that describes the symptoms, possible causes, treatments, and health risks of anorexia. L3

Active Learning Ask students to use a Venn diagram to compare and contrast anorexia and bulimia. L2

Building Health Skills Have students develop strategies that could be used to advocate for a friend who has an eating disorder. L3

Targeted Resources

- ❑ RN Note Taking Guide 4-2 L3 EL
- ❑ ARN Note Taking Guide 4-2 L2
- ❑ TR Practice 4-2
- ❑ TR Enrich 4-2 L4
- ❑ Audio Summary 4-2 L1 L2 EL
- ❑ PHSchool.com: More on eating disorders

3. ASSESS

Evaluate Understanding The assignments listed in the Teacher's Edition can help you assess students' mastery of the section content.

Reteach Have students complete sentences that demonstrate their knowledge of the symptoms of anorexia, bulimia, and binge eating disorder. L2

Targeted Resources

- ❑ TR Section 4-2 Quiz
- ❑ CTB Chapter 4

KEY

L1 Special Needs	L4 Gifted and Talented
L2 Less Proficient Readers	EL English Language Learners
L3 All Students	

Name ______________________ Class ____________________ Date ______

Section 4-2 **Practice**

Decision Making: A Friend With Bulimia

What would you do if you suspected that a friend has bulimia? Imagine your friend is an athlete. Recently you've noticed that your friend seems very concerned about weight. Your friend often rushes to the bathroom right after meals.

Use the DECIDE process to consider how you would respond to your friend. In order to evaluate the results, you will need to imagine your friend's response to your actions.

Define the problem:

____

____

Explore the alternatives and **C**onsider the consequences:

Possible Alternatives	Possible Consequences	
	Positive	Negative

Identify your values:

____

____

Decide and act:

____

____

Evaluate the results:

____

____

____

Name ______________________ Class ____________________ Date ________

Section 4-2 **Enrich**

Family Involvement: Recognizing Eating Disorders

Parents and guardians need to be able to recognize the symptoms of eating disorders. You can help by providing parents and guardians with information about eating disorders. You will work with a partner to design a flyer that can be sent to parents and guardians.

Use the table below to organize the content of your flyer. Remember that the information needs to be brief. Select symptoms that would be easy for a concerned adult to observe. Use a separate piece of paper to show how you will lay out the information on the page.

Disorder	Symptoms
Anorexia nervosa	
Bulimia	
Binge eating disorder	

Name ______________________ Class ______________________ Date ________

Section 4-2

Quiz

Write the letter of the correct answer in the space provided.

a. anorexia nervosa
b. bulimia
c. binge eating disorder

______ **1.** a disorder in which a person doesn't eat enough to maintain a healthy body weight

______ **2.** a disorder that causes excessive weight gain

______ **3.** a disorder that causes erosion of the tooth enamel

______ **4.** a disorder in which an individual eats a large amount and then purges

______ **5.** a disorder in which an individual eats a large quantity of food without purging

______ **6.** a disorder that causes dry skin, growth of fine body hair, and lowered body temperature

Write the letter of the correct answer in the space provided.

______ **7.** Which is *not* a symptom of bulimia?
a. eating in private
b. refusal to eat
c. eating too much food too quickly
d. bathroom visits right after eating

______ **8.** One possible risk of binge eating disorder is
a. extreme weight loss.
b. unhealthy dieting.
c. starving to death.
d. loss of tooth enamel.

______ **9.** A female who has lost a large amount of weight and no longer has menstrual periods may have
a. anorexia nervosa.
b. bulimia.
c. binge eating disorder.
d. personality disorder.

______ **10.** Which is *not* a possible cause of anorexia?
a. an imbalance of brain chemicals
b. a desire for control
c. a strong desire to please others
d. a healthy body image

Name________________ Class__________ Date__________ M T W T F

Section 4-3

Depression and Suicide Lesson Plan

Section Objectives

- **Explain** why it is important to identify and treat clinical depression.
- **Explain** why individuals might deliberately injure themselves.
- **Describe** one major risk factor for suicide.

Vocabulary clinical depression • cutting • suicide • cluster suicides

Time
2 periods
1 block

Local Standards

1. FOCUS

Warm-Up: Health Stats Launch a discussion of ways students can make other students feel more connected to school based on the results of the writing assignment.

Targeted Resources

- ❑ Transparency W14

2. TEACH

Cooperative Learning Have students work in groups to summarize the ways in which depression can affect an individual's ability to function. L3

Differentiated Instruction Have students discuss and compare the everyday usage of the term *depressed* and the correct usage of the term *clinical depression*. EL

Visual Learning: Figure 11 Challenge students to recognize what the suggestions listed in the figure have in common. L2

Building Media Literacy Ask students to analyze examples of suicide portrayed in the media and decide if the portrayal would encourage or discourage teen suicide. L3

Active Learning Have students develop a list of questions about suicide to ask the school guidance counselor. L2

Targeted Resources

- ❑ RN Note Taking Guide 4-3 L3 EL
- ❑ ARN Note Taking Guide 4-3 L2
- ❑ Transparencies and Worksheets 10, 11
- ❑ TR Practice 4-3
- ❑ TR Enrich 4-3 L4
- ❑ Audio Summary 4-3 L1 L2 EL
- ❑ Health Links: Updates on depression

3. ASSESS

Evaluate Understanding The assignments listed in the Teacher's Edition can help you assess students' mastery of the section content.

Reteach Ask students to discuss with a group how depression and suicide are related. L2

Targeted Resources

- ❑ TR Section 4-3 Quiz
- ❑ CTB Chapter 4

KEY

- L1 Special Needs
- L2 Less Proficient Readers
- L3 All Students
- L4 Gifted and Talented
- EL English Language Learners

Name ____________ Class ____________ Date ______

Section 4-3

Practice

Group Activity: The Facts About Suicide

Knowing the facts about suicide can help you effectively advocate for yourself and others. It helps to discuss this information with others.

With a partner, discuss the risk factors and protective factors for suicide. Also discuss things that you would and would not do if a friend is thinking about suicide.

1. Some risk factors for suicide:

2. Protective factors that reduce the risk of suicide:

3. Actions I would take if a friend mentioned suicide at school:

4. Actions I would take if a friend called me at home and described a detailed suicide plan:

5. Things I would avoid doing if a friend was thinking about suicide:

Name ____________________ Class ____________________ Date ________

Section 4-3 **Enrich**

Community Involvement: Raising Awareness of Self-Injury

Self-injury is an unhealthy way to deal with stress and other painful feelings. Many people are not aware of the dangers of self-injury.

With a partner, develop a sixty-second radio public service announcement to raise awareness of self-injury. Use the descriptions below to help organize the announcement. Then write your public service announcement on a separate sheet of paper.

1. Describe self-injury in a way that grabs the attention of the audience.

____

____

____

____

____

____

2. Describe some causes of self-injury.

____

____

____

____

____

3. Describe some dangers of self-injury.

____

____

____

____

____

4. Provide contact information for local resources that help those who self-injure.

____

____

____

____

Name ______________ Class ______________ Date ______

Section 4-3

Quiz

Decide whether each statement is true or false. Write true *or* false *in the space provided.*

______ **1.** Untreated depression can lead to other serious problems.

______ **2.** Medication is one treatment that is used for depression.

______ **3.** All moody, irritable teens are experiencing clinical depression.

______ **4.** Cutting is a form of self-injury.

______ **5.** Every individual who commits suicide shows clear warning signs.

______ **6.** If a friend is thinking about suicide, you should keep his or her secret.

Write the letter of the correct answer in the space provided.

______ **7.** Clinical depression is one type of
a. mood disorder.
b. anxiety disorder.
c. phobia.
d. personality disorder.

______ **8.** Which is *not* a symptom of clinical depression?
a. no change in weight or appetite
b. hopelessness or excessive guilt
c. difficulty thinking and concentrating
d. changes in sleep patterns

______ **9.** What is one thing you should do if a friend is thinking about suicide?
a. analyze his or her motives
b. offer reasons not to commit suicide
c. judge your friend
d. say how concerned you are

______ **10.** Which describes a risk factor for suicide?
a. close friends
b. feeling connected to school
c. lack of access to mental health treatment
d. ability to resolve conflicts in non-violent ways

Name_________________________ Class___________ Date___________ M T W T F

Section 4-4

Treating Mental Disorders Lesson Plan

Section Objectives

- **List** reasons that might prevent a person from seeking help for a mental disorder.
- **Identify** four types of mental health professionals.
- **Describe** some general types of treatment for mental disorders.

Time
1 period
1/2 block

Local Standards

Vocabulary psychiatrist • neurologist • clinical psychologist • psychiatric social worker • therapy

1. FOCUS

Warm-Up: Advice Line Use the activity to start a discussion of how attitudes toward mental illness can be a barrier to treatment.

Targeted Resources

- ❑ Transparency W15

2. TEACH

Class Discussion Ask students to develop strategies that could be used to address each barrier to treatment for mental illness. L2

Active Learning Have students develop a graphic organizer that describes the types of mental health providers listed in the Student Edition. L2

Building Health Skills Have students recall movies with characters who are mental health professionals. Ask if students think that how these characters are portrayed would encourage people to seek help for a mental disorder. L3

Differentiated Instruction Explain the meaning of the word part *psych-* and point out the silent *p*. Have students identify other English words that start with a silent *p*. EL

Cooperative Learning Create a multimedia presentation about types of treatment for mental disorders. L3

Targeted Resources

- ❑ RN Note Taking Guide 4-4 L3 EL
- ❑ ARN Note Taking Guide 4-4 L2
- ❑ TR Practice 4-4
- ❑ TR Enrich 4-4 L4
- ❑ Audio Summary 4-4 L1 L2 EL
- ❑ Health Links: Updates on mental health

3. ASSESS

Evaluate Understanding The assignments listed in the Teacher's Edition can help you assess students' mastery of the section content.

Reteach Have students work in pairs to quiz one another about the section content. L2

Targeted Resources

- ❑ TR Section 4-4 Quiz
- ❑ CTB Chapter 4

KEY

L1 Special Needs	L4 Gifted and Talented
L2 Less Proficient Readers	EL English Language Learners
L3 All Students	

Name ____________________ Class ____________________ Date __________

Section 4-4

Practice

Role-Playing: Helping a Friend

The majority of people with mental disorders do not get the help they need. Some do not recognize that they need help. Others might not know where to get help. Still others may have been told that they can overcome their problems with willpower alone.

With a partner, choose one of the three barriers to treatment described above and write a role-play that addresses that barrier. The role-play should be written as a conversation between Student 1, who recognizes that a friend needs help, and Student 2, the individual who may have a mental disorder.

Barrier to treatment: ____

____

Student 1: ____

____

Student 2: ____

____

Student 1: ____

____

Student 2: ____

____

Student 1: ____

____

Student 2: ____

____

Student 1: ____

____

Student 2: ____

____

Student 1: ____

____

Student 2: ____

____

Name ______________ Class ______________ Date ______

Section 4-4 **Enrich**

Consumer Skills: Accessing Mental Health Services

Most communities have mental health counseling services. Knowing how to access these services is the first step to helping yourself or a friend who is coping with a mental disorder.

Contact a local mental-health agency to obtain answers to the following questions. If the agency you choose has a Web site, see what questions are answered on the site before you contact the agency. Use what you have learned to design a wallet card that contains contact information for this agency.

1. Name of agency: ______________

2. Phone number or address of the agency: ______________

3. Hours the agency is open or accepts calls: ______________

4. Kinds of services provided by the agency: ______________

5. Cost of Service: ______________

6. Specific services for teens: ______________

Front	**Back**

Name ____________ Class ____________ Date ____________

Section 4-4 Quiz

Write the letter of the correct answer in the space provided.

_____ **1.** Which is a medical doctor who specializes in the treatment of mental disorders?
- **a.** mental health counselor
- **b.** social worker
- **c.** psychiatrist
- **d.** clinical psychologist

_____ **2.** In what type of therapy do people work with others who have similar disorders?
- **a.** cognitive therapy
- **b.** group therapy
- **c.** behavioral therapy
- **d.** insight therapy

_____ **3.** What is the goal of cognitive therapy?
- **a.** to identify the triggers of abnormal behavior
- **b.** to work with a group to develop coping skills
- **c.** to understand the reasons for certain behaviors
- **d.** to use medication to treat symptoms of mental disorders

_____ **4.** A physician who treats physical disorders of the nervous system is a
- **a.** psychiatrist.
- **b.** social worker.
- **c.** neurologist.
- **d.** clinical psychologist.

Decide whether each statement is true or false. Write true or false in the space provided.

_____ **5.** Mental disorders can be overcome using willpower alone.

_____ **6.** Insight therapy helps individuals understand the reasons for their behavior.

_____ **7.** Hospitalization is used to treat every person who has a mental disorder.

_____ **8.** Psychiatric social workers help families of individuals with mental disorders.

_____ **9.** Recognizing the need for help is the first step toward recovery from a mental disorder.

_____ **10.** Social workers can prescribe medications for the treatment of mental disorders.

Name ______________________ Class __________________ Date ______

Chapter 4 Test

Write the letter of the correct answer in the space provided.

_____ **1.** A phobia is an example of a(an)
a. anxiety disorder.
b. post-traumatic stress disorder.
c. obsessive-compulsive disorder.
d. mood disorder.

_____ **2.** Which is a symptom of bulimia?
a. excessive weight loss
b. extreme weight gain
c. erosion of tooth enamel
d. lowered body temperature

_____ **3.** Which is a protective factor for suicide?
a. family history of suicide
b. feeling connected to school
c. lack of mental health care
d. feelings of hopelessness

_____ **4.** What is the goal of insight therapy?
a. to identify situations that trigger abnormal behavior
b. to work with others who have a similar disorder
c. to understand the reasons for certain behaviors
d. to use medication to allow patients to function normally

Write the letter of the correct answer in the space provided.

_____ **5.** helps individuals and their families accept and adjust to a mental disorder

_____ **6.** often works with specific groups or specific problems

_____ **7.** has a doctorate degree and at least two years of training

_____ **8.** has a medical degree and can prescribe medication to treat mental disorders

a. mental health counselor
b. psychiatric social worker
c. clinical psychologist
d. psychiatrist
e. neurologist

Name ____________________ Class ________________ Date ________

Chapter 4: Test *(continued)*

Decide whether each statement is true or false. Write true *or* false *in the space provided.*

______ **9.** The majority of individuals with mental disorders do not get the help they need.

______ **10.** All people who cannot sit still have ADHD.

______ **11.** A brain injury is a physical factor that can cause a mental disorder.

______ **12.** Excessive weight loss is a typical symptom of bulimia.

______ **13.** A brief feeling of sadness indicates clinical depression.

______ **14.** Cutting is a strategy that helps individuals solve their underlying problems.

Write the word or phrase that best completes each sentence in the space provided.

15. A mental disorder that causes a split with reality is ______________.

16. An individual who experiences sudden, intense fear for no apparent reason is having a(an) ______________ ______________.

17. An eating disorder that can result in an individual starving to death is ______________ ______________.

18. A series of suicides, called ______________ ______________, is a group of suicides that occur within a short period of time.

Use complete sentences to answer the following questions.

19. Describe the symptoms of bipolar disorder. Explain how these symptoms could affect an individual's ability to function in everyday life.

____

____

____

____

____

20. Miguel has had untreated binge eating disorder for several years. Explain how this disorder may be affecting Miguel's physical and emotional health.

____

____

____

____

____

Name ______________________ Class ____________________ Date ______

Chapter 5

Personal Inventory

Your Family Responsibilities

Families function most effectively when each member does his or her part. As a teen, you can assume more responsibility than you did as a young child. Your responsibilities might include chores, such as doing laundry or mowing the lawn. You may help care for a younger sibling or work at a part-time job.

List some responsibilities you have in your family. Then indicate how often you are expected to do each task. If you do a task almost every day, choose daily. If you do it once or twice a week, choose weekly. For less frequent tasks, choose monthly.

Responsibility	Daily	Weekly	Monthly

Identify and describe one additional responsibility that you could accept in your family.

____

____

____

How would your family benefit if you accepted this responsibility?

____

____

____

Name____________________ Class__________ Date__________ M T W T F

Section 5-1

Families Today Lesson Plan

Section Objectives

- **Explain** why healthy family relationships are important.
- **Identify** three main factors that have changed the form of families.
- **Describe** some family forms that exist today.
- **Summarize** the division of responsibilities within a family.

Vocabulary divorce • nuclear family • adoption • single-parent family • extended family • blended family • foster family • socialization

Time
2 periods
1 block

Local Standards

1. FOCUS

Warm-Up: Health Stats Ask students to identify the trend shown in the graph and speculate on what caused the trend.

Targeted Resources
- ❑ Transparency W16

2. TEACH

Cooperative Learning Have students work in groups to develop a list of words that describe families. L2

Building Health Skills Challenge students to explain how changes in technology can cause changes in the family. L3

Active Learning Ask students to use magazine pictures to make a collage of different types of families. L1

Differentiated Instruction Have students draw stick figures or other symbols on index cards to represent six family structures. EL

Visual Learning: Figure 3 Have students discuss how family and cultural traditions can affect the rules in a given family. L3

Active Learning: Have students make a poster to teach younger students about the benefits of shared responsibilities. L3

Targeted Resources
- ❑ RN Note Taking Guide 5-1 L3 EL
- ❑ ARN Note Taking Guide 5-1 L2
- ❑ TR Practice 5-1
- ❑ TR Enrich 5-1 L4
- ❑ Audio Summary 5-1 L1 L2 EL
- ❑ PHSchool.com: More on families

3. ASSESS

Evaluate Understanding The assignments listed in the Teacher's Edition can help you assess students' mastery of the section content.

Reteach Have students use a Venn diagram to organize the information about responsibilities within the family. L2

Targeted Resources
- ❑ TR Section 5-1 Quiz
- ❑ CTB Chapter 5

KEY

L1 Special Needs	L4 Gifted and Talented
L2 Less Proficient Readers	EL English Language Learners
L3 All Students	

Name ______________ Class ______________ Date ______

Section 5-1 **Practice**

Vocabulary Activity: Families Today

Families today take many forms, all of which share some important characteristics.
Use vocabulary terms from Section 1 to complete this crossword puzzle about families.

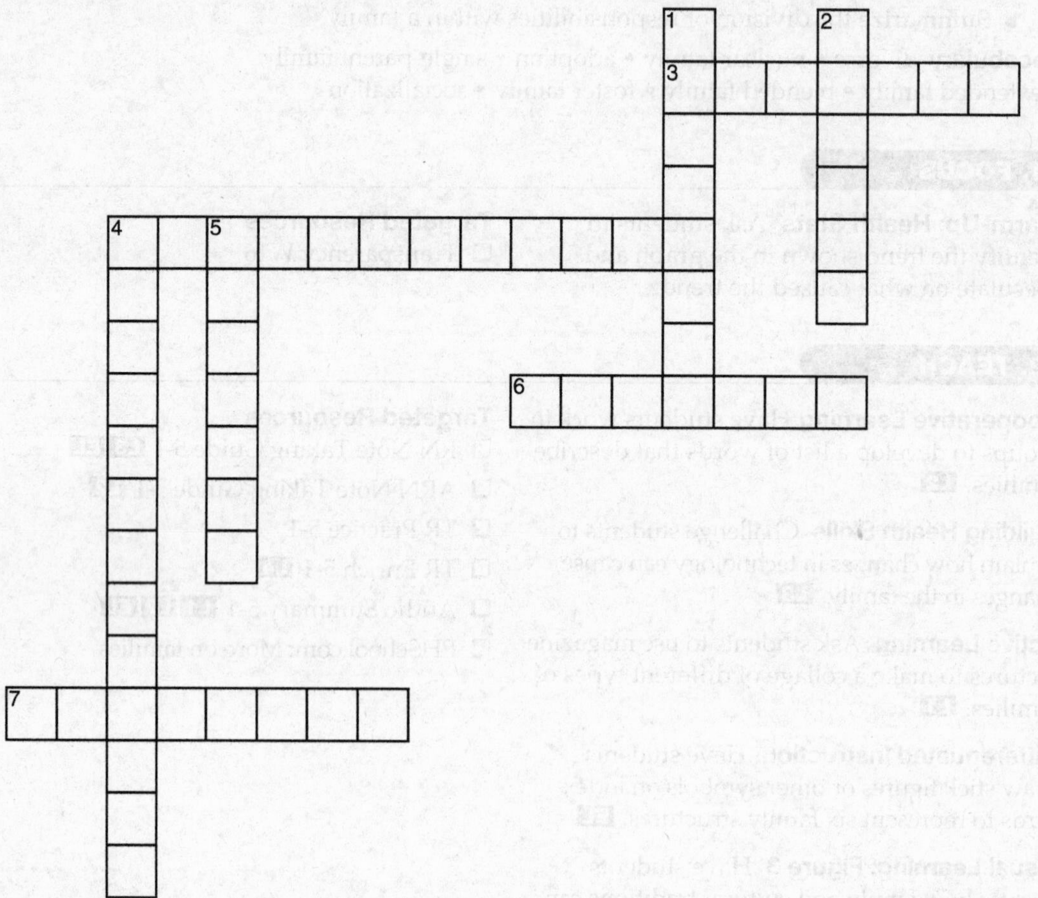

Clues Across

3. a legal arrangement to end a marriage
4. a family that consists of one parent and his or her children
6. a family formed when parents remarry
7. a family that includes relatives such as aunts, grandparents, or cousins

Clues Down

1. the legal process of taking another person's child into the family
2. a family that provides a temporary home for children whose parents are unable to care for them
4. the process by which children learn acceptable behavior
5. a family that consists of a couple and their child or children

Name ______________________ Class ______________________ Date ________

Section 5-1

Enrich

Family Involvement: Responsibilities in Your Family

How families divide up household tasks will vary from family to family. One person may always do a given task, such as taking out the trash. Or maybe one person cooks dinner on week nights and another cooks on weekends. Family members may work together to complete a chore, such as food shopping.

Interview each person in your family who does chores. Use the table to record the answers. Find out which chores they like, which they dislike, and which take the most time. Use what you learn to develop a proposal to assign some chores to different people. For some chores people could work together. Share your proposal with your family.

Person	Like	Dislike	Time-consuming
Myself			

Proposal:

____

____

____

____

____

____

Name ______________________ Class ____________________ Date ______

Section 5-1
Quiz

Write the letter of the correct answer in the space provided.

______ **1.** Grandparents, parents, and children living together form a(an)
- **a.** nuclear family.
- **b.** blended family.
- **c.** extended family.
- **d.** foster family.

______ **2.** What type of family is formed when parents remarry?
- **a.** nuclear
- **b.** blended
- **c.** extended
- **d.** single-parent

______ **3.** Which best describes a nuclear family?
- **a.** a parent, a grandparent, and a child
- **b.** a couple and their foster children
- **c.** a single parent and a child or children
- **d.** a couple and their biological or adopted children

______ **4.** Which best describes the process of socialization?
- **a.** agreeing to legally end a marriage
- **b.** taking another person's child into the family
- **c.** teaching children to behave in an acceptable way
- **d.** adjusting to a blended family when a parent remarries

Decide whether each statement is true or false. Write true *or* false *in the space provided.*

______ **5.** The individual is often called the "basic unit of society."

______ **6.** The trend of postponing marriage has resulted in larger families.

______ **7.** Divorce affects the entire family.

______ **8.** Fathers head most single-parent households.

______ **9.** Providing food, clothing, and shelter is the responsibility of the adults in a family.

______ **10.** Sharing chores is one way that children develop a sense of responsibility.

Name______________________ Class__________ Date__________ M T W T F

Section 5-2

Family Problems — Lesson Plan

Section Objectives

- **List** some causes of stress in families.
- **Describe** three types of abuse that can happen in families.
- **Explain** what problems runaways are likely to have.

Vocabulary separation • domestic abuse • physical abuse • sexual abuse • emotional abuse • neglect • runaway

Time
1 period
1/2 block

Local Standards

1. FOCUS

Warm-Up: Advice Line After students complete their writing, point out that it is normal for families to have problems, but some problems are particularly stressful.

Targeted Resources
- ❑ Transparency W17

2. TEACH

Differentiated Instruction Have students make a concept map that shows the four sources of family stress described in the section. EL

Building Health Skills Have students make posters that inform teens who are dealing with divorce about available resources at school and in the community. L3

Differentiated Instruction Help students create a three-column organizer in which they can record the main ideas about physical abuse, sexual abuse, and emotional abuse. L2

Class Discussion Use the phrase "sticks and stones can break my bones but names will never hurt me" to start a discussion on emotional abuse. L3

Cooperative Learning Ask students to work in small groups to make a list of alternatives to running away. L3

Targeted Resources
- ❑ RN Note Taking Guide 5-2 L3 EL
- ❑ ARN Note Taking Guide 5-2 L2
- ❑ Transparency and Worksheet 12
- ❑ TR Practice 5-2
- ❑ TR Enrich 5-2 L4
- ❑ Audio Summary 5-2 L1 L2 EL
- ❑ Health Links: Updates on divorce

3. ASSESS

Evaluate Understanding The assignments listed in the Teacher's Edition can help you assess students' mastery of the section content.

Reteach Have students write a sentence summarizing the main ideas of the text under each boldface head in the section. L2

Targeted Resources
- ❑ TR Section 5-2 Quiz
- ❑ CTB Chapter 5

KEY

L1 Special Needs	L4 Gifted and Talented
L2 Less Proficient Readers	EL English Language Learners
L3 All Students	

Name ____________ Class ____________ Date ______

Section 5-2 **Practice**

Role-Playing: Dealing With Divorce

Teens whose parents are getting a divorce may experience a wide range of emotions, including anger, sadness, and guilt. A teen's friends can be an important source of support during a divorce.

As a group, read and discuss the first entry in the role-play below. Then complete the role-play to show how one friend can support another who is dealing with a divorce.

Student 1: I can't believe it! My parents just told me that they are getting a divorce. Maybe it's my fault! They argue a lot about me. Anyway, don't expect me to join drama club this year, I couldn't face everyone at the club meetings.

Student 2: ____________________

Student 1: ____________________

Student 2: ____________________

Student 1: ____________________

Student 2: ____________________

Student 1: ____________________

Student 2: ____________________

Name ____________ Class ____________ Date ______

Section 5-2

Enrich

Community Involvement: Family Violence

There are incidents of family violence in every community. Incidents that are reported to police may end up in the local newspaper. There may also be general articles about the overall problem of family violence.

For the next week, cut out and read articles from a local daily newspaper that report incidents of family violence or discuss the general problem of family violence. At the end of the week, answer the following questions.

1. How many articles about family violence did you find? ____________

2. Were the number of reports about family violence in your community higher or lower than you expected? Explain.

____

____

____

3. What were some of the causes of family violence suggested in the articles?

____

____

____

4. What solutions, if any, to the problem of family violence were proposed in the articles?

____

____

____

5. Do you think all incidents of family violence in your community were reported in the paper? Give a reason for your answer.

____

____

____

6. Use your local telephone directory to find two organizations that provide services for victims of family violence.

Name: ____________

Address: ____________

Name: ____________

Address: ____________

Name ______________________ Class __________________ Date ______

Section 5-2

Quiz

Write the letter of the correct answer in the space provided.

______ **1.** when adults fail to provide for children's basic needs		**a.** physical abuse
______ **2.** when a punishment leaves a mark that can be seen the next day		**b.** sexual abuse
______ **3.** when an adult touches a child inappropriately		**c.** emotional abuse
______ **4.** when children constantly hear negative statements about themselves		**d.** neglect

Decide whether each statement is true or false. Write true *or* false *in the space provided.*

______ **5.** When one family member is seriously ill, the whole family experiences stress.

______ **6.** A divorce is when spouses live apart and try to resolve their problems.

______ **7.** Domestic abuse occurs when one spouse abuses the other.

______ **8.** Victims of emotional abuse don't usually require help.

______ **9.** Victims of emotional neglect often have trouble developing a healthy personality.

______ **10.** Runaways often face serious problems, such as illness, crime, and drugs.

Name______________________ Class__________ Date__________ M T W T F

Section 5-3 Keeping the Family Healthy Lesson Plan

Section Objectives

- **List** some characteristics of healthy families.
- **Describe** four skills families need to stay healthy.
- **Identify** places where families can go for help with their problems.

Vocabulary empathy • sibling • support group

Time
2 periods
1 block

Local Standards

1. FOCUS

Warm-Up: Quick Quiz Use the Quick Quiz to start a discussion on the characteristics of a healthy family.

Targeted Resources

- ❑ Transparency W18

2. TEACH

Cooperative Learning Have student groups develop a list of actions that family members can take to demonstrate one characteristic of healthy families. L3

Visual Learning: Figure 9 Challenge students to think of ways to apply the steps for reducing sibling rivalry. Then ask students to make a poster illustrating one of the steps. L2

Differentiated Instruction Have students with mental disorders use role-plays to practice resolving conflicts, expressing emotions, making decisions, and managing time. L1

Cultural Connection Have students describe family traditions from different cultures that can help keep a family healthy. L3

Building Health Skills Have students write to school administrators advocating services for students with family problems. If services are available, have students make posters to make students aware of these services. L3

Targeted Resources

- ❑ RN Note Taking Guide 5-3 L3 EL
- ❑ ARN Note Taking Guide 5-3 L2
- ❑ TR Practice 5-3
- ❑ TR Enrich 5-3 L4
- ❑ Audio Summary 5-3 L1 L2 L3
- ❑ Health Links: Updates on conflict resolution

3. ASSESS

Evaluate Understanding The assignments listed in the Teacher's Edition can help you assess students' mastery of the section content.

Reteach Have students work in pairs, with one student rephrasing the section objectives as questions and the other student locating the answers in the section. L2

Targeted Resources

- ❑ TR Section 5-3 Quiz
- ❑ CTB Chapter 5

KEY

L1 Special Needs	L4 Gifted and Talented
L2 Less Proficient Readers	EL English Language Learners
L3 All Students	

Name ______________ Class ______________ Date ______

Section 5-3

Practice

Group Activity: Characteristics of Healthy Families

Although families come in many different forms, healthy families share certain qualities, or characteristics. When the members of a healthy family interact, these characteristics are evident.

The table below lists characteristics of healthy families. Discuss each characteristic with your group. Then, complete the table by listing three specific statements or actions that could demonstrate each characteristic. The first row is completed for you.

Characteristic	Can be demonstrated by...
Caring and Commitment	**1.** offering to help a sibling study **2.** expressing concern when a parent is ill **3.** not sulking when you get a *No* answer to a request
Respect and Appreciation	**1.** ______________ **2.** ______________ **3.** ______________
Empathy	**1.** ______________ **2.** ______________ **3.** ______________
Communication	**1.** ______________ **2.** ______________ **3.** ______________
Cooperation	**1.** ______________ **2.** ______________ **3.** ______________

Name ______________________ Class ____________________ Date ________

Section 5-3 **Enrich**

Class Debate: Resolving a Family Conflict

Family rules are a common cause of conflict between parents and teens. Many teens want more independence and control over their life. Parents want to be able to set limits for teens.

Read the following description of a family conflict. Then work in small groups to prepare for a debate. Make a list of points you could use to support the mother's point of view and a list of points you could use to support Edgar's point of view. Your teacher will then select teams to debate the issue. After the debate, discuss how Edgar and his mother could resolve this conflict.

It's 11:30 P.M., and Edgar's mother is frantic—and angry. It is the third time this month that Edgar has missed his 11:00 curfew. Edgar hasn't called to say he is running late, so his mother has no idea if he is safe. The other two times Edgar missed curfew, his mother gave him a verbal warning.

When Edgar finally walks through the door at 11:35, his mother is happy to see that he is safe. However, she is still angry. She immediately tells Edgar that he will be grounded for a month and that he can no longer be on the track team. She also takes away Edgar's cell phone. She doesn't give Edgar a chance to explain that it took him 30 minutes to convince the friend who was driving to leave the party.

Mother's Viewpoint: ______________________________

____

____

____

____

____

Edgar's Viewpoint: ______________________________

____

____

____

____

____

Name ______________________ Class ____________________ Date ________

Section 5-3

Quiz

Write the letter of the correct answer in the space provided.

_____ **1.** *Siblings* is a term that means
a. parents and their biological or adopted children.
b. grandparents and parents.
c. brothers and sisters.
d. cousins.

_____ **2.** Which example is a constructive way to express an emotion?
a. All you ever do is criticize me.
b. You never wash the dinner dishes.
c. Why don't you ever listen to me when I talk?
d. I get upset when you borrow my clothes without asking.

_____ **3.** Which best describes a support group?
a. a therapist who works with individuals
b. an agency that deals with many family problems
c. a group of people with a specific problem who help each other cope with the problem
d. a therapist who works with families

_____ **4.** People who answer a crisis hotline can
a. refer people to other sources of help.
b. offer counseling for families.
c. help people receive financial aid.
d. provide therapy for individuals.

_____ **5.** In a healthy family, family members
a. are quick to judge or place blame on others.
b. keep their thoughts and emotions to themselves.
c. consider only their own needs when making decisions.
d. discuss issues and problems in a respectful way.

Write the letter of the correct answer in the space provided.

_____ **6.** understanding another person's thoughts and feelings

_____ **7.** thanking other family members for what they do

_____ **8.** telling other family members what you think and feel

_____ **9.** dividing household chores fairly

_____ **10.** staying together through good times and bad

a. appreciation
b. cooperation
c. empathy
d. commitment
e. communication

Name ____________________ Class ____________________ Date ________

Chapter 5 Test

Write the letter of the correct answer in the space provided..

______ **1.** a couple and their biological or adopted children

______ **2.** grandparents, parents, and children living together

______ **3.** a father and his biological children

______ **4.** a parent, a stepparent, and their children

a. extended family
b. blended family
c. nuclear family
d. single-parent family

Write the letter of the correct answer in the space provided.

______ **5.** Which of these is called the basic unit of society?
a. individual
b. family
c. neighborhood
d. city

______ **6.** Telling a child that he or she is worthless is a form of
a. neglect.
b. emotional abuse.
c. physical abuse.
d. sexual abuse.

______ **7.** The key to conflict resolution is
a. voicing your position loudly and often.
b. ignoring the other person's viewpoint.
c. trying to resolve a problem when you are angry.
d. talking openly, honestly, and lovingly.

______ **8.** Which term describes the ability to understand another person's feelings?
a. empathy
b. appreciation
c. cooperation
d. commitment

______ **9.** A network of people who work together to cope with a particular problem is a
a. crisis center.
b. family therapist.
c. support group.
d. family agency.

Name ______________________ Class ________________ Date ______

Chapter 5: Test *(continued)*

Decide whether each statement is true or false. Write true *or* false *in the space provided.*

_____ **10.** Compared to the 1950s, people today tend to get married at a younger age.

_____ **11.** Children's responsibilities within the family include following family rules.

_____ **12.** A separation always leads to divorce.

_____ **13.** Most abuse stems from one person's desire to have control over others.

_____ **14.** People who answer a crisis hotline need to be sympathetic listeners.

Write the word that best completes each sentence in the space provided.

15. Another term for brothers and sisters is ______________.

16. The process of teaching children to behave in an acceptable way is ______________________.

17. When parents fail to provide love, security, or food for their child, it is called ______________.

18. A fifteen-year-old who stays away from home without permission for two or more nights is called a(an) ______________.

Use complete sentences to answer the following questions.

19. Identify and describe three factors that have changed the American family.

____

____

____

____

____

____

20. Explain why financial problems are a cause of family stress. Then, identify two ways that a teen could help his or her family manage financial problems.

____

____

____

____

____

Name ______________________ Class ______________ Date ________

Chapter 6

Personal Inventory

Checklist for Choosing Friends

Friendships offer the opportunity to build self-esteem, learn more about yourself, and experiment with different roles. Friends can give you a sense of belonging and a chance to be part of a caring, supportive relationship. What qualities do you look for when you choose someone as a friend?

Read the list below, and make checkmarks by the eight characteristics that you consider most important in a friend.

_____ cooperative	_____ tolerant	_____ calm
_____ creative	_____ intelligent	_____ caring
_____ loyal	_____ honest	_____ reliable
_____ supportive	_____ athletic	_____ outgoing
_____ kind	_____ confident	_____ respectful
_____ good listener	_____ responsible	_____ studious
_____ decisive	_____ fun-loving	_____ hard working
_____ sensitive	_____ daring	_____ ambitious

From the qualities you checked, choose the four that you think are most important. List them below and explain why you chose them.

First choice: ____

____

____

Second choice: ____

____

____

Third choice: ____

____

____

Fourth choice: ____

____

____

Name________________________ Class__________ Date__________ M T W T F

Section 6-1

Skills for Healthy Relationships Lesson Plan

Section Objectives

- **Describe** four skills that contribute to effective communication.
- **Explain** how cooperation and compromise help build healthy relationships.

Vocabulary communication • "I" message • active listening • passive • aggressive • assertive • body language • eye contact • cooperation • compromise

Time
1 period
½ block

Local Standards

1. FOCUS

Warm-Up: Advice Line Have students discuss the phrase "stand up for yourself" and describe ways to stand up for oneself.

Targeted Resources

- ❑ Transparency W19

2. TEACH

Building Health Skills Have students make a checklist that can be used to assess their active-listening skills. L3

Cooperative Learning Ask students to work in small groups to demonstrate how active listening can be used in everyday situations. L2

Differentiated Instruction Ask students to verbally restate several sentences as "I" messages. EL

Active Learning Have students examine the use of body language in photographs of people having conversations. L1

Differentiated Instruction Ask students to interview an adult about the importance of cooperation in the workplace. L4

Journal Writing Ask students to write a journal entry about how the ability to compromise can strengthen a relationship. L3

Targeted Resources

- ❑ RN Note Taking Guide 6-1 L3 EL
- ❑ ARN Note Taking Guide 6-1 L2
- ❑ Transparency and Worksheet 13
- ❑ TR Practice 6-1
- ❑ TR Enrich 6-1 L4
- ❑ Audio Summary 6-1 L1 L2 EL
- ❑ PHSchool.com: More on being assertive

3. ASSESS

Evaluate Understanding The assignments listed in the Teacher's Edition can help you assess students' mastery of the section content.

Reteach Have students demonstrate various communication skills. L2

Targeted Resources

- ❑ TR Section 6-1 Quiz
- ❑ CTB Chapter 6

KEY

L1 Special Needs	L4 Gifted and Talented
L2 Less Proficient Readers	EL English Language Learners
L3 All Students	

Name ______________________ Class ____________________ Date ______

Section 6-1 **Practice**

Building Health Skills: Communication Styles

People who are passive may hold back their true feelings. People who are aggressive can appear threatening or disrespectful to others. The most effective communication style is assertive communication. It allows you to express your thoughts and feeling while demonstrating respect for others and for yourself.

Classify each statement below as passive, aggressive, or assertive. Give a reason for your choice. If the statement is passive or aggressive, rewrite it to be assertive.

1. We lost the relay because you were so slow. I don't know why the coach put a loser like you on the team.

Communication Type: ______________________________

Reason: ______________________________

Rewrite (if necessary): ______________________________

____

2. Why would you want to play a duet with me? You play so much better than I do.

Communication Type: ______________________________

Reason: ______________________________

Rewrite (if necessary): ______________________________

____

3. I know you couldn't do much work on our group project while you were ill. What can you do now to help us finish the project?

Communication Type: ______________________________

Reason: ______________________________

Rewrite (if necessary): ______________________________

____

4. Whatever you want to do is fine with me.

Communication Type: ______________________________

Reason: ______________________________

Rewrite (if necessary): ______________________________

____

5. What a crybaby! So you didn't get a part in the school play. It's not important.

Communication Type: ______________________________

Reason: ______________________________

Rewrite (if necessary): ______________________________

Name ______________________ Class ____________________ Date ________

Section 6-1 **Enrich**

Community Involvement: Teaching Cooperation and Compromise

Cooperation and compromise are important skills that can help you maintain healthy relationships. Both cooperation and compromise are skills that get easier with practice.

With a group, plan a lesson to teach students in grades 3 and 4 about cooperation and compromise. Use the questions below to help you get started. Ask your teacher to help you arrange a visit to a classroom to share your lesson.

1. How will you introduce your lesson?

____

____

____

____

2. What activities will the students take part in during the lesson?

____

____

____

____

____

3. How will you conclude your lesson?

____

____

____

____

____

4. How will you assess what the students have learned?

____

____

____

____

____

Name ________________ Class ________________ Date ______

Section 6-1

Quiz

Write the letter of the correct answer in the space provided.

______	**1.** communication that holds back the speaker's true feelings	**a.** aggressive
______	**2.** communication that expresses feelings in a respectful way	**b.** active listening
______	**3.** communication that includes threatening or disrespectful messages	**c.** passive
		d. assertive

Decide whether each statement is true or false. Write true *or* false *in the space provided.*

______ **4.** "I" messages usually put the listener on the defensive.

______ **5.** Showing interest, asking questions, and nodding your head are all active-listening skills.

______ **6.** In every culture, people expect you to make eye contact during a conversation.

______ **7.** Cooperation requires mutual trust.

______ **8.** Body language usually conveys the speaker's true feelings.

______ **9.** You should compromise in every situation.

______ **10.** Compromise involves giving up something to reach an agreement.

Name____________________ Class__________ Date__________ M T W T F

Section 6-2 **Friendships** **Lesson Plan**

Section Objectives

- **Explain** the importance of having friends.
- **Distinguish** different types of friendships.
- **Describe** some problems that occur in friendships.

Vocabulary friendship • gender roles • clique • peer pressure

Time
2 periods
1 block

Local Standards

1. FOCUS

Warm-Up: Quick Quiz After students complete the quiz, have volunteers share their responses with the class.

Targeted Resources

- ❑ Transparency W20

2. TEACH

Class Discussion Ask students to identify and discuss types of support they can offer to their friends. L2

Differentiated Instruction Have students use magazine pictures, words, and drawings to make a poster about friendship. L1

Cooperative Learning Ask students to practice asking questions that require more than a *yes* or *no* answer. EL

Building Health Skills Have students use passages from fiction to illustrate the qualities of a good friend. Discuss the influence these passages might have on readers. L4

Cultural Connection Encourage students to discuss how gender roles vary among cultures, and how people learn traditional roles. L3

Cooperative Learning After students make a list of typical problems that can arise in a friendship, have them discuss one of the problems in detail. L3

Targeted Resources

- ❑ RN Note Taking Guide 6-2 L3 EL
- ❑ ARN Note Taking Guide 6-2 L2
- ❑ TR Practice 6-2
- ❑ TR Enrich 6-2 L4
- ❑ Audio Summary 6-2 L1 L2 EL
- ❑ PHSchool.com: More on friendships

3. ASSESS

Evaluate Understanding The assignments listed in the Teacher's Edition can help you assess students' mastery of the section content.

Reteach Have students work with a partner to identify positive solutions to those problems that can arise in friendships. L2

Targeted Resources

- ❑ TR Section 6-2 Quiz
- ❑ CTB Chapter 6

KEY

L1 Special Needs	L4 Gifted and Talented
L2 Less Proficient Readers	EL English Language Learners
L3 All Students	

Name ______________________ Class ____________________ Date ________

Section 6-2

Practice

Concept Check: Understanding Friendship

Friends provide encouragement, support, and understanding. Interacting with friends gives you a chance to build self-esteem and try new experiences.

Use the information from the section to complete the concept map about friendships and to answer the question below.

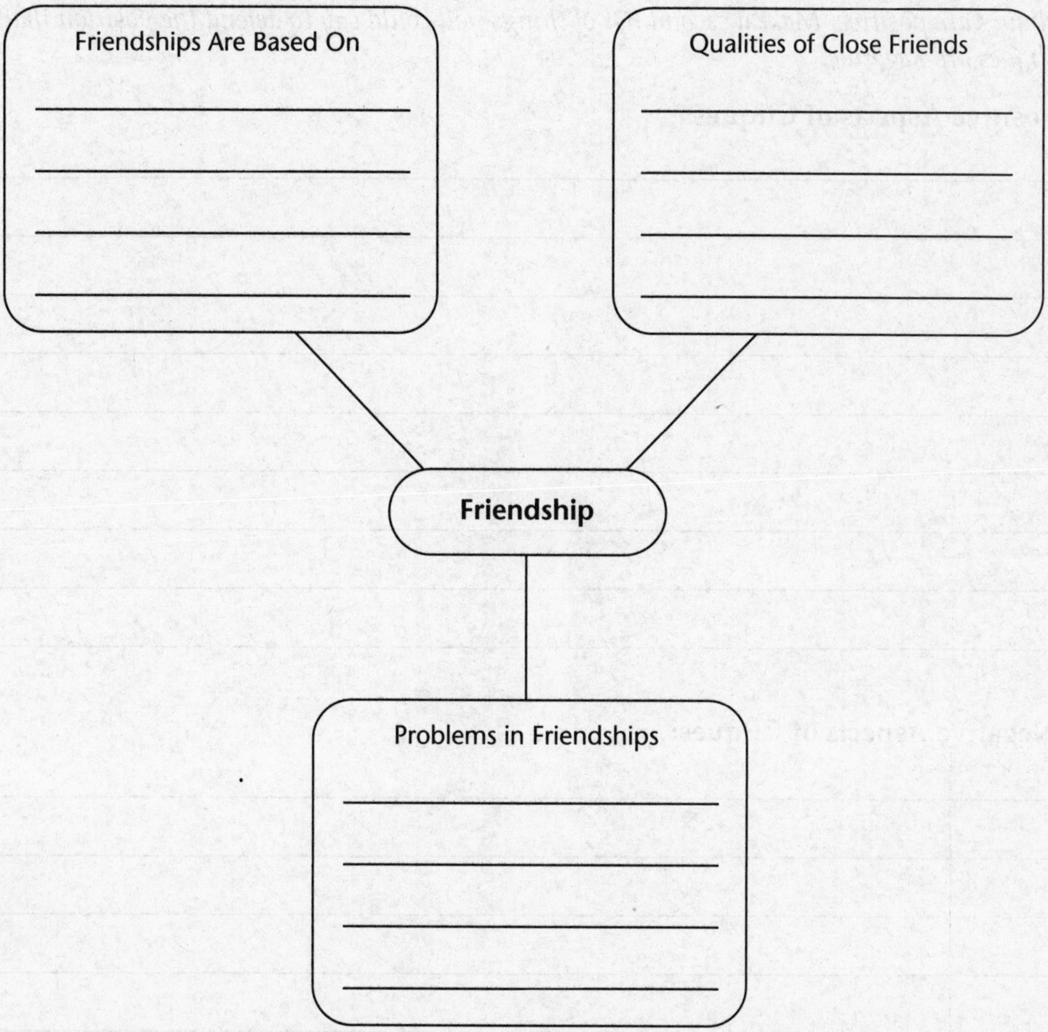

Friendships Are Based On

____

____

____

____

Qualities of Close Friends

____

____

____

____

Friendship

Problems in Friendships

____

____

____

____

What is one positive strategy that can be used to solve a problem in a friendship?

____

____

____

____

Name ______________________ Class ____________________ Date __________

Section 6-2 **Enrich**

Class Debate: Are Cliques Positive or Negative?

Cliques are small, closed circles of friends. Members of a clique tend to have similar backgrounds and interests. People disagree on whether the presence of cliques at school has a positive or negative effect on the school environment. There are arguments that can be made in support of cliques and against cliques.

Work in small groups to make a list of things you could say to defend the position that cliques are positive. Make a second list of things you could say to defend the position that cliques are negative.

Positive Aspects of Cliques:

Negative Aspects of Cliques:

Name ______________ Class ______________ Date ______

Section 6-2

Quiz

Write the letter of the correct answer in the space provided.

_____ **1.** sticking with a friend through good times and bad

_____ **2.** being truthful, even when it is not easy

_____ **3.** trying not to let a friend down

_____ **4.** being caring and sensitive to feelings

a. honesty
b. reliability
c. jealousy
d. loyalty
e. empathy

Write the letter of the correct answer in the space provided.

_____ **5.** A movie that shows females as less assertive than males is portraying traditional
a. gender roles.
b. attitudes.
c. behaviors.
d. communication styles.

_____ **6.** A problem in a friendship that may occur when one friend has something the other does not have is
a. cruelty. **b.** envy.
c. jealousy. **d.** cliques.

_____ **7.** Which tip gives good advice for making new friends?
a. Be yourself.
b. Put on an act.
c. Be disrespectful.
d. Avoid people with similar interests.

_____ **8.** Which term describes an exclusive, closed group of friends?
a. peer group **b.** in group
c. social circle **d.** clique

_____ **9.** When one member of a close friendship wants to make additonal close friends, the other friend may experience
a. cruelty. **b.** envy.
c. jealousy. **d.** cliques.

_____ **10.** When people dress in the same style as their friends, they may be
a. experiencing peer pressure.
b. searching for an identify.
c. reflecting traditional gender roles.
d. being empathetic.

Name____________________ Class__________ Date__________ M T W T F

Section 6-3

Responsible Relationships Lesson Plan

Section Objectives

- **List** some things you can learn about a person by dating.
- **Describe** the cycle of violence.

Vocabulary infatuation • dating violence • date rape

Time
1 period
½ block

Local Standards

1. FOCUS

Warm-Up: Myth/Fact Have students discuss the myth and identify precautions that can be taken to reduce the risk of being raped by a friend or acquaintance.

Targeted Resources
- ❑ Transparency W21

2. TEACH

Active Learning Ask students to use index cards to organize information about qualities they would like to find in a date. L2

Addressing Misconceptions Point out to students that not all teens date. L3

Active Learning Ask students to do brief presentations about dating customs in their cultures. EL

Differentiated Instruction Ask students to prepare outlines of the section and to review their outlines after they complete the section. L2

Cooperative Learning Have students work together to make posters about the warning signs of abuse. L1

Building Health Skills Ask students to work in small groups to develop a plan to advocate for a friend who is in an abusive relationship. L3

Targeted Resources
- ❑ RN Note Taking Guide 6-3 L3 EL
- ❑ ARN Note Taking Guide 6-3 L2
- ❑ Transparency and Worksheet 14
- ❑ TR Practice 6-3
- ❑ TR Enrich 6-3 L4
- ❑ Audio Summary 6-3 L1 L2 EL
- ❑ Health Links: Updates on dating responsibly

3. ASSESS

Evaluate Understanding The assignments listed in the Teacher's Edition can help you assess students' mastery of the section content.

Reteach Ask students to work in pairs to review the boldface headings in the chapter and identify the main ideas and vocabulary terms associated with each heading. L2

Targeted Resources
- ❑ TR Section 6-3 Quiz
- ❑ CTB Chapter 6

KEY

L1 Special Needs
L2 Less Proficient Readers
L3 All Students
L4 Gifted and Talented
EL English Language Learners

Name ______________________ Class __________________ Date ______

Group Activity: The Cycle of Violence

Dating violence is a pattern of emotional, physical, or sexual abuse that occurs in some dating relationships. Understanding the cycle of violence can help you avoid abuse in your own relationships and recognize when others are experiencing abuse.

Use the diagram to describe how an abuser might behave at different stages of the cycle of violence. For each stage of the cycle, an example is provided to get you started.

Tension-Building

picks fights all of the time

____

____

____

____

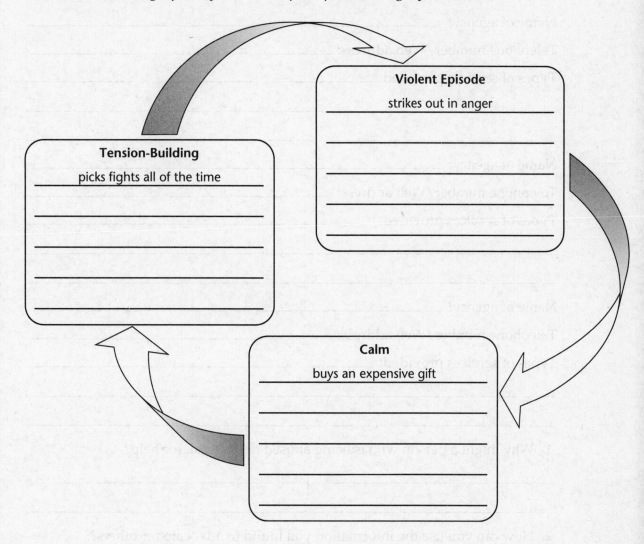

Violent Episode

strikes out in anger

____

____

____

____

Calm

buys an expensive gift

____

____

____

____

Name ____________________ Class ____________________ Date ________

Consumer Skills: Locating Community Resources

In most communities, there are organizations that help people who are in abusive relationships. These organizations include counseling services, shelters, and information hotlines.

Use the Internet, a telephone directory, or other resources to find information about services in your community for those who are being abused. Record the information below. Then answer the questions.

Name of agency: ____________________

Telephone number/Web address: ____________________

Types of services provided: ____________________

____

____

Name of agency: ____________________

Telephone number/Web address: ____________________

Types of services provided: ____________________

____

____

Name of agency: ____________________

Telephone number/Web address: ____________________

Types of services provided: ____________________

____

____

1. Why might a person who is being abused need to ask for help?

____

____

2. How can you use the information you found to advocate for others?

____

____

3. What are some warning signs that a relationship may lead to abuse?

____

____

Name ______________________ Class ________________ Date ______

Section 6-3

Quiz

Decide whether each statement is true or false. Write true *or* false *in the space provided.*

______ **1.** Infatuation is an intense attraction to another person.

______ **2.** In abusive dating relationships, the abuser is always male.

______ **3.** A person who is abused often has an increase in self-confidence.

______ **4.** Date rape is a form of abuse.

______ **5.** Abuse in a dating relationship is never the victim's fault.

Write the letter of the correct answer in the space provided. You can use a letter more than once.

______ **6.** The abuser shows jealous and possessive behavior.

______ **7.** The abuser asks for forgiveness.

______ **8.** The abuser causes serious injury.

______ **9.** The abuser buys presents.

______ **10.** The abuser has unpredictable mood swings.

a. tension-building

b. violent episode

c. calm

Name________________________ Class__________ Date__________ M T W T F

Section 6-4

Choosing Abstinence — Lesson Plan

Section Objectives

- **Identify** some risks of sexual intimacy.
- **Explain** why emotional intimacy is important in close relationships.
- **List** some skills that can help you choose abstinence.

Vocabulary emotional intimacy • abstinence

Time
1 period
½ block

Local Standards

1. FOCUS

Warm-Up: Health Stats Ask students to discuss the influences on teens' decisions about sex.

Targeted Resources
- ❑ Transparency W22

2. TEACH

Visual Learning: Figure 11 Ask students to discuss how having to take care of a baby would affect a teen mother. L1

Differentiated Instruction Have students use a graphic organizer to outline the information about the risks of sexual intimacy. L2

Building Vocabulary Discuss the general meaning of the term *abstinence*. EL

Building Media Literacy Ask students to analyze television programs about teens to see if information about abstinence or the risks of sexual intimacy are included. L3

Cooperative Learning Have students work in small groups to identify high-pressure dating situations and low-pressure alternatives to these situations. L2

Building Health Skills Have students work in small groups to practice refusal skills. L3

Targeted Resources
- ❑ RN Note Taking Guide 6-4 L3 EL
- ❑ ARN Note Taking Guide 6-4 L2
- ❑ TR Practice 6-4
- ❑ TR Enrich 6-4 L4
- ❑ Audio Summary 6-4 L1 L2 EL
- ❑ Health Links: Updates on abstinence

3. ASSESS

Evaluate Understanding The assignments listed in the Teacher's Edition can help you assess students' mastery of the section content.

Reteach Ask students to make a bulleted list of risks associated with sexual intimacy and to write a one-sentence description of each abstinence skill. L2

Targeted Resources
- ❑ TR Section 6-4 Quiz
- ❑ CTB Chapter 6

KEY

L1	Special Needs	L4	Gifted and Talented
L2	Less Proficient Readers	EL	English Language Learners
L3	All Students		

Name ______________________ Class ______________________ Date ________

Building Health Skills: Abstinence Skills

Abstinence skills are healthful behaviors that you can practice to protect your emotional and physical health. When you use abstinence skills, you are also using other essential health skills.

For each abstinence skill, explain how the skill builds on communicating or making decisions. Be as specific as possible. For example, you may want to refer to specific communication skills or steps in the DECIDE process.

1. Setting clear limits:

____

____

____

____

____

2. Communicating your limits:

____

____

____

____

____

3. Avoiding high-pressure situations:

____

____

____

____

____

4. Asserting yourself:

____

____

____

____

____

Name ______________________ Class ____________________ Date ______

Section 6-4 **Enrich**

Family Involvement: Influences on Teens' Decisions

Teens receive messages from many sources about sexual intimacy and the importance of choosing abstinence. These sources include parents or other adult family members, peers, teachers, clergy, and media.

Give a copy of this worksheet to a parent or other trusted adult. Working on your own, fill in the table. Record the message you think a typical teen receives from each source. Rank the sources from 1 to 5, with 1 having the most influence and 5 having the least influence on a typical teen. Meet to discuss your responses. Then answer the questions.

Source	Message About Abstinence	Influence
Parents or Guardians		
Friends		
Teachers		
Clergy		
Media		

1. If there were any major differences between the messages you and the adult wrote for any source, describe the difference. How would you explain the difference?

____

____

____

2. Did you and the adult have the same rankings for the sources? If not, why do you think the rankings were different?

____

____

____

3. Do you think that doing this activity helped you improve your ability to communicate with your parent or other trusted adult? Why or why not?

____

____

____

Name ______________________ Class ___________________ Date ______

Section 6-4

Quiz

Write the letter of the correct answer in the space provided.

______ **1.** A decision to be sexually intimate
- **a.** does not change a relationship.
- **b.** always leads to increased emotional intimacy.
- **c.** adds complications that may end a relationship.
- **d.** always makes a relationship stronger.

______ **2.** Which of these does *not* build emotional intimacy in a relationship?
- **a.** being honest with each other
- **b.** trying to control the other person's behavior
- **c.** sharing your feelings and dreams
- **d.** being supportive of each other

______ **3.** What proportion of teenage girls who engage in sexual intercourse become pregnant?
- **a.** one in six
- **b.** one in twenty-five
- **c.** one in fifty
- **d.** one in one hundred

______ **4.** Which of these can help teens choose abstinence?
- **a.** making hasty decisions
- **b.** having a passive communication style
- **c.** never talking about sexual feelings
- **d.** avoiding high-pressure situations

Decide whether each statement is true or false. Write true *or* false *in the space provided.*

______ **5.** Teen parents often feel trapped and overwhelmed.

______ **6.** Emotional intimacy includes honesty, openness, and affection.

______ **7.** In teen relationships, sexual intimacy always increases emotional intimacy.

______ **8.** Setting clear limits is a skill that can be used to make healthy decisions about sex.

______ **9.** Sexually transmitted infections can cause serious health problems.

______ **10.** All teens are sexually active.

Name ______________________ Class ____________________ Date ________

Chapter 6 Test

Write the letter of the correct answer in the space provided.

______ **1.** The process of sharing thoughts, feelings, and information is
a. cooperation. **b.** loyalty.
c. communication. **d.** empathy.

______ **2.** A friend you can always count on demonstrates the quality of
a. loyalty. **b.** honesty.
c. empathy. **d.** reliability.

______ **3.** A teen who has a intense crush on a movie star is experiencing
a. emotional intimacy.
b. casual friendship.
c. infatuation.
d. admiration.

______ **4.** Which term describes the decision to refrain from sexual activity?
a. empathy **b.** abstinence
c. intimacy **d.** infatuation

______ **5.** Which of these is a warning sign of abuse in a dating relationship?
a. Each person shows a willingness to compromise.
b. The couple likes to spend time with family and friends.
c. One person always worries about saying and doing the right thing.
d. Each person tries to boost the self-esteem of the other.

Write the letter of the correct answer in the space provided.

______ **6.** a communication style that demonstrates respect for yourself and others

______ **7.** a communication style that demonstrates a lack of respect for others

______ **8.** a communication style that demonstrates a lack of self-respect for yourself

a. aggressive
b. passive
c. active
d. assertive

Name ______________________ Class ________________ Date ______

Chapter 6: **Test** *(continued)*

Write the word or phrase that best completes each sentence in the space provided.

9. Working together toward a common goal, or ______________, is an important skill at home and at school.

10. When two people ______________, both give up something in order to reach agreement.

11. A narrow, exclusive group of friends is a(an) ______________.

12. A pattern of emotional, physical, or sexual abuse that occurs in a dating relationship is ______________.

13. The ______________ that can develop in close relationships is demonstrated by honesty, respect, and trust.

Decide whether each statement is true or false. Write true or false in the space provided.

______ **14.** Active listening is important only in the classroom.

______ **15.** Friendships offer a sense of belonging.

______ **16.** Gender roles are the same in every culture.

______ **17.** Going out with a group is one strategy for avoiding date rape.

______ **18.** Teens who engage in sexual intimacy risk pregnancy and sexually transmitted infections.

Use complete sentences to answer the following questions.

19. Restate the following sentence as an "I" message: *You never do your part of our group projects!* Then explain why "I" messages are an effective way to communicate.

20. Describe one advantage and one disadvantage of steady dating.

Name ______________________ Class ________________ Date ______

Chapter 7

Personal Inventory

Your Anger Style

This inventory will help you better understand how you usually deal with anger. Be honest as you answer the questions. After you complete the inventory, your teacher will explain how to evaluate your answers.

Consider each statement below and circle the letter of the answer that most closely represents how you would probably react.

1. A friend is dancing too close with your steady date. You would
a. challenge your friend to a fight.
b. ignore what is happening, but decide that the friendship is over.
c. talk with your friend and your date about what is going on.

2. A friend tells some crude jokes about your ethnic group. You would
a. respond with challenging words and aggressive body language.
b. not respond at all because you really like this particular friend.
c. explain why you dislike the jokes.

3. A sibling has really been getting on your nerves. You would
a. beat up your sibling the next time he or she bothers you.
b. decide that there isn't much you can do about the problem.
c. arrange a family meeting where you can discuss the problem.

4. Someone you never liked is spreading rumors about you. You would
a. slap the person the next time your paths cross.
b. try to avoid running into the person.
c. tell the person to stop spreading rumors about you.

5. When you are in a situation that makes you angry, you often think
a. no one is going to push *me* around.
b. all I want to do is get out of here.
c. I have to find a way to make this situation better.

6. If you were thinking of ways to get even with a person, you would
a. decide which plan you like best and go ahead with it.
b. tell a friend about your plan, but not go through with it.
c. decide that it is time to tell the person how you feel.

7. When you are angry, you often
a. think about hitting someone or something.
b. go for a walk or take a nap.
c. talk things over with a friend.

Name____________________ Class__________ Date__________ M T W T F

Section 7-1

What Is Violence? Lesson Plan

Section Objectives

- **Describe** all of the costs related to violence.
- **Identify** five risk factors for violence.

Vocabulary violence • homicide • victim • assailant • territorial gang

Time
2 periods
1 block

Local Standards

1. FOCUS

Warm-Up: Myth/Fact Ask students to share their ideas about why many people believe strangers commit most violent acts.

Targeted Resources
- ❑ Transparency W23

2. TEACH

Building Media Literacy Give each group a newspaper article about a non-fatal violent act, and ask them to analyze the coverage of costs to the victim, the assailant, and society. L3

Class Discussion Ask students to brainstorm a list of factors that would make a person more likely to become involved with violence. L2

Cooperative Learning Have small groups develop proposals for how to reduce violence in poor neighborhoods. L3

Differentiated Instruction Have students who are visually impaired use a modified version of the checklist for analyzing video games to analyze audio games. L1

Cooperative Learning Have students discuss what needs a gang might meet and brainstorm other ways to meet those needs. L2

Journal Writing Have students evaluate which of the six risks factors for violence influence their lives. L3

Targeted Resources
- ❑ RN Note Taking Guide 7-1 L3 EL
- ❑ ARN Note Taking Guide 7-1 L2
- ❑ TR Practice 7-1
- ❑ TR Enrich 7-1 L4
- ❑ Audio Summary 7-1 L1 L2 EL
- ❑ PHSchool.com: More on media violence

3. ASSESS

Evaluate Understanding The assignments listed in the Teacher's Edition can help you assess students' mastery of the section content.

Reteach Work with students to make an outline of section content. L2

Targeted Resources
- ❑ TR Section 7-1 Quiz
- ❑ CTB Chapter 7

KEY

L1 Special Needs	L4 Gifted and Talented
L2 Less Proficient Readers	EL English Language Learners
L3 All Students	

Name ______________________ Class ______________________ Date ________

Section 7-1

Practice

Skill-Building Activity: Risk Factors For Violence

Health professionals, educators, and government officials need to work together to reduce the major risk factors for violence, which are poverty, family violence, media violence, availability of weapons, drug abuse, and membership in gangs. You can help by advocating for strategies that address these risk factors.

Work with a partner. For each risk factor, propose one strategy that you think would help to reduce this risk. For example, what could be done to reduce the frustration of people living in poor neighborhoods?

Poverty: ____

____

____

Family Violence: ____

____

____

Media Violence: ____

____

____

Availability of Weapons: ____

____

____

Drug Abuse: ____

____

____

Membership in Gangs: ____

____

____

Name ______________ Class ______________ Date ______

Section 7-1 **Enrich**

Research Project: **Violence on Television**

The amount of violence on television is of great concern to parents, educators, and psychologists. How much violence do you see on TV?

Pick two of your favorite television shows that tend to include violence. Before you watch an episode of each show, read the questions below. Record what you observe in the spaces provided. Use your completed worksheet for a class discussion on TV violence.

Name of show: ______________

Time of day: ______________

How many violent acts occurred in the show? ______________

What kind of violent acts were they? ______________

Did any characters try to stop a fight from occurring? If so, how?

Name of show: ______________

Time of day: ______________

How many violent acts occurred in the show? ______________

What kind of violent acts were they? ______________

Did any characters try to stop a fight from occurring? If so, how?

Name ______________________ Class ____________________ Date ______

Section 7-1

Quiz

Write the letter of the correct answer in the space provided.

______ **1.** What is the second leading cause of death for people aged 15 to 24?
- **a.** gang violence
- **b.** homicide
- **c.** drug abuse
- **d.** motor vehicle crashes

______ **2.** The people who experience fear after violent acts are
- **a.** victims.
- **b.** assailants.
- **c.** society as a whole.
- **d.** all of the above.

______ **3.** The rate of violence is highest in
- **a.** poor urban communities.
- **b.** suburban communities.
- **c.** foreign countries.
- **d.** wealthy communities.

______ **4.** Television and movies show violent acts
- **a.** because violence is a part of life.
- **b.** to warn about the dangers of violence.
- **c.** to encourage violence as a response to conflict.
- **d.** to keep viewers glued to the screen.

______ **5.** Alcohol is a risk factor for violence because people who abuse alcohol
- **a.** think before they act.
- **b.** have poor judgment.
- **c.** avoid confrontations.
- **d.** belong to gangs.

Write the letter of the correct answer in the space provided.

______ **6.** the threat of or actual use of physical force against oneself or another person

______ **7.** a group that is organized to control a specific neighborhood or "turf"

______ **8.** a person who is attacked

______ **9.** the intentional killing of one person by another

______ **10.** a person who attacks another person

- **a.** victim
- **b.** homicide
- **c.** territorial gang
- **d.** violence
- **e.** abuse
- **f.** assailant

Name____________________ Class__________ Date__________ M T W T F

Section 7-2

Violence in Schools Lesson Plan

Section Objectives

- **Explain** the relationship between harassment and the use of weapons at school.
- **Describe** effective ways to reduce bullying, hazing, sexual harassment, and hate violence in schools.

Time
2 periods
1 block

Local Standards

Vocabulary harassment • bullying • cyber bullying • hazing • sexual harassment • hate violence • prejudice • stereotype • intolerance • discrimination • vandalism

1. FOCUS

Warm-Up: Health Stats Ask students to explain the trend shown on a graph of students who felt unsafe at school.

Targeted Resources
- ❑ Transparency W24

2. TEACH

Active Learning Ask students to interview a school administrator about the school's policy on weapons brought to school. L3

Visual Learning: Figure 5 Call on volunteers to describe incidents of bullying they have witnessed and suggest ways the bullying could have been stopped. L2

Class Discussion Lead a class discussion on the dangers of hazing. L2

Building Health Skills Have pairs of students write a role-play that shows how a female student could communicate her displeasure to a male student who is sexually harassing her or to school authorities. L3

Building Health Skills Have students work in small groups to develop a creative way to address intolerance at school. L4

Targeted Resources
- ❑ RN Note Taking Guide 7-2 L3 EL
- ❑ ARN Note Taking Guide 7-2 L2
- ❑ Transparency and Worksheet 15
- ❑ TR Practice 7-2
- ❑ TR Enrich 7-2 L4
- ❑ Audio Summary 7-2 L1 L2 EL
- ❑ Health Links: Updates on bullying

3. ASSESS

Evaluate Understanding The assignments listed in the Teacher's Edition can help you assess students' mastery of the section content.

Reteach Ask students to rewrite the section objectives as questions and then write answers to the questions. L2

Targeted Resources
- ❑ TR Section 7-2 Quiz
- ❑ CTB Chapter 7

KEY

L1 Special Needs	L4 Gifted and Talented
L2 Less Proficient Readers	EL English Language Learners
L3 All Students	

Name ______________ Class ______________ Date ______

Section 7-2

Practice

Vocabulary Activity: Terms That Describe Violence

Respond to the clues by writing the correct terms in the blanks. Use the numbered letters to find the hidden vocabulary term. Then write the definition for this term.

Clues	Vocabulary Terms
1. speech or behavior aimed at a person or group based on personal characteristics	_ _ _ _ _ _ _ _ _ _ (1)
2. requiring a person to do degrading, risky, or illegal acts in order to join a group	_ _ _ _ _ _ (2)
3. the use of e-mail, instant messaging, or text messaging to make threats or spread rumors	_ _ _ _ _ _ _ _ _ _ _ _ _ (3)
4. negative feelings about a group based on stereotypes	_ _ _ _ _ _ _ _ _ _ (4)
5. unwanted remarks or actions that cause emotional or physical pain	_ _ _ _ _ _ _ _ _ _ (5)
6. a lack of acceptance of another person's opinions, beliefs, or actions	_ _ _ _ _ _ _ _ _ _ _ _ (6)
7. the use of threats or physical force to intimidate and control another person	_ _ _ _ _ _ _ _ (7)
8. an exaggerated belief or overgeneralization about an entire group of people	_ _ _ _ _ _ _ _ _ _ (8)
9. the unfair treatment of a person or group based on prejudice	_ _ _ _ _ _ _ _ _ _ _ _ _ _ (9)

10. Hidden term: _ _ _ _ _ _ _ _ _
1 2 3 4 5 6 7 8 9

Definition: ______________________________

____

Name ____________________ Class ____________________ Date ________

Enrich

Class Debate: Controlling Bullies

How serious do you think the problem of bullying is? Once a bully is identified, should he or she be expelled from school? Or, should a bully be given counseling and possibly some lesser punishment?

Prepare for a debate on whether bullies should be expelled from school or given counseling. Read the arguments below, and add additional information that supports an argument for each side. Be prepared to argue either side of the issue in a class debate.

Arguments for expelling bullies from school:

- The climate of fear a bully produces at school makes it difficult for others to concentrate and learn.
- Victims of bullies have increased levels of anxiety and depression. They may think about suicide, or they may strike back in a violent way.
- Once a bully, always a bully. No amount of counseling will change a bully.
- Other arguments: ______________________________

____

____

____

____

____

Arguments for counseling bullies:

- Bullying is a serious, but common problem. It would not be possible to expel all the bullies.
- A bully may be taking out feelings of frustration and insecurity on others. If the reasons for bullying are addressed, the bullying will stop.
- The purpose of school is to teach people new ideas and behaviors. Everyone deserves a second chance to learn and change his or her behavior.
- Other arguments: ______________________________

____

____

____

____

____

Name ____________ Class ____________ Date ______

Section 7-2

Quiz

Write the letter of the correct answer in the space provided.

______ **1.** unwanted remarks or actions that cause a person emotional or physical harm		**a.** bullying
______ **2.** requiring a person to do degrading, risky, or illegal acts in order to join a group		**b.** vandalism
______ **3.** the unfair treatment of a person or group based on prejudice		**c.** harassment
______ **4.** the use of threats or physical force to intimidate and control another person		**d.** stereotype
______ **5.** an exaggerated belief or overgeneralization about an entire group of people		**e.** hazing
		f. discrimination

Write the letter of the correct answer in the space provided.

______ **6.** Students who use weapons at school often are acting on the rage they feel as victims of
- **a.** hazing.
- **b.** harassment.
- **c.** poor grades.
- **d.** bystanders.

______ **7.** The most effective way to stop bullying is to
- **a.** get bystanders involved.
- **b.** never tell anyone about it.
- **c.** threaten to fight the bully.
- **d.** try to be nice to the bully.

______ **8.** Which is an example of sexual harassment?
- **a.** having to wear a ridiculous costume in public
- **b.** receiving poor service in a restaurant
- **c.** making uninvited comments about a person's body
- **d.** destroying another person's property

______ **9.** Hate violence might be aimed at a person because of race, ethnicity, gender, or
- **a.** income.
- **b.** religion.
- **c.** intelligence.
- **d.** behavior.

______ **10.** What is a lack of acceptance of another person's opinions, beliefs, or actions?
- **a.** harassment
- **b.** prejudice
- **c.** intolerance
- **d.** discrimination

Name__________________ Class__________ Date__________ M T W T F

Section 7-3

How Fights Start — Lesson Plan

Section Objectives

- **Explain** how anger and a desire for revenge can lead to fights.
- **Describe** the role that friends and bystanders play in fights.
- **Explain** the relationship between a need for control and violence.

Time
1 period
1/2 block

Local Standards

Vocabulary escalate • instigator

1. FOCUS

Warm-Up: Advice Line Have students discuss how they would respond to whispered and shouted insults.

Targeted Resources
- ❑ Transparency W25

2. TEACH

Visual Learning: Figure 10 Discuss why strategies for dealing with stress can be applied to dealing with anger. L1

Cooperative Learning Have pairs of students role-play a conversation between a person who is seeking revenge and a friend. L2

Cultural Connection Discuss how common sayings about revenge can influence a person's attitude toward violence. L3

Cooperative Learning Have groups role-play a situation of peers instigating a fight. L3

Visual Learning: Figure 11 Discuss how bystanders affect the actions of those involved in a conflict. L2

Building Health Skills Have students identify alternatives for helping a friend who is being abused and consider the consequences of each alternative. L3

Targeted Resources
- ❑ RN Note Taking Guide 7-3 L3 EL
- ❑ ARN Note Taking Guide 7-3 L2
- ❑ TR Practice 7-3
- ❑ TR Enrich 7-3 L4
- ❑ Audio Summary 7-3 L1 L2 EL
- ❑ Health Links: Updates on anger management

3. ASSESS

Evaluate Understanding The assignments listed in the Teacher's Edition can help you assess students' mastery of the section content.

Reteach Ask students to make a bulleted list of what to tell a younger sibling about how fights start. L2

Targeted Resources
- ❑ TR Section 7-3 Quiz
- ❑ CTB Chapter 7

KEY

L1 Special Needs	L4 Gifted and Talented
L2 Less Proficient Readers	EL English Language Learners
L3 All Students	

Name ______________________ Class ______________________ Date ________

Section 7-3

Practice

Group Activity: How Fights Start

Fights start for a variety of reasons, including anger, hurt pride, embarrassment, revenge, peer pressure, and control. Each paragraph below describes a situation that may lead to a fight.

As a group, analyze each situation described below. In the spaces provided, describe what might cause a fight to start and how a fight might be avoided.

1. Marcus wishes he were as tall as Brendan. Brendan won't admit it, but he wishes he were as good at schoolwork as Marcus. Brendan often teases Marcus about being short and smart in school. This really angers Marcus.

____

____

____

____

____

____

2. In the hallway between classes, Ashante accuses Teresa of stealing money from her locker. Teresa denies it. Ashante's friends encourage her to search Teresa's locker for the money. They press Ashante forward, urging her to fight Teresa.

____

____

____

____

____

____

3. Terence tripped Derek, causing him to drop his books and papers. Derek was hurt and angry. He threatened to get back at Terence.

____

____

____

____

____

Name ______________________ Class ______________________ Date ________

Section 7-3

Enrich

Community Involvement: Domestic Violence

Most communities have a shelter where victims of domestic violence can get help. Your teacher will invite a person who works at one of these shelters to class to answer the questions below and additional questions that students have.

In the spaces below, record what you learn. Before the interview, decide what other question you would like answered.

Name of Center: ____

Description of center: ____

____

____

____

Safety measures to protect victims: ____

____

____

____

Counseling services offered: ____

____

____

Legal services offered: ____

____

____

Other services: ____

____

____

24-hour emergency telephone number: ____

Your question: ____

____

____

____

Name ______________________ Class __________________ Date ________

Section 7-3

Quiz

Decide whether each statement is true or false. Write true *or* false *in the space provided.*

______ **1.** Anger is at the root of most arguments and many fights.

______ **2.** If you resort to fighting when someone makes you angry, you give the other person control over you.

______ **3.** A cycle of revenge between gangs may last for years.

______ **4.** It is easier to avoid a fight when friends or bystanders are present.

______ **5.** In domestic violence, the victim may begin to believe that he or she deserves to be hit.

Write the letter of the correct answer in the space provided.

______ **6.** When a fight escalates,
- **a.** it stops for a brief period and then begins again.
- **b.** there is a greater chance that the argument will be resolved.
- **c.** the number of people involved is likely to increase.
- **d.** the participants are less likely to be seriously injured.

______ **7.** People are less likely to start a fight when they are
- **a.** excited.
- **b.** calm.
- **c.** embarrassed.
- **d.** angry.

______ **8.** A person who encourages a fight while staying out of the fight is called a(an)
- **a.** instigator.
- **b.** victim.
- **c.** assailant.
- **d.** bully.

______ **9.** Which of these statements do you think is most accurate?
- **a.** There are always bystanders at a fight.
- **b.** Bystanders have no affect on whether a fight will occur.
- **c.** People are less likely to fight when bystanders are present.
- **d.** People are more likely to fight when bystanders are present.

______**10.** What is the main reason for domestic violence and dating violence?
- **a.** the desire for revenge between gangs
- **b.** one person's desire to have control over another
- **c.** people who gather hoping to see a fight
- **d.** the desire for everyone to be equal

Name______________________ Class__________ Date__________ M T W T F

Section 7-4

Preventing Fights — Lesson Plan

Section Objectives

- **Describe** two general approaches for resolving conflicts.
- **Explain** why safety should be a person's first concern in any conflict.
- **Summarize** how to confront a person wisely.
- **Identify** ways to help others avoid fighting.

Vocabulary mediation

Time
1 period
1/2 block

Local Standards

1. FOCUS

Warm-Up: Quick Quiz Use the Quick Quiz to discuss the qualities of a peacemaker.

Targeted Resources
- ❑ Transparency W26

2. TEACH

Visual Learning: Figure 13 Ask volunteers to describe an example of a situation for each of the criteria listed in the figure. For each situation, have other students decide if it would be wise to ignore the conflict. L2

Cooperative Learning Have pairs role-play a conflict between two teens in which one teen tries to ignore the conflict. L3

Journal Writing Ask students to record ways they could stay calm if they needed to confront a person. L3

Building Health Skills Have the class brainstorm a list of possible opening lines to use when confronting a person. L3

Building Vocabulary Explain that *mediation* comes from a Latin word that means "to be in the middle." EL

Targeted Resources
- ❑ RN Note Taking Guide 7-4 L3 EL
- ❑ ARN Note Taking Guide 7-4 L2
- ❑ TR Practice 7-4
- ❑ TR Enrich 7-4 L4
- ❑ Audio Summary 7-4 L1 L2 EL
- ❑ PHSchool.com: More on handling conflicts

3. ASSESS

Evaluate Understanding The assignments listed in the Teacher's Edition can help you assess students' mastery of the section content.

Reteach Ask students how they would respond to a friend who said there was no choice but to fight. L2

Targeted Resources
- ❑ TR Section 7-4 Quiz
- ❑ CTB Chapter 7

KEY

L1 Special Needs	L4 Gifted and Talented
L2 Less Proficient Readers	EL English Language Learners
L3 All Students	

Name ______________________ Class ______________ Date ________

Section 7-4 **Practice**

Role-Playing: Preventing a Fight

Anyone can get into an argument, and any argument can lead to a fight if the participants let it. How can a fight be prevented?

With a partner, complete the role-play below to show how a fight can be prevented. Use another sheet of paper, if necessary.

Title: *To Fight or Not to Fight*

Characters: two high school students

Setting: school cafeteria

Setup: Student 1, who's in a bad mood today, is sitting at a table in the school cafeteria. Student 2 walks by and knocks Student 1's books off the table onto the floor. To Student 1, it looks like Student 2 knocked the books off on purpose. Actually, Student 2 wasn't paying attention and did not intend to knock the books off the table. These two students have a long history of not getting along.

Student 1: Hey, you jerk! You did that on purpose, didn't you?

Student 2: No I didn't.

Student 1: ______________________________

Student 2: ______________________________

Student 1: ______________________________

Student 2: ______________________________

Student 1: ______________________________

Student 2: ______________________________

Student 1: ______________________________

Student 2: ______________________________

Name ______________ Class ______________ Date ______

Section 7-4

Enrich

Family Involvement: How to Prevent Fights

Older relatives can be good sources of information about ways to avoid fights. As people mature, they usually learn techniques for preventing fights.

Interview two adult relatives about their experiences with conflicts, fights, and ways to prevent fights. Then, answer the following questions in the spaces provided.

1. Describe some conflicts that you learned about from the first relative. Did any conflicts escalate to fights?

2. Were any fights prevented? How were they prevented?

3. Describe some conflicts that you learned about from the second relative. Did any conflicts escalate to fights?

4. Were any fights prevented? How were they prevented?

5. What did you learn from your interviews about preventing fights?

Name ______________________ Class ____________________ Date ________

Section 7-4

Quiz

Write the letter of the correct answer in the space provided.

______ **1.** Being able to ignore a conflict is a sign of
a. fear.
b. pride.
c. anger.
d. self-control.

______ **2.** What should be your first concern in deciding to deal with any conflict?
a. ignoring the conflict
b. getting friends involved
c. confronting the person
d. your safety

______ **3.** When you want to confront a person wisely, you should *not*
a. choose the right time and place.
b. negotiate a solution.
c. refuse to apologize.
d. stay calm.

______ **4.** Mediation is a process for resolving conflicts that requires
a. an assailant and a victim.
b. a neutral third party.
c. three bystanders.
d. an adult.

______ **5.** If a friend reveals plans of violence to you, it is important to
a. keep the plans to yourself.
b. offer to join the fight.
c. ask an adult for help.
d. threaten to tell an adult.

Decide whether each statement is true or false. Write true *or* false *in the space provided.*

______ **6.** It is best to wait until people get angry to deal with a conflict.

______ **7.** Ignoring a conflict is a sign of cowardice.

______ **8.** Learning to control your anger is an important skill to master if you want to avoid conflicts.

______ **9.** Mediators must think about their own safety first.

______ **10.** A good time to confront people is when they are relaxed because they have been using alcohol.

Name ____________ Class ____________ Date ______

Chapter 7 Test

Write the letter of the correct answer in the space provided.

______ **1.** The threat of or actual use of physical force against oneself or another person is
- **a.** hazing.
- **b.** violence.
- **c.** instigation.
- **d.** mediation.

______ **2.** Students who use weapons at school often are acting on the rage they feel as
- **a.** parties in a mediation.
- **b.** victims of harassment.
- **c.** members of gangs.
- **d.** friends and bystanders.

______ **3.** What is the intentional damaging or destroying of another person's property?
- **a.** discrimination
- **b.** hazing
- **c.** bullying
- **d.** vandalism

______ **4.** What is at the root of most arguments and many fights?
- **a.** anger
- **b.** weapons
- **c.** media violence
- **d.** poverty

______ **5.** It is best *not* to ignore a conflict when
- **a.** the other person or issue isn't very important to you.
- **b.** you will probably not see the other person again.
- **c.** ignoring the situation will make the other person angrier.
- **d.** you are trying to "save face" or impress your friends.

Decide whether each statement is true or false. Write true *or* false *in the space provided.*

______ **6.** The costs to an assailant may include criminal charges.

______ **7.** Cyber bullying is requiring a person to do degrading, risky, or illegal acts in order to join a group.

______ **8.** The most effective way to deal with violence based on hate is through education.

______ **9.** It is often easier for a person to avoid a fight when friends or bystanders are present.

______ **10.** You need to stay calm to confront a person wisely.

Name ______________________ Class ___________________ Date ______

Chapter 7: Test *(continued)*

Write the letter of the correct answer in the space provided.

______ **11.** the use of threats or physical force to intimidate and control another person		**a.** victim
______ **12.** a person who attacks another person		**b.** discrimination
______ **13.** an exaggerated belief or overgeneralization about an entire group of people		**c.** bullying
______ **14.** a person who encourages fighting between others while staying out of the fight		**d.** assailant
______ **15.** a person who is attacked		**e.** instigator
		f. stereotype

Write the word that best completes each sentence in the space provided.

16. The intentional killing of one person by another is ______________.

17. A lack of acceptance of another person's opinions, beliefs, or actions is

______________________.

18. A process for resolving conflicts that involves a neutral third party is

______________________.

Use complete sentences to answer the following questions.

19. What are six risk factors for violence?

20. What are the two general approaches you can take once you recognize that a conflict exists?

Name ____________________ Class ____________________ Date __________

Chapter 8

Personal Inventory

Food Diary

Eating a well-balanced diet is critical for good health. Your body relies on the nutrients from food for energy, building blocks for growth and repair, and substances that regulate body processes. Are you choosing foods that give your body the nutrients it needs? One way to find out is to keep a food diary. In a food diary, you record everything you eat. For example, if you eat a ham sandwich, you might list bread, ham, lettuce, Swiss cheese, and tomato.

In the table below, record everything you eat in one day. Use additional paper if needed. For each food eaten, estimate its amount in ounces or cups, and record the amount.

Foods Eaten	Grains (ounces)	Vegetables (cups)	Fruits (cups)	Milk (cups)	Meat/Beans (ounces)
Totals					

Compare what you ate with the recommended daily servings in the chart on page 213 in your text. To correctly use the chart, you must first identify your activity level: You are sedentary if you exercise less than 30 minutes each day. You are moderate if you exercise 30 to 60 minutes each day. You are active if you exercise more than 60 minutes daily.

Based on the daily recommendations for your gender and activity level, what should you eat more of?

____

____

What should you eat less of?

____

____

Name________________________ Class__________ Date__________ M T W T F

Section 8-1 Carbohydrates, Fats, and Proteins Lesson Plan

Section Objectives

- **Name** the three classes of nutrients that supply your body with energy.
- **Explain** how the body obtains energy from foods.
- **Describe** the roles that carbohydrates, fats, and proteins play in your body.

Vocabulary nutrient • metabolism • calorie • carbohydrate • fiber • fat • unsaturated fat • saturated fat • cholesterol • trans fat • protein • amino acid

Time
3 periods
1½ blocks

Local Standards

1. FOCUS

Warm-Up: Quick Quiz Survey students' knowledge of food and nutrition. Address any misconceptions while teaching this section.

Targeted Resources
- ❑ Transparency W27

2. TEACH

Class Discussion Lead a discussion about where nutrients come from and which nutrients supply the body with energy. L2

Teacher Demo Burn two potato chips that differ in calorie content to demonstrate how calories are a measure of energy. L3

Active Learning Have students create a bulletin board display of simple and complex carbohydrates. L1

Addressing Misconceptions Have students explain the role of fats in the body to address the misconception that fats are always "bad." L2

Cultural Connection Have students find and share recipes for dishes that have complementary plant proteins, such as rice and beans. L3

Targeted Resources
- ❑ RN Note Taking Guide 8-1 L3 EL
- ❑ ARN Note Taking Guide 8-1 L2
- ❑ Transparency and Worksheet 16
- ❑ TR Practice 8-1
- ❑ TR Enrich 8-1 L4
- ❑ Audio Summary 8-1 L1 L2 EL
- ❑ PHSchool.com: More on healthy eating

3. ASSESS

Evaluate Understanding The assignments listed in the Teacher's Edition can help you assess students' mastery of the section content.

Reteach List vocabulary terms on the board, and have students give facts about each term. L2

Targeted Resources
- ❑ TR Section 8-1 Quiz
- ❑ CTB Chapter 8

KEY

L1 Special Needs	L4 Gifted and Talented
L2 Less Proficient Readers	EL English Language Learners
L3 All Students	

Name ______________________ Class ________________ Date ________

Section 8-1 **Practice**

Vocabulary Activity: Nutrients That Supply Energy

Complete the crossword puzzle using the vocabulary terms from the section.

Clues Across

2. links in a protein chain (2 words)

4. nutrient that contains twice as many calories as carbohydrates

6. sugar or starch, for short

7. waxy, fatlike substance found only in animal products

8. fats made when manufacturers add hydrogen to vegetable oils

9. nutrient important for growth and repair of body tissues

Clues Down

1. fats that are usually solid at room temperature

3. chemical process by which the body breaks down nutrients for energy

4. type of complex carbohydrate found in plants

5. substance in food that supplies energy and materials for growth, repair, and regulation of bodily functions

6. unit that measures the amount of energy released by nutrients

Name ______________________ Class __________________ Date ________

Section 8-1 **Enrich**

Cultural Connection: Sources of Nutrients in Egypt

Egypt is a country located in the northeastern corner of Africa. The *fellahin,* or country people, constitute more than half of Egypt's total population. The rest of the people live in cities, such as Alexandria and Cairo.

The fellahin are farmers. Although they work from dawn to sunset, many fellahin still earn a poor living. Both men and women work in the fields. The entire family gathers at home for a hot evening meal.

The staple foods of the fellahin are rice and beans. The fellahin also eat bread at nearly every meal. The bread is made from corn flour, has no yeast, and looks like a thick, crusty pancake. A common meal is bread dipped in *dukka,* a mixture made of mashed chickpeas seasoned with salt and pepper. Children often enjoy chewing on sugarcane and eating roasted ears of corn. Fellahin who are wealthy enough to own a goat can include goat milk or yogurt in their family's diet. Wealthier fellahin also might have fruit. Meat is too expensive for most fellahin and is rarely eaten, except on special holidays.

Egyptian city dwellers live very differently. They eat their main meal of the day at about two o'clock in the afternoon. Their midday menu may include an assortment of smoked sardines, stuffed eggs, and beans served in olive oil. This is generally followed by rice, chopped onions and vegetables, lamb, broiled pigeons, fish, or poultry. Yellow saffron rice topped with boiled lamb is very popular, as are grape leaves stuffed with a mixture of rice and minced meat. Fruit is the most popular dessert. Children usually drink *laban,* which is yogurt made from goat milk diluted with water and flavored with salt. Adults often drink root beer or tea with their meals.

Answer the following questions about the reading using what you know about carbohydrates, fats, and proteins.

1. Compare the diets of the fellahin and city dwellers. Whose diet is more varied? Explain.

____

____

____

____

____

2. What foods are sources of carbohydrates for the fellahin? Are those carbohydrates simple or complex?

____

____

____

____

Name ______________________ Class ____________________ Date ________

Section 8-1: Enrich *(continued)*

3. What foods are sources of carbohydrates for the city dwellers? Are those carbohydrates simple or complex?

4. What foods are sources of protein for the fellahin? Are those proteins complete or incomplete?

5. Do you think the fellahin get all the essential amino acids? Explain.

6. What foods are sources of protein for the city dwellers? Are those proteins complete or incomplete?

7. Do you think the city dwellers get all the essential amino acids? Explain.

Name ______________________ Class __________________ Date ______

Section 8-1 Quiz

Decide whether each statement is true or false. Write true *or* false *in the space provided.*

______ **1.** The body uses carbohydrates, fats, and proteins as sources of energy.

______ **2.** The energy in food is released during a series of chemical reactions inside body cells.

______ **3.** Most of a person's daily calorie intake should come from proteins.

______ **4.** The only role that fats play in the body is to supply energy.

______ **5.** Carbohydrates are important for the growth and repair of body tissues.

Write the letter of the correct answer in the space provided.

______ **6.** fat that is solid at room temperature

______ **7.** unit that measures the amount of energy released in food

______ **8.** small substance that make up the "links" in proteins

______ **9.** substance from food that the body uses for growth, repair, and energy

______ **10.** type of complex carbohydrate found in plants

a. nutrient
b. calorie
c. fiber
d. unsaturated fat
e. saturated fat
f. amino acid

Name_______________________ Class__________ Date__________ M T W T F

Section 8-2 Vitamins, Minerals, and Water Lesson Plan

Section Objectives

Time
2 periods
1 block

- **Identify** the two main classes of vitamins.
- **List** seven minerals your body needs in significant amounts.
- **Explain** why water is so important to your body.

Local Standards

Vocabulary vitamin • antioxidant • mineral • anemia • homeostasis • electrolyte • dehydration

1. FOCUS

Warm-Up: Myth/Fact Discuss how some sources of nutritional information create myths about nutritional needs.

Targeted Resources
- ❑ Transparency W28

2. TEACH

Differentiated Instruction Have students prepare a chart to compare fat-soluble and water-soluble vitamins. L2

Cooperative Learning Have groups prepare a menu for one day that supplies all of the essential vitamins. L2

Cultural Connection Explain that Americans of African, Asian, and Mexican descent are often lactose-intolerant. Challenge students to find alternative food sources of calcium. L3

Differentiated Instruction Have students collect a variety of food labels and use them to identify the amount of sodium in a serving of each food. L1

Building Media Literacy Have students critique an ad for a vitamin or mineral supplement. L3

Teacher Demo Demonstrate how much water is in various foods by weighing samples before and after they have been dried. L2

Targeted Resources
- ❑ RN Note Taking Guide 8-2 L3 EL
- ❑ ARN Note Taking Guide 8-2 L2
- ❑ TR Practice 8-2
- ❑ TR Enrich 8-2 L4
- ❑ Audio Summary 8-2 L1 L2 EL
- ❑ Health Links: Updates on nutrients

3. ASSESS

Evaluate Understanding The assignments listed in the Teacher's Edition can help you assess students' mastery of the section content.

Reteach Have students write five questions that cover the objectives for this section. Then have them exchange questions with a partner and answer the questions. L2

Targeted Resources
- ❑ TR Section 8-2 Quiz
- ❑ CTB Chapter 8

KEY

L1 Special Needs
L2 Less Proficient Readers
L3 All Students
L4 Gifted and Talented
EL English Language Learners

Name ____________ Class ____________ Date ________

Section 8-2

Practice

Group Activity: The Seven Significant Minerals

Minerals are nutrients required by the body in small amounts. Unlike vitamins, which are made by living things, minerals occur naturally in rocks and soil. Plants absorb minerals from the soil through roots. Animals get minerals by eating plants or by eating animals that have eaten plants.

Of the 24 different minerals that are essential to good health, seven are required in significant amounts. List these seven minerals in the table below. Then complete the table using information from your text. In the "Foods I Eat" column, brainstorm a list of food sources of each mineral that you would actually eat.

Mineral	Main Functions	Good Sources	Foods I Eat

Name ______________________ Class ______________________ Date __________

Section 8-2 **Enrich**

Consumer Skills: Vitamin and Mineral Supplements

Your doctor suggested that you take a vitamin and mineral supplement. When you go to the pharmacy, you're faced with an entire aisle of vitamin and mineral supplements. Which one should you choose?

Go to a store that sells vitamin and mineral supplements, and follow these steps.

Step 1. Choose a supplement and read the label. Avoid supplements that provide "megadoses," or more than 100 percent of the Daily Value (%DV) of a vitamin or mineral. Some vitamins and minerals can cause negative side effects when taken in excessive amounts.

Step 2. Look for "USP" on the label. Supplements labeled "USP" have been tested and meet the standards set by U.S. Pharmacopeia.

Step 3. Look for an expiration date. Avoid supplements with no expiration date or that will expire before you can finish them.

Step 4. Look for other claims on the label. Supplements labeled "natural" are not necessarily better. "Natural" ingredients often have the same chemical makeup as synthetic ingredients. Compare the ingredients lists to make sure.

Step 5. Look for supplements that best fit your nutritional requirements. Some multivitamin and mineral supplements are formulated specifically to meet the nutritional needs of men, women, children, or older adults. Teenagers have different nutritional needs than young children and older adults.

Step 6. Choose three brands of similar supplements to compare for nutrient content and price. Use the back side of this worksheet if you want to compare additional brands.

Feature	Brand A	Brand B	Brand C
Vitamins and Minerals Supplied (Name and % DV)			
Cost per pill			

Step 7. Which brand do you think is the best buy? Explain why using the data from your table.

____

____

Name ________________________ Class ____________________ Date ______

Section 8-2

Quiz

Write the letter of the correct answer in the space provided.

______ **1.** Which is *not* a characteristic of vitamins?
- **a.** They are made by living things.
- **b.** They are required by the body in small amounts.
- **c.** They occur naturally in rocks and soil.
- **d.** They assist in many chemical reactions in the body.

______ **2.** Which of the following protects healthy cells from damage during the normal aging process?
- **a.** electrolytes
- **b.** minerals
- **c.** water
- **d.** antioxidants

______ **3.** Which of the following is a mineral?
- **a.** folate
- **b.** magnesium
- **c.** pantothenic acid
- **d.** biotin

______ **4.** Which mineral is needed for healthy red blood cells?
- **a.** calcium
- **b.** potassium
- **c.** iron
- **d.** sodium

______ **5.** The process of maintaining a steady state inside the body is called
- **a.** homeostasis.
- **b.** dehydration
- **c.** anemia.
- **d.** nausea.

Decide whether each statement is true or false. Write true *or* false *in the space provided.*

______ **6.** Water-soluble vitamins can be stored by the body.

______ **7.** Only plants can absorb minerals from rocks and soil.

______ **8.** An excess of vitamins or minerals can damage your health.

______ **9.** Water regulates body temperature.

______ **10.** Water can be obtained only by drinking beverages.

Name______________________ Class__________ Date__________ M T W T F

Section 8-3 Guidelines for Healthful Eating Lesson Plan

Section Objectives

- **Explain** how the *Dietary Guidelines for Americans* can help you plan a healthful diet.
- **Summarize** the recommendations in the MyPyramid plan.

Vocabulary *Dietary Guidelines for Americans* • nutrient-dense food • MyPyramid plan

Time
1 period
1/2 block

Local Standards

1. FOCUS

Warm-Up: Advice Line Help students understand how their food choices can affect their overall health.

Targeted Resources

- ❑ Transparency W29

2. TEACH

Cooperative Learning Have student groups create a brochure that describes the four recommendations of the *Dietary Guidelines for Americans.* L3

Visual Learning: Figure 15 Use the figure to help students understand the MyPyramid nutrition plan. L3

Differentiated Instruction Give students a copy of Figure 15 with blank boxes, and have them fill in the boxes with familiar foods. EL

Building Health Skills Have students visit the USDA's MyPyramid Web site to create a personalized MyPyramid plan. L3

Building Health Skills Have students make posters that offer tips to help students follow the dietary guidelines. L2

Targeted Resources

- ❑ RN Note Taking Guide 8-3 L3 EL
- ❑ ARN Note Taking Guide 8-3 L2
- ❑ Transparency and Worksheet 17
- ❑ TR Practice 8-3
- ❑ TR Enrich 8-3 L4
- ❑ Audio Summary 8-3 L1 L2 EL
- ❑ PHSchool.com: More on MyPyramid plans

3. ASSESS

Evaluate Understanding The assignments listed in the Teacher's Edition can help you assess students' mastery of the section content.

Reteach Have students label the food groups on an unlabeled copy of the MyPyramid plan. L2

Targeted Resources

- ❑ TR Section 8-3 Quiz
- ❑ CTB Chapter 8

KEY

L1 Special Needs	L4 Gifted and Talented
L2 Less Proficient Readers	EL English Language Learners
L3 All Students	

Name ______________________ Class __________________ Date ______

Section 8-3 **Practice**

Skill-Building Activity: Following the Food Guidelines

Use the MyPyramid plan and the Dietary Guidelines *to evaluate the menu below. Draw a line through foods that should be eliminated, write your change in the second column, and your reason for your change in the third column. Add foods to the menu, using the blank lines at the end of each meal. Write your reasons for the added foods in the third column.*

Meal	Your Change	Your Reason
Breakfast		
whole-grain cereal		
sugar		
milk		
white toast		
butter		
jelly		
coffee		
cream		
sugar		
orange slices		
Lunch		
hot dog		
bun		
salsa		
mustard		
French fries		
catsup		
coleslaw		
cabbage		
carrots		
mayonnaise dressing		

Section 8-3: **Practice** *(continued)*

Meal	Your Change	Your Reason
After school snack		
canned ravioli		
milk		
Supper		
tossed salad		
lettuce		
tomatoes		
thousand island dressing		
chicken breast, broiled		
rice		
butter		
carrots		
pear slices, fresh		
lemonade		
Evening snack		
popcorn		
butter		
salt		
soft drink		

Name ______________ Class ______________ Date ______

Section 8-3 **Enrich**

Community Involvement: Community Cafeterias

Many places in your community routinely plan and serve nutritious meals for large groups of people. Most have dietitians on staff to plan menus based on the nutritional requirements and the food habits of the people they serve.

To learn what is involved in running a meal program, first select a site in your community that serves meals to a large group of people, such as a nursing home, school, day-care center, Meals On Wheels program, or hospital. Telephone the facility, and set up a telephone or personal interview with the person in charge of the food-service program. Ask the questions below, and add more questions that you would like answered.

1. Community site: ______________

   Name of interviewee: ______________

2. What nutritional requirements do you consider in ordering and preparing food?

3. How do you develop weekly menus? ______________

4. Where does the food come from? ______________

5. How do you select food vendors? ______________

6. How much do you charge for meals? How are meal prices determined?

7. What influence do the people you serve have on food selection and preparation?

8. Question: ______________

9. Question: ______________

Name ______________________ Class __________________ Date ______

Section 8-3

Quiz

Decide whether each statement is true or false. Write true *or* false *in the space provided.*

______ **1.** The *Dietary Guidelines* recommend that teens be active for 60 minutes most days.

______ **2.** To prevent food-borne illnesses, thaw foods on the counter.

______ **3.** According to the MyPyramid plan, your diet should include more meats and beans than grains.

______ **4.** Exercise is important for balancing the calories you consume with the calories you use.

______ **5.** According to the MyPyramid plan, you must consume every food group at each meal.

Write the letter of the correct answer in the space provided.

______ **6.** The *Dietary Guidelines for Americans* provides information on
- **a.** planning a low-sodium diet.
- **b.** calculating how many calories certain foods have.
- **c.** finding the daily recommended servings of grains.
- **d.** handling food safely.

______ **7.** Which is an example of a nutrient-dense food?
- **a.** soft drinks
- **b.** potato chips
- **c.** peanuts
- **d.** cookies

______ **8.** The MyPyramid plan
- **a.** differs according to the foods people eat.
- **b.** differs according to a person's age, sex, and activity level.
- **c.** is the same for all people.
- **d.** is the same for people at all activity levels.

______ **9.** According to the MyPyramid plan, pasta and breads belong to the
- **a.** meat and beans group.
- **b.** vegetables group.
- **c.** fruits group.
- **d.** grains group.

______ **10.** Which is *not* a tip that can help you follow the *Dietary Guidelines* and the MyPyramid plan?
- **a.** Skip breakfast if you do not have time.
- **b.** Choose unbuttered popcorn at the movies.
- **c.** Use mustard or ketchup instead of mayonnaise.
- **d.** Choose a grilled chicken sandwich instead of a burger.

Name ______________ Class ______________ Date ______

Chapter 8 Test

Write the letter of the correct answer in the space provided.

_____ **1.** nutrient made by living things; assists many chemical reactions in the body

_____ **2.** nutrient that supplies energy, maintains body temperature, protects nerves, forms cells

_____ **3.** nutrient that occurs naturally in rocks and soil; needed only in small amounts

_____ **4.** nutrient that supplies energy for body functions; can be simple or complex

_____ **5.** nutrient that is important for the growth and repair of body tissues

a. carbohydrate
b. fat
c. protein
d. vitamin
e. mineral
f. water

Write the word that best completes each sentence in the space provided.

6. Food provides ______________, which are substances that the body needs to regulate bodily functions, promote growth, repair body tissues, and obtain energy.

7. The amount of energy released from food is measured in units called ______________.

8. ______________ is a type of complex carbohydrate found in plants that cannot be digested by the body.

9. Vitamins called ______________ help protect healthy cells from damage during aging.

10. Foods that are ______________ contain lots of vitamins and minerals relative to the number of calories.

Decide whether each statement is true or false. Write true *or* false *in the space provided.*

_____ **11.** A series of chemical reactions take place in cells to release the energy from nutrients.

_____ **12.** All vitamins are soluble in water.

_____ **13.** Potassium is one mineral that you need in significant amounts.

_____ **14.** The MyPyramid plan is the same for people of all ages.

_____ **15.** Physical activity is a part of the MyPyramid plan.

Chapter 8: Test *(continued)*

Write the letter of the correct answer in the space provided.

_______ **16.** A fat that is solid at room temperature and has all the hydrogen the carbon atoms can hold is a(an)
a. unsaturated fat. **b.** saturated fat.
c. monounsaturated fat. **d.** polyunsaturated fat.

_______ **17.** The chemical process by which the body breaks down foods to release energy is called
a. anemia. **b.** metabolism.
c. homeostasis. **d.** dehydration.

_______ **18.** Which is *not* a tip to help you follow the *Dietary Guidelines?*
a. Consume every food group at every meal.
b. Satisfy your sweet tooth with fruit.
c. Instead of fried meats or fish, try them grilled.
d. Limit pastries, eggs, and bacon.

Use complete sentences to answer the following questions.

19. Give at least three reasons why water is an essential nutrient for the body.

20. What factors should you consider to create your own MyPyramid plan? According to the MyPyramid plan, which kind of foods should you eat most of, and which should you eat least of?

Name ______________________ Class ____________________ Date ________

Chapter 9

Personal Inventory

Food Choices

Food choices are affected by many things, including moods, companions, and family background. What kinds of foods do you choose in different situations? *Complete each statement below. Then, answer the questions that follow.*

1. When I am home sick with a cold,
   I usually eat ______________________________

2. When I eat out with friends,
   I usually eat ______________________________

3. When I am in a hurry for breakfast,
   I usually eat ______________________________

4. When I have plenty of time for breakfast,
   I usually eat ______________________________

5. When I eat lunch at school,
   I usually eat ______________________________

6. When I eat lunch at home on weekends,
   I usually eat ______________________________

7. When I am bored or depressed,
   I usually eat ______________________________

8. When there is a special family celebration,
   I usually eat ______________________________

9. When I have an important test or game the next day,
   I usually eat ______________________________

How do different situations influence your food choices? ____________

Do any of your food choices reflect your family background or traditions? Which ones? ______________________________

Name______________________ Class__________ Date__________ M T W T F

Section 9-1

Choosing Food Wisely — Lesson Plan

Section Objectives

- **Summarize** three main reasons why you eat.
- **Analyze** the information contained on food labels.

Vocabulary hunger • appetite • basal metabolic rate (BMR) • Daily Values

Time
1 period
1/2 block

Local Standards

1. FOCUS

Warm-Up: Quick Quiz Have students respond to the questions privately. Discuss the most common eating triggers.

Targeted Resources
- ❑ Transparency W30

2. TEACH

Building Health Skills Have students list ways that each factor listed under "The Foods You Choose" influences their food choices. Have volunteers share their responses. L3

Visual Learning: Figure 1 Have students use the number of calories burned during sleep to estimate the basal metabolic rate of a 125-pound person per day (about 1,200 calories). L2

Differentiated Instruction Contrast the definitions of *hunger* and *appetite*. Help students understand the difference by asking; which makes you want dessert after a big meal? (appetite) EL

Active Learning Have students identify the nutrition facts and other food label information on food containers they bring in. L1

Visual Learning: Figure 2 Have students study the nutrient and health claims in the table, and ask them how they differ from what they might have thought previously. L2

Targeted Resources
- ❑ RN Note Taking Guide 9-1 L3 EL
- ❑ ARN Note Taking Guide 9-1 L2
- ❑ Transparencies and Worksheets 18, 19
- ❑ TR Practice 9-1
- ❑ TR Enrich 9-1 L4
- ❑ Audio Summary 9-1 L1 L2 EL
- ❑ PHSchool.com: More on appetite and eating

3. ASSESS

Evaluate Understanding The assignments listed in the Teacher's Edition can help you assess students' mastery of the section content.

Reteach Ask students to locate various kinds of information on a food label, such as the number of servings, percent Daily Values, health claims, and open dates. L2

Targeted Resources
- ❑ TR Section 9-1 Quiz
- ❑ CTB Chapter 9

KEY

L1 Special Needs	L4 Gifted and Talented
L2 Less Proficient Readers	EL English Language Learners
L3 All Students	

Name ______________________ Class ______________________ Date __________

Section 9-1

Practice

Decision Making: Comparing Food Labels

Food labels provide information on calories, Daily Values for nutrients contained in the food, ingredients, and health claims. This worksheet will give you practice making informed food choices based on comparing food labels.

Study the two food labels from breakfast cereals. Then complete the table and answer the questions on the next page.

Cereal A

Nutrition Facts
Serving Size ¾ cup (30g)
Servings Per Container about 11

Amount Per Serving	
Calories	100
Calories from Fat	5
	% Daily Value
Total Fat 0.5g*	**1%**
Saturated Fat 0g	**0%**
Trans Fat 0g	
Polyunsaturated Fat 0g	
Monounsaturated Fat 0g	
Cholesterol 0mg	**0%**
Sodium 190mg	**8%**
Potassium 90mg	**3%**
Total Carbohydrate 23g	**8%**
Dietary Fiber 3g	**10%**
Sugars 5g	
Other Carbohydrate 15g	
Protein 2g	
Vitamin A	10%
Vitamin C	100%
Calcium	100%
Iron	100%
Vitamin D	10%
Vitamin E	100%
Thiamin	100%
Riboflavin	100%
Niacin	100%
Vitamin B_6	100%
Folic Acid	100%
Vitamin B_{12}	100%
Pantothenic Acid	100%
Phosphorus	8%
Magnesium	6%
Zinc	100%
Copper	4%

Cereal B

Nutrition Facts
Serving Size ¾ cup (42g)
Servings Per Container about 10

Amount Per Serving	
Calories	220
Calories from Fat	40
	% Daily Value
Total Fat 4.5g*	**7%**
Saturated Fat 0.5g	**3%**
Trans Fat 0g	
Polyunsaturated Fat 1.5g	
Monounsaturated Fat 2g	
Cholesterol 0mg	**0%**
Sodium 250mg	**10%**
Potassium 180mg	**5%**
Total Carbohydrate 42g	**14%**
Dietary Fiber 4g	**17%**
Sugars 16g	
Other Carbohydrate 22g	
Protein 5g	
Vitamin A	0%
Vitamin C	10%
Calcium	2%
Iron	25%
Vitamin D	0%
Thiamin	25%
Riboflavin	25%
Niacin	25%
Vitamin B_6	25%
Folic Acid	25%
Vitamin B_{12}	25%
Phosphorus	15%
Magnesium	15%
Zinc	25%
Copper	6%

Name ______________ Class ______________ Date ______

Section 9-1: **Practice** *(continued)*

Nutrient	Cereal A (per serving)	Cereal B (per serving)
Calories		
Total Fat (% DV)		
Cholesterol (% DV)		
Sodium (% DV)		
Dietary Fiber (% DV)		
Sugars (g)		
Proteins (g)		
Vitamin A (% DV)		
Vitamin C (% DV)		
Calcium (% DV)		
Iron (% DV)		

1. Which cereal has more vitamins and minerals overall? ______________

2. Which cereal is lower in fat, sodium, and sugars? ______________

3. Which cereal is a better source of protein? ______________

4. Which cereal is lower in calories? ______________

5. Which cereal would you choose? Explain your choice.

____

____

____

____

____

Name ______________________ Class ______________________ Date __________

Section 9-1 **Enrich**

Consumer Skills: Food Additives

On every can, box, bag, and container of food in your grocery store, you can find a food label that lists all the ingredients in the food. Many of the ingredients are familiar ones that you would expect to find in a particular food. Other ingredients, however, may be unfamiliar or surprising to you. Some of these unfamiliar ingredients may be food additives—ingredients added to a food during processing to improve its appearance, taste, shelf-life, nutritional value, or some other quality.

To investigate which food additives are found in the foods you eat, collect ten food labels from a variety of foods. Be sure to include foods such as canned soups, snack foods, beverages, prepared meals, frozen foods, and other things you commonly eat. You and your classmates will use the labels to identify the various additives in different foods. Then you will do research to learn more about why those particular substances are added to foods.

For the additives listed in the chart below, fill in the missing information based on what you learned from your research. Then, in the blank rows, write the names of three other additives from the labels you gathered. Do research about those additives to complete the chart.

Additive	Function	Used in
1. coloring agents		soft drinks, cake mixes, cereals, cheese, margarine
2. sodium benzoate	preservative	
3. calcium propionate	preservative, mold inhibitor	
4. sodium chloride		
5. sucrose	enhances flavor	
6. aspartame		diet sodas, chewing gum, diet foods
7. gelatin		
8.		
9.		
10.		

Name ________________ Class ________________ Date ______

Section 9-1

Quiz

Write the letter of the correct answer in the space provided.

______ **1.** Your basal metabolic rate is
a. the rate at which you eat.
b. the rate at which your body uses energy at rest.
c. the rate at which you exercise.
d. your heart rate.

______ **2.** What is appetite?
a. a desire for food that is based on emotional factors
b. hunger
c. a feeling of physical discomfort caused by the need for nutrients
d. basal metabolic rate

______ **3.** What information is *not* required on food labels?
a. nutrition facts
b. price
c. Daily Values
d. ingredients

______ **4.** Daily Values are recommendations for the average person for which of the following?
a. daily exercise
b. daily calorie intake
c. daily intake of certain nutrients
d. daily intake of trans fats

______ **5.** The "sell by" date tells you
a. how long the product will be at peak quality.
b. the last date a product can be used.
c. the expiration date.
d. the last date the product can be sold.

Decide whether each statement is true or false. Write true *or* false *in the space provided.*

______ **6.** The nutrient claim *light* means that one serving of a particular food contains 50 percent less fat.

______ **7.** Older people tend to have a higher basal metabolic rate (BMR) than younger people.

______ **8.** Convenience has very little influence on a person's food choices.

______ **9.** Hunger is an inborn response, while appetite is a learned response.

______ **10.** Health claims on food labels are statements that link the use of a food to certain health risks or benefits.

Name________________________ Class__________ Date__________ M T W T F

Section 9-2

Safely Managing Your Weight Lesson Plan

Section Objectives

- **Examine** how heredity, activity level, and body composition influence a person's weight.
- **Calculate** your body mass index.
- **Identify** health problems associated with being overweight and underweight.
- **Summarize** strategies for losing or gaining weight.

Vocabulary body composition • body mass index (BMI) • overweight • obesity • underweight • fad diet

Time
2 periods
1 block

Local Standards

1. FOCUS

Warm-Up: Health Stats Use the statistics to encourage students to think about why the number of overweight teens is increasing.

Targeted Resources

- ❑ Transparency W31

2. TEACH

Class Discussion Ask students which factor that influences weight—heredity, activity, or body composition—they think is most important. Point out that it is possible to control weight with proper diet and exercise. L3

Visual Learning: Figure 4 Show students how to use the Body Mass Index graphs so they can privately determine where their BMI falls. L2

Differentiated Instruction Help students understand the significance of portion size by showing them French fry wrappers and soft drink containers of different sizes. L1

Cultural Connection Have interested students find out how the concept of the ideal body shape varies from society to society. L4

Addressing Misconceptions Make sure students understand that there are no shortcuts to permanent weight loss. Eating and exercise habits must be changed for a lifetime. L2

Targeted Resources

- ❑ RN Note Taking Guide 9-2 L3 EL
- ❑ ARN Note Taking Guide 9-2 L2
- ❑ Transparency and Worksheet 20
- ❑ TR Practice 9-2
- ❑ TR Enrich 9-2 L4
- ❑ Audio Summary 9-2 L1 L2 EL
- ❑ Health Links: Updates on food and diet

3. ASSESS

Evaluate Understanding The assignments listed in the Teacher's Edition can help you assess students' mastery of the section content.

Reteach Have students write e-mails to hypothetical friends advising them about sensible weight loss or weight gain. L2

Targeted Resources

- ❑ TR Section 9-2 Quiz
- ❑ CTB Chapter 9

KEY

L1 Special Needs	L4 Gifted and Talented
L2 Less Proficient Readers	EL English Language Learners
L3 All Students	

Name ______________________ Class ____________________ Date ______

Section 9-2

Practice

Decision Making: Dieting Dilemmas

Below are descriptions of several teens facing different weight management issues. For each person, make a recommendation about what the person should do in the situation described. Be sure to consider all of the factors that could influence the person's decision before making your recommendation.

1. Josh's doctor has told Josh that he needs to lose some weight. But Josh's friends always want to go out to fast food restaurants. How can Josh eat healthily when out with his friends?

____

____

____

2. Teresa leads a busy life—she's on Student Council, sings in the school chorus, and has a lead in the school play. She doesn't have time to exercise or eat right, although she knows she should. What can she do?

____

____

____

3. Hector is tall and thin, like the rest of his family. He wants to put on some weight and hopes to make the football team next year. Hector's family has never been concerned about healthy eating, but now, Hector thinks he should be.

____

____

____

4. Sophia and her best friend have challenged each other to a weight loss competition. Sophia is planning to go on the new "low-carb" diet she has heard a lot of people talking about. What advice would you give Sophia?

____

____

____

Name ______________ Class ______________ Date ______

Section 9-2

Enrich

Community Involvement: Weight Management Strategies

How sensible are the weight management strategies that people in your community use? To find out, ask four adults in your community to complete the survey below. Add three questions of your own. Use the following scale for responses: 1 = always; 2 = sometimes; 3 = never.

Survey Question	Person 1	Person 2	Person 3	Person 4
1. Do you read the nutritional information on food labels before you purchase foods?				
2. Do you follow the recommendations in the MyPyramid plan for your age, sex, and activity level?				
3. When you eat out, do you ask how foods are prepared in order to avoid extra fat, sugar, or salt?				
4. Do you monitor and limit portion sizes of meals and snacks?				
5. Do you know and avoid your triggers for overeating, such as boredom or stress?				
6. Do you avoid fad diets and diet aids when trying to gain or lose weight?				
7. Do you incorporate regular exercise into your daily schedule?				
8.				
9.				
10.				

After you have completed your survey, compare your results with those of your classmates. On a separate sheet of paper, summarize your findings about the weight management strategies of people in your community.

Name ____________________ Class ____________________ Date ________

Section 9-2

Quiz

Write the letter of the correct answer in the space provided.

______ 1. body composition	a. lighter than the standard for one's weight
______ 2. body mass index	b. refers to adults with a BMI of 30 or more
______ 3. obesity	c. how much body fat you have compared to muscle and bone
______ 4. overweight	d. rate at which body uses energy at rest
______ 5. underweight	e. heavier than the standard for one's height
	f. a ratio of weight to height

Write the letter of the correct answer in the space provided.

______ **6.** Which is *not* a good strategy for gaining weight?
a. taking larger portions of food at meals
b. eating snacks right before mealtimes
c. exercising
d. choosing nutrient-dense foods

______ **7.** Which of the following factors does *not* play a role in determining a person's weight?
a. heredity
b. activity level
c. body compostion
d. body mass index

______ **8.** A fad diet
a. is a good way to begin a weight-loss program.
b. usually includes extra carbohydrates.
c. may lead to temporary weight loss.
d. is perfectly safe as long as exercise is also included.

______ **9.** In general, it is best to lose weight
a. quickly so that it stays off.
b. by eating whatever you want.
c. by using diet pills.
d. gradually, by changing your eating and exercise habits.

______ **10.** One health risk of being underweight is
a. high blood pressure.
b. diabetes.
c. anemia.
d. excess cholestrol in the blood.

Name____________________ Class__________ Date__________ M T W T F

Section 9-3 Nutrition for Individual Needs Lesson Plan

Section Objective

- **Examine** how diabetics, vegetarians, people with food sensitivities, and athletes can meet their nutritional needs.

Vocabulary vegetarian • vegan • food allergy • food intolerance • carbohydrate loading

Time
2 periods
1 block

Local Standards

1. FOCUS

Warm-Up: Advice Line Use the Warm-Up to challenge students to consider how vegetarians can meet their nutritional needs.

Targeted Resources
- ❑ Transparency W32

2. TEACH

Differentiated Instruction Have students make a concept map for type 2 diabetes, including a definition of the condition, symptoms, and dietary requirements. L2

Cooperative Learning Have groups of students develop a menu of vegetarian meals and snacks for one day. The meal plan should provide complete protein combinations, adequate vitamins and minerals, and a good balance of protein, fats, and carbohydrates. L3

Cultural Connection Have student use restaurant menus or cookbooks from a variety of cultures to identify complete protein combinations. L2

Active Learning Provide students with food labels, and have them use the information in Figure 10 to identify possible sources of food allergies or intolerances listed on the labels. L2

Building Media Literacy Have students do Internet research on carbohydrate loading. They should determine if the sites they select are research-based, based on personal anecdotes, or selling a product. L3

Targeted Resources
- ❑ RN Note Taking Guide 9-3 L3 EL
- ❑ ARN Note Taking Guide 9-3 L2
- ❑ TR Practice 9-3
- ❑ TR Enrich 9-3 L4
- ❑ Audio Summary 9-3 L1 L2 EL
- ❑ PHSchool.com: More on meals for individual needs

3. ASSESS

Evaluate Understanding The assignments listed in the Teacher's Edition can help you assess students' mastery of the section content.

Reteach Help students create a chart listing the special dietary requirements for each of the conditions or lifestyle choices discussed in the section. L2

Targeted Resources
- ❑ TR Section 9-3 Quiz
- ❑ CTB Chapter 9

KEY
- L1 Special Needs
- L2 Less Proficient Readers
- L3 All Students
- L4 Gifted and Talented
- EL English Language Learners

Name ______________ Class ______________ Date ______

Section 9-3

Practice

Group Activity: Special Diets

Individuals with special dietary needs include diabetics, vegetarians, people with food sensitivities, and athletes. Healthy meals for special diets should include the nutrients a person needs while minimizing or eliminating foods that cause problems.

Work with three other students. After each student in your group has filled in the information on this page, share your answers with the rest of your group. You may want to modify some of your answers as you discuss them.

1. Diabetics:

Health Concerns: ______________

Diet Tips: ______________

2. Vegetarians:

Health Concerns: ______________

Diet Tips: ______________

3. People With Food Sensitivities:

Health Concerns: ______________

Diet Tips: ______________

4. Athletes:

Health Concerns: ______________

Diet Tips: ______________

Name ______________________ Class __________________ Date ______

Section 9-3 **Enrich**

Consumer Skills: Select a Meal

When eating out, many people need to be careful selecting items from a menu. Three friends—Jeffrey, Vanessa, and Cruz—are having dinner together in a restaurant. Each wants to enjoy a nutritious meal that meets the person's dietary needs.

Read the description of each friend. Then choose a nutritious meal from the menu provided and explain your choices.

Menu

Appetizers

Fried Mozzarella Sticks
Cream of Turkey Soup
Chopped Chicken Liver on Toast
Fresh Fruit Cup
Asparagus with Cheese Sauce
Clams on the Half Shell

Entrees

Broiled Sirloin Steak
Broiled Swordfish
Fried Clams
Lentil Casserole
Spaghetti with Meatballs

All entrees served with whole-wheat bread and butter and a choice of two of the following accompaniments:

Potato (baked, mashed, or fried)
Vegetable (string beans)
Salad (oil and vinegar, Russian, or Thousand Island dressing)

Desserts

Fresh Melon
Ice Cream
Rice Pudding
Apple Pie

1. Jeffrey's family has a history of diabetes. His doctor has advised him to watch his sugar and fat intake, as well as his weight.

Appetizer ______________________________

Entree ______________________________

Accompaniments ______________________________

Dessert ______________________________

Reasons for choices ______________________________

____

____

Name ______________________ Class ____________________ Date ______

Section 9-3: Enrich *(continued)*

2. Vanessa is a vegan. She avoids all animal products, including eggs, milk, butter, and other dairy products.

Appetizer ______________________

Entree ______________________

Accompaniments ______________________

Dessert ______________________

Reasons for choices ______________________

____

____

____

3. Cruz is allergic to shellfish. He is also trying to lose ten pounds.

Appetizer ______________________

Entree ______________________

Accompaniments ______________________

Dessert ______________________

Reasons for choices ______________________

____

____

____

4. What meal would you choose for yourself and why?

Appetizer ______________________

Entree ______________________

Accompaniments ______________________

Dessert ______________________

Reasons for choices ______________________

____

____

____

Name ______________________ Class ____________________ Date ________

Section 9-3 **Quiz**

Write the letter of the correct answer in the space provided.

_____ **1.** vegetarian

_____ **2.** vegan

_____ **3.** food allergy

_____ **4.** food intolerance

_____ **5.** carbohydrate loading

a. the inability to digest a particular food

b. a person who does not eat meat

c. a person who eats only animal protein

d. a practice followed by some endurance athletes

e. an immune system response to certain foods

f. a person who eats no animal products

Write the letter of the correct answer in the space provided.

_____ **6.** People with diabetes
a. must control their weight.
b. may have poor nutritional habits.
c. must monitor their diet carefully.
d. all of the above

_____ **7.** The nutrient that diabetics must monitor most carefully is
a. protein.
b. carbohydrates.
c. vitamins.
d. minerals.

_____ **8.** Vegetarians tend to have
a. a lower risk of heart disease than other people.
b. too much calcium in their diet.
c. a higher risk of diabetes than other people.
d. a higher body mass index than other people.

_____ **9.** A food allergy is a response by the immune system to the
a. carbohydrates in certain foods.
b. fats in certain foods.
c. proteins in certain foods.
d. vitamins in certain foods.

_____ **10.** Compared to nonathletes, most athletes need to consume
a. more calories and more fluids.
b. more fluids and more fats.
c. more fats and more proteins.
d. as little fat as possible.

Name ______________________ Class ____________________ Date ______

Chapter 9 Test

Write the letter of the correct answer in the space provided.

______ **1.** A measure of the amount of body fat a person has as compared to muscle and bone is known as
a. basal metabolic rate.
b. obesity.
c. body composition.
d. body mass index.

______ **2.** Fad diets are not recommended because
a. there are too many types to choose from.
b. weight loss occurs too slowly.
c. they do not restrict enough foods.
d. they often exclude essential nutrients.

______ **3.** Which foods should diabetics limit to help control blood sugar levels?
a. foods high in protein
b. foods high in fiber
c. foods low in fat
d. foods high in sugar

______ **4.** When nutrients are added to canned food to replace those lost during canning, the food is said to be
a. enriched.
b. spoiled.
c. preserved.
d. fortified.

Write the letter of the correct answer in the space provided.

______ **5.** basal metabolic rate
______ **6.** hunger
______ **7.** appetite
______ **8.** carbohydrate loading
______ **9.** fad diet
______ **10.** vegetarian
______ **11.** body mass index

a. a person who does not eat meat
b. a weight loss program that may be lacking in proper nutrition
c. body's rate of energy use at rest
d. physical sensation due to the body's need for nutrients
e. a practice followed by some endurance athletes
f. a ratio of a person's weight to height
g. a desire for food based on emotional factors

Name ______________________ Class ____________________ Date ________

Chapter 9: Test *(continued)*

Decide whether each statement is true or false. Write true *or* false *in the space provided.*

______ **12.** The term *overweight* refers specifically to adults with a BMI of 30 or higher.

______ **13.** Any weight loss achieved with a fad diet is usually temporary.

______ **14.** Underweight people who want to gain weight should make sure to exercise regularly.

______ **15.** Body composition is a ratio of your weight to your height.

Write the word or phrase that best completes each sentence in the space provided.

16. *Low in sodium* is an example of a ______________________.

17. Recommendations that specify the amounts of certain nutrients that an average person should obtain each day are called ______________________.

18. A person who is lighter than the standard for the person's height is considered ______________________.

Use complete sentences to answer the following questions.

19. What are three facts people can learn from a food label? Why is each fact important to know?

____

____

____

____

____

____

____

____

20. Describe two factors on which a person's weight depends. How does each factor affect weight?

____

____

____

____

____

Name ______________________ Class ________________ Date ______

Chapter 10

Personal Inventory

Healthy Mealtimes

There is more to mealtime than just enjoying what you eat. In fact, two other factors also influence the health of your digestive system: how you eat and the safe preparation of your food.

Complete each statement below. Then, answer the last question based on how you completed the statements.

1. My favorite meal of the day is ______________________

because ______________________

____

2. I drink these beverages with my meals ______________________

____

3. On an average day, I spend this much time eating each meal:

breakfast ______________________

lunch ______________________

dinner ______________________

4. The people I eat my meals with are ______________________

____

5. I usually eat meals while sitting ______________________

____

6. If I prepare a meal, I handle food safely by ______________________

____

Read through your answers. Which of your habits do you think are good ones? Explain which habits could use improvement.

____

____

____

____

____

____

____

Name________________________ Class__________ Date__________ M T W T F

Section 10-1

Your Digestive System Lesson Plan

Section Objectives

- **Describe** the three main functions of the digestive system.
- **Identify** the organs of the digestive system and their functions.

Vocabulary digestion • enzyme • absorption • pharynx • epiglottis • peristalsis • chyme • bile • gallbladder • villi

Time
2 periods
1 block

Local Standards

1. FOCUS

Warm-Up: Myth/Fact Have students think of questions they have about the digestive system and then seek the answers.

Targeted Resources

- ❑ Transparency W33

2. TEACH

Building Health Skills During a class discussion, students will analyze the influences that contribute to snacking. L2

Visual Learning: Figure 1 Ask students to identify the organs of the digestive system. L2

Building Vocabulary Explain the origin of the word *peristalsis*. Then use a bead and a straw to model peristalsis. L3

Differentiated Instruction Have students write down the names of the digestive system structures in English and in their first language. They should write a sentence describing each structure's function. EL

Differentiated Instruction Help students visualize the relative lengths of the small and large intestine using ropes. L1

Targeted Resources

- ❑ RN Note Taking Guide 10-1 L3 EL
- ❑ ARN Note Taking Guide 10-1 L2
- ❑ Transparencies and Worksheets 21, 22
- ❑ TR Practice 10-1
- ❑ TR Enrich 10-1 L4
- ❑ Audio Summary 10-1 L1 L2 EL
- ❑ PHSchool.com: More on the digestive system

3. ASSESS

Evaluate Understanding The assignments listed in the Teacher's Edition can help you assess students' mastery of the section content.

Reteach Write the names of digestive structures on index cards. Have students sequence the cards in the order that food travels through the system. Then have students write the functions on the back of the cards. L2

Targeted Resources

- ❑ TR Section 10-1 Quiz
- ❑ CTB Chapter 10

KEY

L1 Special Needs	L4 Gifted and Talented
L2 Less Proficient Readers	EL English Language Learners
L3 All Students	

Name ______________________ Class ________________ Date ______

Section 10-1 **Practice**

Concept Check: Steps in the Digestive Process

As soon as food enters your body, the process of digestion begins. Digestion proceeds in a series of steps that involve the mechanical and chemical breakdown of food.

Name the structures indicated by the numbers on the diagram. Write a short description of what happens to food at each structure. Include both mechanical and chemical digestion in your descriptions.

1. ______________________________

____

____

2. ______________________________

____

____

3. ______________________________

____

____

4. ______________________________

____

____

5. ______________________________

____

____

6. ______________________________

____

____

7. ______________________________

____

____

1
2
3
4
5
6
7

Name ______________________ Class ____________________ Date ________

Section 10-1 **Enrich**

Class Activity: The Mathematics of Digestion

Mechanical digestion makes chemical digestion more efficient. By tearing, grinding, and mixing food, mechanical digestion increases the ratio of food surface area to food volume. The following activity will help you determine how this ratio is important to digestion.

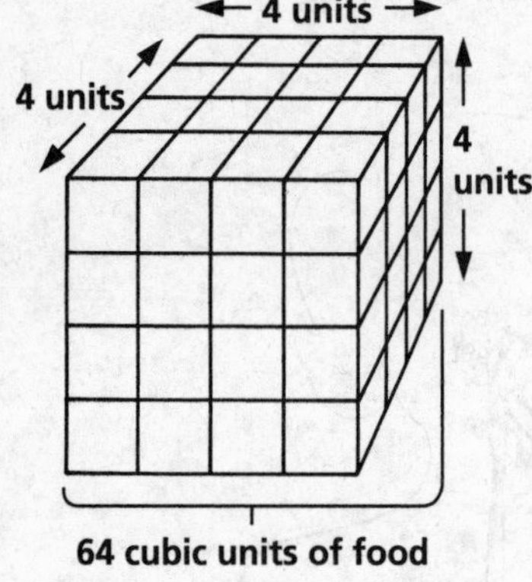

Step 1 Calculate the volume of the cube by multiplying the length × width × height (4 units × 4 units × 4 units = 64 cubic units).

Step 2 To calculate the surface area of the cube, first calculate the area of one side (4 units × 4 units = 16 square units). Then multiply the area of one side by the number of sides: 16 square units × 6 = 96 square units.

Step 3 The ratio of surface area to volume in this example is 96:64, or 1.5. Gastric juice could work on 1.5 square units of surface to digest 1 cubic unit of food.

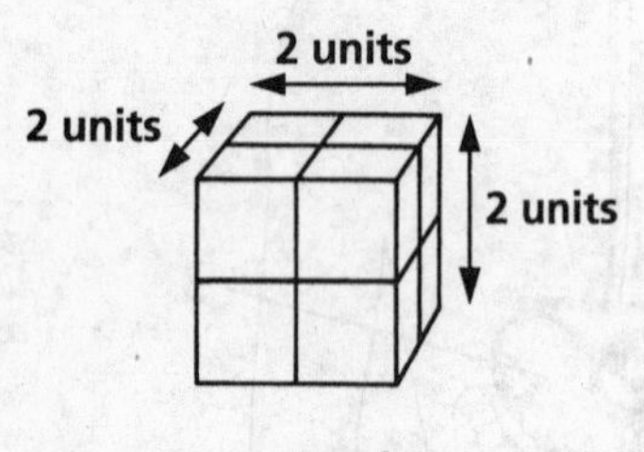

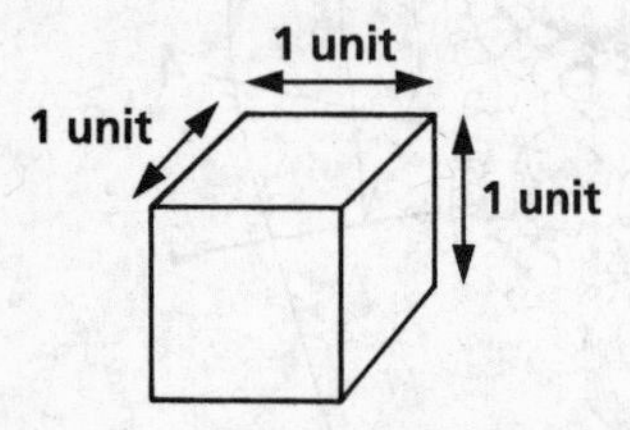

1. Now suppose you bite, chew, and grind the single piece of food into 8 pieces. Each piece is 2 units × 2 units × 2 units.

a. What is the volume of one piece? ____________

b. What is the surface area of one piece? __________

c. What is the ratio of surface area to volume? ____________________

d. In other words, gastric juice has ____________ square units of surface available to digest each cubic unit of food.

2. Now you bite the smaller food pieces again, so each piece is 1 unit × 1 unit × 1 unit.

a. What is the volume of one piece? ______________________________

b. What is the surface area of one piece? ____________________________

c. What is the ratio of surface area to volume? ______________________

d. In other words, gastric juice has ________________ square units of surface available to digest each cubic unit of food.

3. Which cube has the highest surface area to volume ratio? ______________

4. Why do you think a high surface area to volume ratio makes chemical digestion occur faster? ____

____

Name ______________________ Class ______________________ Date ________

Section 10-1

Quiz

Write the letter of the correct answer in the space provided.

______ **1.** A flap of tissue that keeps you from choking when you swallow is the
a. pharynx.
b. epiglottis.
c. esophagus.
d. villus.

______ **2.** Which statement is true?
a. Chemical digestion occurs only in the small intestine.
b. Mechanical digestion occurs only in the mouth.
c. Chemical digestion occurs in the mouth, stomach, and small intestine.
d. Fat digestion takes place in the liver.

______ **3.** Which is the major function of the large intestine?
a. absorption of water
b. chemical digestion of protein
c. absorption of nutrients
d. breaking up large fat droplets

______ **4.** The pancreas secretes digestive enzymes into the
a. gallbladder.
b. stomach.
c. small intestine.
d. large intestine.

______ **5.** Hydrochloric acid
a. is produced by the stomach during chemical digestion.
b. is produced by the salivary glands during the breakdown of starch.
c. is produced by the gallbladder to help break up fat droplets.
d. All of the above

Write the letter of the correct answer in the space provided.

______ **6.** muscular tube that connects the throat and stomach

______ **7.** thick liquid created as a result of food mixing with gastric juice

______ **8.** substance that helps carry out chemical reactions in the body

______ **9.** substance that breaks up fat droplets

______ **10.** long, tubelike organ in which chemical digestion is completed

a. bile
b. large intestine
c. small intestine
d. chyme
e. enzyme
f. esophagus

Name______________________ Class__________ Date__________ M T W T F

Section 10-2

Keeping Your Digestive System Healthy

Lesson Plan

Section Objectives

- **Identify** behaviors that keep your digestive system healthy.
- **Evaluate** whether you practice proper food safety methods.

Vocabulary foodborne illness • cross-contamination

Time
1 period
1/2 block

Local Standards

1. FOCUS

Warm-Up: Quick Quiz Use the Warm-Up activity to uncover misconceptions about food safety and digestive system health.

Targeted Resources
- ❑ Transparency W34

2. TEACH

Visual Learning: Figure 4 Verify that students understand the information in the table. Ask a series of questions, such as "Which of these problems can be cured only with surgery?" L1

Cooperative Learning Invite an internist to talk about how medical knowledge regarding digestive system disorders has changed over the years. Have small groups brainstorm questions to ask. L2

Cooperative Learning Have small groups make a picnic menu. After groups exchange menus have them create food-safety plans. L2

Active Learning Coordinate with school food-service employees to arrange for class tours of the cafeteria and kitchen. L3

Targeted Resources
- ❑ RN Note Taking Guide 10-2 L3 EL
- ❑ ARN Note Taking Guide 10-2 L2
- ❑ TR Practice 10-2
- ❑ TR Enrich 10-2 L4
- ❑ Audio Summary 10-2 L1 L2 EL
- ❑ Health Links: Updates on food safety

3. ASSESS

Evaluate Understanding The assignments listed in the Teacher's Edition can help you assess students' mastery of the section content.

Reteach On index cards, write a problem associated with food safety on one side and its solution or solutions on the back. Show students the problems, and have them respond with the solutions. L2

Targeted Resources
- ❑ TR Section 10-2 Quiz
- ❑ CTB Chapter 10

KEY

L1 Special Needs
L2 Less Proficient Readers
L3 All Students
L4 Gifted and Talented
EL English Language Learners

Name ______________ Class ______________ Date ______________

Section 10-2 **Practice**

Vocabulary Activity: Digestive Disorders

Create flashcards to help you remember details about the different types of digestive disorders discussed in this activity. Follow the example below.

Front

Appendicitis

Back

Cause: Microorganisms infect the appendix

Treatment: Surgery

What are five steps you can take to help keep your digestive system healthy?

____

____

____

____

____

Name ______________________ Class ____________________ Date ______

Section 10-2 **Enrich**

Community Involvement: **Foodborne Illness**

Your local health department enforces regulations to help prevent cases of foodborne illness. When cases of foodborne illness are reported, the health department takes action to determine the cause.

Conduct a telephone interview to learn what procedures are followed by your local health department to ensure public safety. Ask the questions below, and add another question of your own.

1. Name of health department representative ____________________

2. How many instances of food poisoning were reported last year? __________

3. What are the most frequent causes of food poisoning? ____________________

____

____

4. What steps are taken when a case of food poisoning is reported to the health department? ____________________

____

____

5. How often are restaurants inspected by the health department? __________

6. What happens during a restaurant inspection? ____________________

____

____

____

____

7. What happens when a restaurant is found in violation of health-code regulations?

____

____

____

8. What suggestions do you have for preventing food poisoning at school or at home? ____________________

____

____

9. Question: ____________________

____

Name ______________ Class ______________ Date ______

Section 10-2

Quiz

Write the letter of the correct answer in the space provided.

_____ **1.** Which condition may be caused by an infection with *H. pylori*?
a. lactose intolerance
b. appendicitis
c. hemorrhoids
d. peptic ulcer

_____ **2.** Which condition is most likely caused by overeating?
a. hemorrhoids
b. heartburn
c. peptic ulcer
d. irritable bowel syndrome

_____ **3.** Identify the action that could lead to foodborne illness from cross-contamination.
a. thawing meat at room temperature
b. failing to quickly refrigerate cut up fruit
c. eating chicken that is not fully cooked
d. chopping meat and vegetables on the same cutting board

_____ **4.** What is the best way to determine when fish has been fully cooked?
a. if it can be flaked with a fork, it is cooked
b. taste it
c. if it is translucent, it is cooked
d. follow recipe instructions

_____ **5.** Abnormal peristalsis is a cause of which digestive system condition?
a. lactose intolerance
b. colon cancer
c. irritable bowel syndrome
d. appendicitis

Decide whether each statement is true or false. Write true *or* false *in the space provided.*

_____ **6.** To treat diarrhea, you should reduce your fluid intake.

_____ **7.** Heartburn is caused by stomach acids irritating the lining of the esophagus.

_____ **8.** Paper towels are safer than sponges for cleanup in the kitchen.

_____ **9.** You should allow hot leftovers to cool before refrigerating them.

_____ **10.** Eggs should be cooked until the whites and yolks are firm.

Name________________ Class________ Date________ M T W T F

Section 10-3

Your Excretory System — Lesson Plan

Section Objectives

- **Identify** the organs of excretion in the body and their functions.
- **Explain** how the kidneys remove wastes from the blood and produce urine.
- **Describe** behaviors that can keep your excretory system healthy.

Vocabulary excretion • urea • kidney • urine • nephron • glomerulus • dialysis

Time
1 period
1/2 block

Local Standards

1. FOCUS

Warm-Up: Health Stats The Warm-Up will introduce students to the role of the excretory system in water balance.

Targeted Resources

- ❑ Transparency W35

2. TEACH

Visual Learning: Figure 7 Have students study the figure to trace the removal of wastes from the body by the excretory system. L2

Building Vocabulary Help students brainstorm ways to distinguish the terms *ureter* and *urethra*. EL

Differentiated Instruction Have students place plastic bags over their hands and secure them with tape. Moisture in the bag will reveal the work of the excretory system. L1

Building Health Skills Ask students to make a chart to keep track of how much water they drink. L3

Cooperative Learning Have student pairs come up with various strategies to increase fluid intake. L2

Targeted Resources

- ❑ RN Note Taking Guide 10-3 L3 EL
- ❑ ARN Note Taking Guide 10-3 L2
- ❑ Transparency and Worksheet 23
- ❑ TR Practice 10-3
- ❑ TR Enrich 10-3 L4
- ❑ Audio Summary 10-3 L1 L2 EL
- ❑ Health Links: Updates on the excretory system

3. ASSESS

Evaluate Understanding The assignments listed in the Teacher's Edition can help you assess students' mastery of the section content.

Reteach Mix colored water and marbles. Pour the mixture into a colander to reinforce the concept of filtration in a nephron. L2

Targeted Resources

- ❑ TR Section 10-3 Quiz
- ❑ CTB Chapter 10

KEY

L1 Special Needs	L4 Gifted and Talented
L2 Less Proficient Readers	EL English Language Learners
L3 All Students	

Name ______________________ Class __________________ Date ______

Section 10-3 **Practice**

Vocabulary Activity: Word Search

Read each clue and decide which vocabulary word fits the description. Then, find that word in the puzzle. Words can read left to right, straight down, or diagonally.

Clues

1. the process by which the body removes wastes
2. a waste product from the breakdown of proteins
3. major organ of excretion
4. fluid excreted from the kidneys
5. filtering unit of the kidney
6. cluster of vessels where blood enters a nephron
7. process in which a machine does the job of the kidneys

Name ______________________ Class ____________________ Date ______

Section 10-3 **Enrich**

Consumer Skills: Urinalysis

Urinalysis is a set of tests that are useful in detecting some medical problems. As a health consumer, it is useful for you to understand what urinalysis can reveal. During urinalysis, a healthcare professional inserts a strip of paper or plastic, called a dipstick, into a urine sample. If the dipstick changes color, the patient has the condition being tested for. Healthcare professionals also examine the overall color and look of the sample. They may also use a microscope to look for specific cells. The table lists some common urine tests, possible results, and what these results indicate.

Review the information in the table and then answer the questions on a separate piece of paper.

Test	Results	Condition Indicated by Test Results
Color	pale to dark yellow	normal
	bright blue	presence of drug
	foamy	presence of protein
	red or red-brown	presence of red blood cells
Presence of protein	slight color change in dipstick	kidney disease
	major color change in dipstick	severe kidney disease
Presence of glucose	dipstick changes color	diabetes
Presence of ketones	dipstick changes color	severe diabetes
Presence of nitrite	dipstick changes color	bacteria in urine (urinary infection)
Presence of red blood cells	observed with microscope	kidney disease
Presence of white blood cells	observed with microscope	bacteria in urine (urinary infection)

1. A patient's urine tests positive for glucose and ketones. What do these results indicate?
2. A patient's urine test shows the presence of nitrite. What condition does this indicate? What other test could you perform to confirm this result?
3. What should a doctor check for in the urine of a person who might have kidney disease?
4. Use reliable Web sites to find a definition of *ketones*. Why are people with diabetes likely to have ketones in their urine?

Name ______________________ Class ____________________ Date ________

Section 10-3

Quiz

Write the letter of the correct answer in the space provided.

______	**1.** bladder	**a.**	a small unit that contains a long, twisting tube
______	**2.** urethra	**b.**	cluster of blood vessels surrounding a capsule
______	**3.** kidney	**c.**	stores urine before it is released from the body
______	**4.** nephron	**d.**	tube urine travels through to the bladder
______	**5.** glomerulus	**e.**	tube urine travels through to exit the body
		f.	contains millions of tiny filtering units

Write the letter of the correct answer in the space provided.

______ **6.** The ureter
- **a.** stores urine.
- **b.** carries urine to the kidneys.
- **c.** carries urine to the bladder.
- **d.** removes urine from the body.

______ **7.** As the kidneys filter wastes,
- **a.** glucose is returned to the blood.
- **b.** urea is returned to the blood.
- **c.** protein collects in the urine.
- **d.** glucose collects in the urine.

______ **8.** Urinary tract infections usually involve the
- **a.** ureter or bladder.
- **b.** nephron or urethra.
- **c.** kidney or ureter.
- **d.** urethra or bladder.

______ **9.** Protein in the urine can be a sign that
- **a.** the kidneys are functioning properly.
- **b.** the kidneys are functioning poorly.
- **c.** a person has a urinary tract infection.
- **d.** a person needs more protein in the diet.

______ **10.** Which is *not* a function of the kidneys?
- **a.** formation of urea
- **b.** filtering urea from the blood
- **c.** formation of urine
- **d.** maintaining water balance

Name ______________ Class ______________ Date ______

Chapter 10 Test

Write the letter of the correct answer in the space provided.

_____ **1.** What is a benefit of eating high-fiber foods?
a. They play a critical role in controlling lactose intolerance.
b. They increase the production of digestive enzymes.
c. They help prevent constipation and hemorrhoids.
d. They are broken down into substances that can be easily absorbed.

_____ **2.** Which actions best serve to keep your kidneys healthy?
a. limiting your intake of saturated fats
b. drinking plenty of water every day
c. eating 10 ounces of fiber a day
d. all of the above

_____ **3.** Which is *not* a mechanical process involved in the breakdown of food?
a. action of digestive enzymes
b. peristalsis
c. swallowing
d. mixing of food by stomach muscles

_____ **4.** Substances found in urine include
a. water and complex carbohydrates.
b. starch and carbon dioxide.
c. starch and water.
d. water and urea.

Write the letter of the correct answer in the space provided.

_____ **5.** organ that releases water and urea to lower body temperature

_____ **6.** organ that removes carbon dioxide from the body

_____ **7.** organ that stores urine

_____ **8.** organ that churns and mixes food

_____ **9.** organ that absorbs the most nutrients

_____ **10.** organ that stores bile

a. stomach
b. lung
c. skin
d. liver
e. gallbladder
f. bladder
g. small intestine

Name ______________________ Class __________________ Date ______

Chapter 10: **Test** *(continued)*

Decide whether each statement is true or false. Write true or false in the space provided.

______**11.** The small intestine is longer than the large intestine.

______**12.** *Salmonella* bacteria are killed by cooking food thoroughly.

______**13.** Appendicitis is a chronic inflammation of the lower part of the small intestine.

______**14.** Organs of excretion include the skin, kidneys, lungs, and liver.

Write the word or phrase that best completes each sentence in the space provided.

15. Urea is produced by the ______________ and excreted by the ______________.

16. Digestion involves two processes: ______________ digestion and ______________ digestion.

17. Food is pushed through the esophagus by ______________.

18. Gastric juice contains ______________, an enzyme that breaks down protein, and ______________ ______________.

Use complete sentences to answer the following questions.

19. Describe the four precautions you can take to avoid foodborne illness.

20. How are the lungs, skin, and liver involved in excretion?

Name ____________________ Class ________________ Date ______

Chapter 11

Personal Inventory

Healthy Bones, Muscles, and Nerves

There are a number of ways that you can maintain the health of your skeletal, muscular, and nervous systems. Consider the following healthy choices. How often do you make them part of your life?

For each example, check the appropriate column.

Healthy Choices	Always	Usually	Sometimes	Seldom/ Never
I eat foods high in calcium, such as milk products, dark green leafy vegetables, tofu, and legumes.				
I get regular medical checkups.				
I exercise regularly.				
I vary my exercise routine.				
I warm up, stretch, and cool down as part of my exercise routine.				
I drink plenty of water before and during exercise.				
I practice good posture when using the computer.				
I use a seat belt when riding in a motor vehicle.				
I wear a helmet when I ride a bicycle, play contact sports, or use inline skates.				
I refuse to use illegal drugs, including anabolic steroids.				

Review your responses. In what ways can you improve your habits?

____

____

What is your favorite form of exercise? List the kinds of risks that are part of that activity and choices you can make to reduce those risks.

____

____

____

Name_________________________ Class__________ Date__________ M T W T F

Section 11-1

Your Skeletal System Lesson Plan

Section Objectives

- **Identify** the five main roles of the skeletal system.
- **Decribe** the functions of bones and joints.
- **Explain** how you can keep your skeletal system healthy.

Time
2 periods
1 block

Local Standards

Vocabulary joint • cartilage • ossification • marrow • ligament • osteoporosis • fracture • sprain • dislocation • scoliosis

1. FOCUS

Warm-Up: Quick Quiz Discuss how the behaviors described in the quiz help maintain the health of the body.

Targeted Resources
- ❑ Transparency W36

2. TEACH

Class Discussion Use what students know about the framework of a house to discuss the five main roles of the skeletal system. L2

Differentiated Instruction Provide students with the materials to design a board game that teaches the names and locations of the bones in the skeleton. EL

Visual Learning: Figure 2 Use the diagram of a bone to discuss how the structure of bones contributes to the functions of the skeletal system. L2

Class Discussion Have students describe how joints are important to movement by imagining their fingers without joints. L2

Building Health Skills Challenge students to determine the reasons why they do not wear helmets while participating in certain activities. L1

Targeted Resources
- ❑ RN Note Taking Guide 11-1 L3 EL
- ❑ ARN Note Taking Guide 11-1 L2
- ❑ Transparencies and Worksheets 24, 25
- ❑ TR Practice 11-1
- ❑ TR Enrich 11-1 L4
- ❑ Audio Summary 11-1 L1 L2 EL
- ❑ PHSchool.com: More on movable joints

3. ASSESS

Evaluate Understanding The assignments listed in the Teacher's Edition can help you assess students' mastery of the section content.

Reteach Have students create a concept map that describes the structures and functions of the skeletal system. L2

Targeted Resources
- ❑ TR Section 11-1 Quiz
- ❑ CTB Chapter 11

KEY

L1 Special Needs	L4 Gifted and Talented
L2 Less Proficient Readers	EL English Language Learners
L3 All Students	

Name ____________________ Class ____________________ Date ________

Section 11-1 **Practice**

Decision Making: To Play or Not to Play?

Your coach has selected you to play in the starting lineup for the big game tomorrow night. You hurt your knee during practice today, but have not told the coach for fear of not being allowed to play in the game tomorrow. You can walk without limping, most of the time. Tonight, you plan to apply ice and take a pain reliever.

The following questions will lead you through the process of deciding whether you should play in the game tomorrow night.

1. What decision do you need to make?

____

2. In the chart below, list the possible solutions to the problem and their positive and negative consequences.

Possible Solutions	Possible Consequences	
	Positive	**Negative**

3. What would you do in this situation? Explain the reasons for your decision.

____

____

____

____

Name ____________________ Class ____________________ Date ____________

Section 11-1 **Enrich**

Research Project: Factors That Affect Osteoporosis

Betty felt fine last night, and she slept well. But when she tried to get out of bed this morning, she felt a sharp pain. X-rays show that while she slept one of the vertebrae in her spinal column collapsed—just crumbled!

Well, I measured Grandma's height today. I thought she was getting shorter, but I had no idea. She is two inches shorter than she used to be!

Both of these stories are not unusual. Many older women and some men have osteoporosis, a condition in which the bones become weak and break easily. People with osteoporosis might become shorter as their vertebrae crumble. Although there is no cure for osteoporosis, doctors can treat patients with medications that help rebuild bone or prevent bone from losing more calcium. Doctors recommend certain behavior changes to prevent or slow the progress of osteoporosis.

Use up-to-date library or online resources to answer these questions about osteoporosis.

1. Identify two health problems or symptoms that could cause a person with osteoporosis to seek medical care.

a. ____________________

b. ____________________

2. Find three risk factors that may lead to the development of osteoporosis. Place a check next to any that a patient can control.

a. ____________________

b. ____________________

c. ____________________

3. Name one condition that can lead to osteoporosis during the teen years.

____

4. Give three recommendations that a doctor might make to patients to help prevent osteoporosis.

a. ____________________

b. ____________________

c. ____________________

Name ______________________ Class ____________________ Date ________

Section 11-1 **Quiz**

Write the letter of the correct answer in the space provided.

______ **1.** a tissue found in the spaces of bones		**a.** cartilage
______ **2.** the ends of bones in a joint are forced out of place		**b.** marrow
______ **3.** a break in a bone		**c.** ligament
______ **4.** a soft, flexible supportive tissue that is replaced by bone during ossification		**d.** fracture
______ **5.** a strong, fibrous band that connects bones at joints		**e.** dislocation
		f. scoliosis

Decide whether each statement is true or false. Write true *or* false *in the space provided.*

______ **6.** The skeleton gives the body its basic shape.

______ **7.** One role of the skeletal system is to produce blood cells.

______ **8.** Bones are nonliving structures that do not change once you are finished growing.

______ **9.** Joints enable the skeletal system to move.

______ **10.** If you consume enough calcium, you don't need to exercise for bone health.

Name______________________ Class__________ Date__________ M T W T F

Section 11-2

Your Muscular System Lesson Plan

Section Objectives

- **Describe** the functions of the three types of muscles.
- **Explain** how you can keep your muscular system healthy.

Vocabulary smooth muscle • cardiac muscle • skeletal muscle • tendon • muscle tone • atrophy • anabolic steroid • strain • tendonitis

Time
1 period
1/2 block

Local Standards

1. FOCUS

Warm-Up: Myth/Fact Ask students to write down where they get information about muscles and how correct this information is. Volunteers should share their responses.

Targeted Resources
- ❑ Transparency W37

2. TEACH

Cooperative Learning Instruct students to build a model to show how skeletal muscles move bones. L3

Differentiated Instruction Have students eat a cracker and then discuss how food travels from the mouth to the stomach. Students can squeeze a toothpaste tube to model this movement. L1

Building Health Skills Ask students to assess their exercise routines, including the time spent warming up, stretching, and cooling down, and develop an exercise plan to address any weaknesses. L3

Targeted Resources
- ❑ RN Note Taking Guide 11-2 L3 EL
- ❑ ARN Note Taking Guide11-2 L2
- ❑ Transparency and Worksheet 26
- ❑ TR Practice 11-2
- ❑ TR Enrich 11-2 L4
- ❑ Audio Summary 11-2 L1 L2 EL
- ❑ Health Links: Updates on stretching

3. ASSESS

Evaluate Understanding The assignments listed in the Teacher's Edition can help you assess students' mastery of the section content.

Reteach Have students design a table that describes the functions and locations of the three types of muscles. L2

Targeted Resources
- ❑ Section 11-2 Quiz
- ❑ CTB Chapter 11

KEY

L1 Special Needs	L4 Gifted and Talented
L2 Less Proficient Readers	EL English Language Learners
L3 All Students	

Name ______________________ Class ________________ Date ________

Section 11-2 **Practice**

Concept Check: Muscles in the Body

Look at the pictures below. Then answer the question next to each picture.

1. a. When a runner uses her leg muscles to run, which of the three types of muscle is she using?

____

b. Are these muscle movements voluntary or involuntary? Explain.

____

____

____

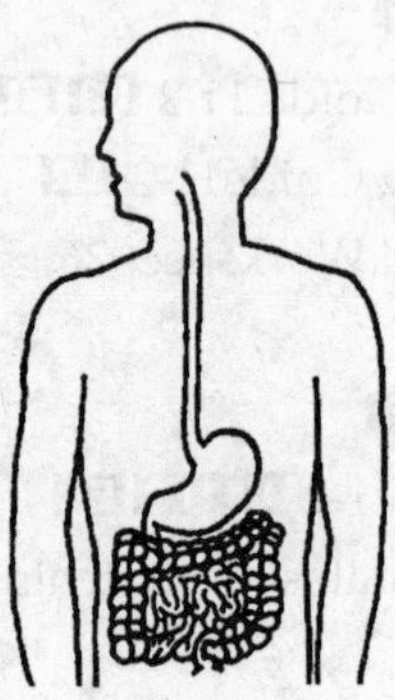

2. a. When food moves through the esophagus, stomach, and intestines, which type of muscle is at work?

____

b. Are these muscle movements voluntary or involuntary? Explain.

____

____

____

3. a. When the heart pumps blood, which type of muscle is being used?

____

b. Are these muscles voluntary or involuntary? Explain.

____

____

____

4. While eating, you lift food to your mouth, chew it, swallow it, and digest it. Explain how all three types of muscle tissue are used during this process.

____

____

____

Name ______________________ Class ________________ Date ______

Section 11-2 **Enrich**

***Community Involvement:* Physical Therapy**

Physical therapy and rehabilitation medicine involve conditioning the bones, muscles, and joints. Some athletes need this kind of therapy to strengthen muscles or bones after an injury. Other people may need to recuperate from a fall or car crash, while still others need therapy for conditions such as arthritis.

Use the yellow pages in your local telephone book to identify places offering physical therapy or rehabilitation services in your community. Choose one of the facilities and prepare questions suitable for a telephone interview. The questions below are some examples. Add another question that is of interest to you.

1. Name of interviewee: ______________________

2. Place of employment: ______________________

3. What types of physical therapy are offered? ______________________

____

____

4. What kinds of equipment are used to help someone recover from a knee injury? ______________________

____

____

5. What kinds of treatment and equipment are used to ease joint pain related to arthritis? ______________________

____

____

6. What exercises are recommended for a person with back pain? ______________________

____

____

7. What training do physical therapists receive? ______________________

____

____

8. Your question: ______________________

____

____

____

Name ______________________ Class ____________________ Date ______

Section 11-2 **Quiz**

Decide whether each statement is true or false. Write true *or* false *in the space provided.*

______ **1.** You consciously control involuntary muscles.

______ **2.** All muscles work by contracting.

______ **3.** To keep up your muscle strength you should always practice the same exercise routine.

______ **4.** Treatment for muscle injuries includes strenuous exercise.

______ **5.** Some muscle soreness after exercise is normal.

Write the letter of the correct answer in the space provided.

______ **6.** Involuntary muscle found only in the heart is called
a. smooth muscle.
b. cardiac muscle.
c. skeletal muscle.
d. voluntary muscle.

______ **7.** Smooth muscles are involved in which one of the following activities?
a. pumping blood
b. walking
c. digesting food
d. playing a piano

______ **8.** A tendon is a thick strand of tissue that attaches
a. muscles to nerves.
b. muscles to muscles.
c. bones to bones.
d. muscles to bones.

______ **9.** Which is a condition that occurs when muscles weaken or shrink due to little use?
a. atrophy
b. muscle tone
c. strain
d. tendonitis

______ **10.** A muscle strain is a(an)
a. overused tendon.
b. strong, uncontrolled muscle contraction.
c. pulled muscle.
d. strengthening exercise.

Name________________________ Class__________ Date__________ M T W T F

Section 11-3

Your Nervous System Lesson Plan

Section Objectives

- **Explain** the functions of the nervous system and the role of neurons.
- **Describe** the roles of the central nervous system and the peripheral nervous system.
- **Identify** the most important thing you can do to keep your nervous system healthy.

Time
3 periods
1 1/2 blocks

Local Standards

Vocabulary neuron • cerebrum • cerebellum • brain stem • spinal cord • reflex • concussion • coma • paralysis • meningitis • seizure • epilepsy

1. FOCUS

Warm-Up: Health Stats Have students write and share reasons why teens do not always choose healthful behaviors.

Targeted Resources
- ❑ Transparency W38

2. TEACH

Visual Learning: Use the diagram of a neuron to discuss the structure and function of neurons. L3

Addressing Misconceptions: Explain to students that the neuron connections in their brains will continue to develop into their early twenties. L3

Differentiated Instruction Have students make a flowchart that follows the path of an impulse from sensory nerves to the central nervous system and motor nerves. L2

Building Health Skills: Have students prepare a public service announcement that advocates the prevention of bacterial meningitis through vaccination. L3

Cooperative Learning Challenge student groups to identify whether sensory nerves or autonomic or somatic nerves are responsible for certain actions. L2

Targeted Resources
- ❑ RN Note Taking Guide 11-3 L3 EL
- ❑ ARN Note Taking Guide 11-3 L2
- ❑ Transparencies and Worksheets 27, 28, 29
- ❑ TR Practice 11-3
- ❑ TR Enrich 11-3 L4
- ❑ Audio Summary 11-3 L1 L2 EL
- ❑ Health Links: Updates on overuse injuries

3. ASSESS

Evaluate Understanding The assignments listed in the Teacher's Edition can help you assess students' mastery of the section content.

Reteach Instruct student pairs to use the figures in the chapter as a guide to help them write a description of the functions of the different parts of the nervous system. L2

Targeted Resources
- ❑ TR Section 11-3 Quiz
- ❑ CTB Chapter 11

KEY
L1 Special Needs
L2 Less Proficient Readers
L3 All Students
L4 Gifted and Talented
EL English Language Learners

Name ______________________ Class ____________________ Date ________

Section 11-3 **Practice**

Vocabulary Activity: The Nervous System

Complete the concept map that shows the divisions of the nervous system.

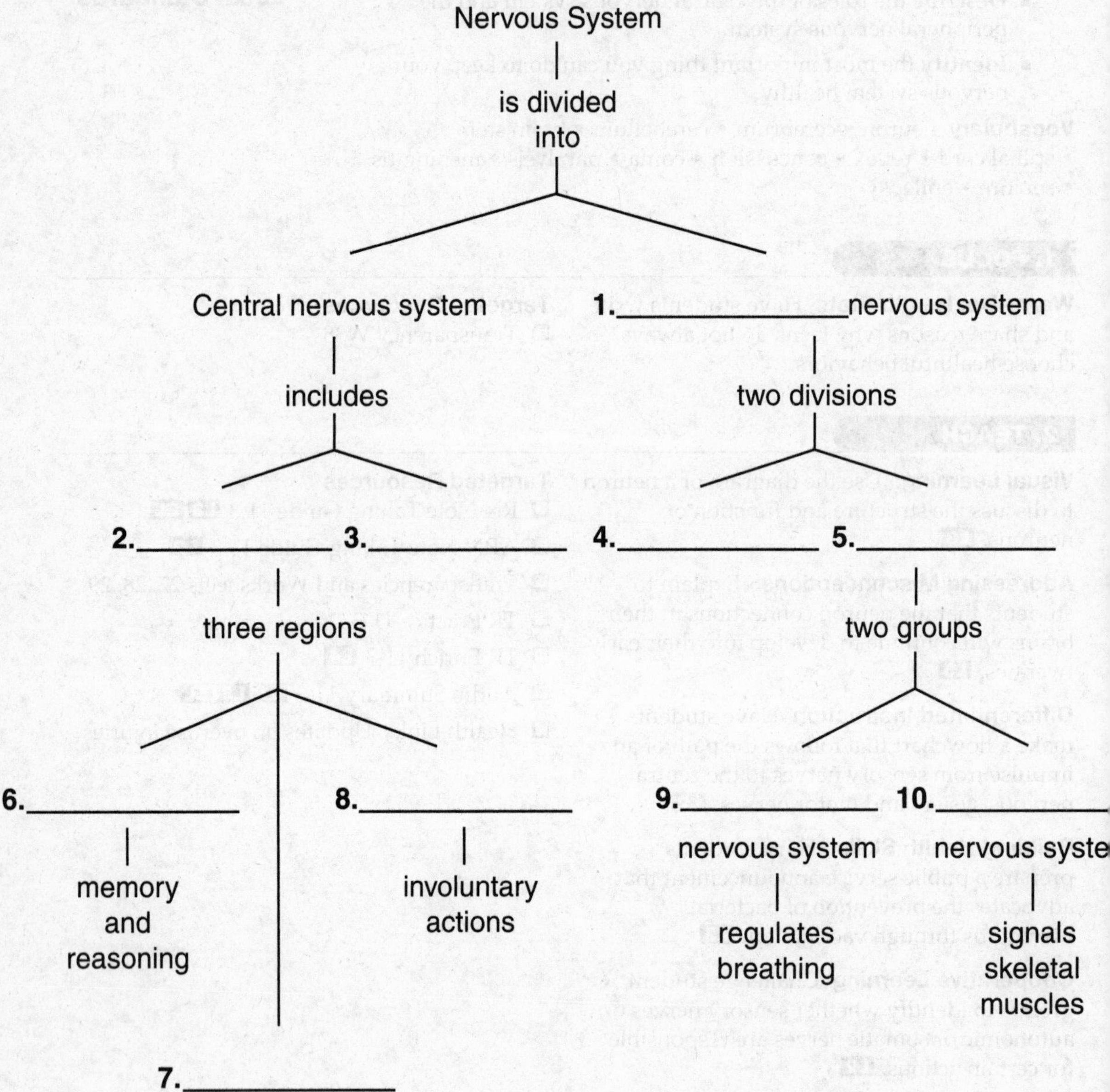

Name ____________________ Class ____________________ Date ________

Section 11-3 **Enrich**

Class Debate: To Helmet or Not?

Do you wear a helmet when you ride a bike? In the United States, 21 states have laws requiring bicyclists to wear helmets. At least 148 cities also have laws requiring bicycle helmets. Most of these laws require people under the age of 16 years to wear a helmet. A few laws require all bicyclists to wear a helmet.

Are these laws necessary? In 2003, 85 percent of the bicyclists killed were not wearing a helmet. In California, which has a state law requiring bicyclists under 16 years of age to wear a helmet, there was an 18.2 percent decrease in head injuries in this age group after the law was passed. There was no change in the adult rate of head injuries. Studies also show that after a state law is passed, helmet use increases by an average of 18.4 percent.

Many groups oppose helmet laws. They cite evidence from the Centers for Disease Control and Prevention that only 1 percent of head injuries result from riding a bicycle. In contrast, 43 percent of head injuries result from motor vehicle crashes. Studies also show that the typical bicycle helmet cannot withstand an impact of more than 14 mph.

Should laws require people to wear bicycle helmets? Your teacher will assign you to one side of the debate. List three to five points to support the side you are arguing. Be prepared to participate in a class debate.

For Helmet Laws	Against Helmet Laws

Name ______________________ Class __________________ Date ______

Section 11-3

Quiz

Write the letter of the correct answer in the space provided.

______	**1.** loss of ability to move and feel some part of the body	**a.** concussion
______	**2.** sudden, uncontrolled nerve impulses in the brain	**b.** coma
______	**3.** inflammation of the membranes surrounding the brain and spinal cord	**c.** paralysis
______	**4.** prolonged period of deep unconsciousness	**d.** meningitis
______	**5.** bruiselike injury to the brain	**e.** epilepsy
		f. seizure

Write the letter of the correct answer in the space provided.

______ **6.** The nervous system can directly perform all of the following actions *except*

a. processing information.
b. moving the skeleton in response to information.
c. receiving information from inside and outside the body.
d. forming a response to information.

______ **7.** The basic unit of the nervous system is the

a. neuron. **b.** cerebrum.
c. spinal cord. **d.** synapse.

______ **8.** Which function below is *not* performed by the central nervous system?

a. thinking and reasoning
b. coordinating balance
c. sensing the environment
d. coordinating reflex actions

______ **9.** Which *best* describes the peripheral nervous system?

a. the basic unit of the nervous system
b. the center of memory, speech, and abstract thought
c. the link between the body and the brain and spinal cord
d. the control center of the body

______ **10.** Which is the most important step you can take to care for your nervous system?

a. eat well-balanced meals
b. consume plenty of calcium
c. exercise regularly
d. protect it from injury

Name ______________________ Class ______________________ Date ________

Chapter 11 Test

Decide whether each statement is true or false. Write true *or* false *in the space provided.*

______ **1.** The skeletal system stores important substances such as calcium.

______ **2.** A newborn's skeleton has completed ossification.

______ **3.** Exercise programs that include periods of warming up and cooling down help prevent muscular system injuries.

______ **4.** The nervous system supports the body and protects internal organs.

______ **5.** A reflex action involves only the brain.

Write the letter of the correct answer in the space provided.

______ **6.** The main role of joints in the skeletal system is to
- **a.** store materials the body needs.
- **b.** gather information inside and outside the body.
- **c.** allow for movement.
- **d.** attach muscles to bones.

______ **7.** Involuntary muscle tissue that pushes food through the digestive system is
- **a.** skeletal muscle.
- **b.** cardiac muscle.
- **c.** sensory muscle.
- **d.** smooth muscle.

______ **8.** Which structures carry messages from one part of your body to another?
- **a.** neurons
- **b.** tendons
- **c.** ligaments
- **d.** marrow

______ **9.** The central nervous system
- **a.** links the body to the brain and spinal cord.
- **b.** is made up of the brain and spinal cord.
- **c.** is divided into the sensory and motor divisions.
- **d.** contains only sensory neurons.

______ **10.** Carpal tunnel syndrome is a nerve injury that
- **a.** only affects people who type all day.
- **b.** occurs when tendons in the lower arm swell.
- **c.** can lead to migraines.
- **d.** can be prevented with a vaccine.

Write the letter of the correct answer in the space provided.

______ **11.** a bruiselike injury to the brain

______ **12.** an overstretched or torn ligament

______ **13.** a break in a bone

______ **14.** inability to move or feel a part of the body

- **a.** fracture
- **b.** sprain
- **c.** paralysis
- **d.** concussion

Chapter 11: Test *(continued)*

Write the word that best completes each sentence in the space provided.

15. A place where two or more bones come together is called a(an) ____________________.

16. The process in which cartilage is replaced by bone is called ____________________.

17. Voluntary muscle tissue that moves arms and legs is called ____________________ muscle.

18. The region of the brain that coordinates movement and balance is the ____________________.

Use complete sentences to answer the following questions.

19. What are four things you can do to maintain the health of your skeletal system?

____

____

____

____

____

____

20. Describe the pathway of nerve impulses from when you hear the timer buzz on a microwave oven to when you open the microwave door.

____

____

____

____

____

____

____

____

Name ____________________ Class ______________ Date ______

Chapter 12

Personal Inventory

Habits for a Healthy Heart and Lungs

Your cardiovascular and respiratory systems work closely together. Often, the health of one of these systems influences the health of the other system. What do you do to keep both systems healthy?

Complete the statements below. Your answers will identify ways you can improve your habits to keep your heart and lungs healthy. You may want to review your answers after you have read Chapter 12.

Eating Healthy Foods

1. My favorite healthy foods are ______________________________

____

____

2. I ______________ eat fried and processed foods.

3. To maintain a healthy weight, I ______________________________

____

____

Exercising Regularly

4. The types of exercises I like to do include ______________________

____

____

5. To relieve stress through exercise, I ___________________________

____

____

6. Every day, I try to do ______________ minutes of physical activity.

Breathing Clean Air

7. When someone near me lights a cigarette, I _______________________

____

8. When I do work that generates fumes or dust, I ___________________

____

9. On days when the outside air quality is poor, I ___________________

____

Name____________________ Class__________ Date__________ M T W T F

Section 12-1

Your Cardiovascular System Lesson Plan

Time
2 periods
1 block

Local Standards

Section Objectives

- **Describe** the main functions of the cardiovascular system.
- **Trace** the pathway of blood through the heart.
- **Identify** three types of blood vessels and the four components of blood.

Vocabulary atrium • ventricle • pacemaker • artery • capillary • vein • blood pressure • hypertension • plasma • red blood cell • white blood cell • platelet

1. FOCUS

Warm-Up: Myth/Fact Ask students to explain in writing knowledge they hope to gain about the cardiovascular system.

Targeted Resources
- ❑ Transparency W39

2. TEACH

Building Vocabulary Reinforce students' understanding of the cardiovascular system by examining the derivation of *cardiovascular.* L2

Visual Learning: Figure 1 Ask students to use the diagram to respond to questions about blood flow through the chambers of the heart. L3

Teacher Demo Demonstrate for students which way the blood flows through a vein in the arm. L3

Differentiated Instruction Help students create a cycle diagram to demonstrate the flow of blood through the heart and blood vessels. L2

Building Health Skills Have groups of students make posters to inform the public about blood pressure and blood pressure readings. L3

Active Learning Have students make clay models of the different types of blood cells. L1

Targeted Resources
- ❑ RN Note Taking Guide 12-1 L3 EL
- ❑ ARN Note Taking Guide 12-1 L2
- ❑ Transparency and Worksheet 30
- ❑ TR Practice 12-1
- ❑ TR Enrich 12-1 L4
- ❑ Audio Summary 12-1 L1 L2 EL
- ❑ PHSchool.com: More on the heart

3. ASSESS

Evaluate Understanding The assignments listed in the Teacher's Edition can help you assess students' mastery of the section content.

Reteach List each of the section's vocabulary terms on the board and have students brainstorm facts about each term. L2

Targeted Resources
- ❑ TR Section 12-1 Quiz
- ❑ CTB Chapter 12

KEY

L1 Special Needs
L2 Less Proficient Readers
L3 All Students
L4 Gifted and Talented
EL English Language Learners

Name ______________ Class ______________ Date ______

Section 12-1 **Practice**

Vocabulary Activity: Structures of the Heart

The major structures of the heart include the right atrium, the left atrium, the right ventricle, the left ventricle, and the aorta. Each structure has a different role in directing the flow of blood.

In the spaces provided, list the structure that corresponds to the number and explain the structure's function.

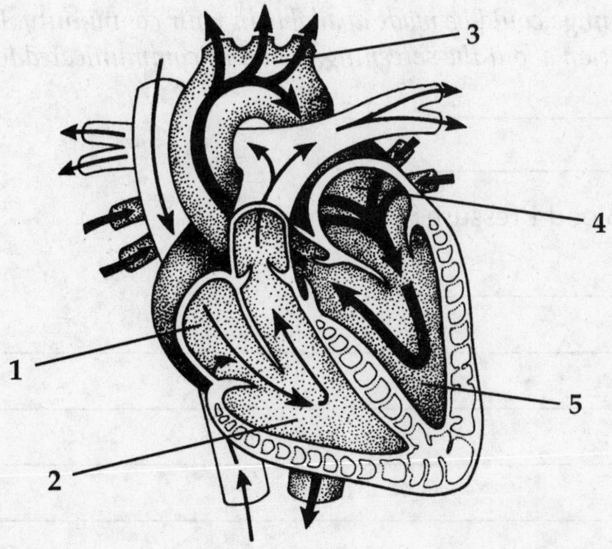

1. ____

____

2. ____

____

3. ____

____

4. ____

____

5. ____

____

Name ______________________ Class ____________________ Date ________

Section 12-1

Enrich

Community Involvement: Blood Pressure Screenings

About one third of people with high blood pressure do not know they have it. Some people have high blood pressure for many years without knowing it. Meanwhile, their cardiovascular systems could suffer damage that might have been prevented with treatment. What action could be taken in your community to ensure more people have their blood pressure screened?

Write an e-mail to your local health department presenting at least two ideas for how blood pressure screenings could be made available in your community. In your e-mail explain how information about the screenings could be communicated to the public.

To: ______________________________

cc: ______________________________

Subject: Ideas for Blood Pressure Screenings

Dear ___________________________,

Respectfully,

____

Name ______________________ Class ____________________ Date ______

Section 12-1

Quiz

Write the letter of the correct answer in the space provided.

______ **1.** blood vessels that carry blood to the heart		**a.** atrium
______ **2.** a lower chamber of the heart that pumps blood from the heart		**b.** ventricle
______ **3.** cells that carry oxygen from the lungs to all parts of the body		**c.** arteries
______ **4.** an upper chamber of the heart that receives blood		**d.** veins
______ **5.** blood vessels that carry blood away from the heart		**e.** red blood cells
		f. white blood cells

Decide whether each statement is true or false. Write true *or* false *in the space provided.*

______ **6.** One main function of the cardiovascular system is delivering materials to cells.

______ **7.** Blood flows from the atria to the ventricles.

______ **8.** The smallest blood vessels are capillaries.

______ **9.** The main role of white blood cells is to aid with the clotting process.

______ **10.** A person with type O blood can accept blood from any donor.

Name______________________ Class__________ Date__________ M T W T F

Section 12-2

Cardiovascular Health — Lesson Plan

Section Objectives

- **Identify** two factors that contribute to cardiovascular disease.
- **Describe** behaviors that can reduce your risk of cardiovascular disease.

Vocabulary low-density lipoprotein • plaque • atherosclerosis • high-density lipoprotein • arrhythmia

Time
2 periods
1 block

Local Standards

1. FOCUS

Warm-Up: Quick Quiz Ask students to choose the true statement about cardiovascular health and explain their choice in writing.

Targeted Resources
- ❑ Transparency W40

2. TEACH

Teacher Demo Use a bicycle pump and tubing to model atherosclerosis. Students should feel the difference in the pressure of an open tube and a pinched tube. L2

Building Health Skills Ask students to plan two meals, one that would contribute to the development of atherosclerosis and another that might help prevent the condition. L3

Differentiated Instruction Use an analogy of delivery trucks and garbage trucks to help students grasp the roles of LDL and HDL. L1

Building Health Skills Have small groups create a pamphlet that advocates developing habits that would help a teenager maintain cardiovascular health. L3

Targeted Resources
- ❑ RN Note Taking Guide 12-2 L3 EL
- ❑ ARN Note Taking Guide 12-2 L2
- ❑ TR Practice 12-2
- ❑ TR Enrich 12-2 L4
- ❑ Audio Summary 12-2 L1 L2 EL
- ❑ Health Links: Update on preventing heart disease

3. ASSESS

Evaluate Understanding The assignments listed in the Teacher's Edition can help you assess students' mastery of the section content.

Reteach Have students work in pairs. One student should name a cardiovascular disorder and the other should state two facts about that disorder. L2

Targeted Resources
- ❑ TR Section 12-2 Quiz
- ❑ CTB Chapter 12

KEY

L1	Special Needs	L4	Gifted and Talented
L2	Less Proficient Readers	EL	English Language Learners
L3	All Students		

Name ______________________ Class ______________________ Date __________

Section 12-2 **Practice**

Skill-Building Activity: Advocating Healthy Behavior

Sometimes people who have cardiovascular disease need the support of their family members. What would you do in the following situations?

In the spaces provided, explain what you could do to advocate for healthy behaviors.

1. Your mother has been diagnosed with hypertension. She is overweight and is trying to stay on a very strict diet. How can you support her efforts? What can you do or say to help her?

2. Your father has learned that he has a high level of LDL. He smokes and is overweight. His doctor told him that he must stop smoking, go on a strict diet, and exercise. How can you support him as he makes these changes?

3. Your brother eats many high-fat foods and rarely consumes fruits and vegetables. He also does not exercise often. He is of normal weight and does not think he needs to change his habits. Based on the recent diagnoses of your parents, what advice would you give your brother?

Name ______________________ Class ______________________ Date ________

Section 12-2 **Enrich**

Family Involvement: Heart-Healthy Meals

Find a book at the library that contains information about which foods are healthiest for the heart. The best books are ones that were published recently and contain menus and recipes for heart-healthy foods. As an alternative, search online for a reliable Web site that provides heart-healthy menus and recipes. *Review the information with your family. Together, plan dinner menus for a week that are both heart-healthy and appealing to everyone in your family. Write your family's menus below.*

Monday	Tuesday	Wednesday	Thursday

Friday	Saturday	Sunday

Suppose a member of your family is reluctant to try some of the meals. How would you try to convince him or her of the importance of eating heart-healthy meals?

____

____

____

____

Name ______________ Class ______________ Date ______

Section 12-2 **Quiz**

Decide whether each statement is true or false. Write true *or* false *in the space provided.*

______ **1.** High levels of LDL and low levels of HDL increase a person's risk of heart attack and stroke.

______ **2.** Low-density lipoproteins carry cholesterol to body tissues for use or storage.

______ **3.** The only treatment for hypertension is medication.

______ **4.** Atherosclerosis is a condition in which an artery wall hardens and thickens due to plaque buildup.

______ **5.** A heart murmur may be caused by a valve in the heart not closing properly.

Write the letter of the correct answer in the space provided.

______ **6.** The substance that builds up in artery walls is called
a. HDL.
b. atherosclerosis.
c. plaque.
d. arrhythmia.

______ **7.** Almost half of all children are diagnosed with a(an)
a. heart murmur.
b. arrhythmia.
c. opening in the heart wall.
d. stroke.

______ **8.** Which substance carries excess cholesterol to the liver to be broken down?
a. platelets
b. low-density lipoprotein
c. high-density lipoprotein
d. plaque

______ **9.** Which condition is known as a "silent killer"?
a. hypertension
b. atherosclerosis
c. heart attack
d. stroke

______ **10.** Which of the following is *not* a benefit of exercise?
a. an overall decrease in blood pressure
b. an increase in LDL levels
c. lowered stress levels
d. strengthened heart muscles

Name________________________ Class__________ Date__________ M T W T F

Section 12-3

Respiratory Health — Lesson Plan

Section Objectives

- **List** the functions of the respiratory system.
- **Describe** how air travels through your respiratory system, and how you breathe.
- **Identify** ways to keep the respiratory system healthy.

Vocabulary alveoli • diaphragm • asthma • bronchitis

Time
1 period
1/2 block

Local Standards

1. FOCUS

Warm-Up: Health Stats Ask students to interpret trends in asthma rates from a graph of asthma emergency room visits over a 10-year period and describe factors that could contribute to asthma rates.

Targeted Resources

- ❑ Transparency W41

2. TEACH

Visual Learning: Figure 9 Have students write the name of each label on an index card. Then they should organize the cards in the order in which air travels through the respiratory system. EL

Differentiated Instruction Have each student trace the outline of the person in Figure 9 and then add structures of the respiratory system to the outline. L1

Cooperative Learning Have small groups express the suggestions for keeping the respiratory system healthy as a list of "Do's" and "Don'ts." L3

Differentiated Instruction Have interested students further investigate asthma. L4

Class Discussion Have students list and discuss the different sources of respiratory system irritants they are exposed to each day. L2

Targeted Resources

- ❑ RN Note Taking Guide 12-3 L3 EL
- ❑ ARN Note Taking Guide 12-3 L2
- ❑ Transparencies and Worksheets 31, 32
- ❑ TR Practice 12-3
- ❑ TR Enrich 12-3 L4
- ❑ Audio Summary 12-3 L1 L2 EL
- ❑ PHSchool.com: More on asthma

3. ASSESS

Evaluate Understanding The assignments listed in the Teacher's Edition can help you assess students' mastery of the section content.

Reteach Play a quiz game in which you describe the function of a part of the respiratory system and students name that part. L2

Targeted Resources

- ❑ TR Section 12-3 Quiz
- ❑ CTB Chapter 12

KEY

L1 Special Needs	L4 Gifted and Talented
L2 Less Proficient Readers	EL English Language Learners
L3 All Students	

Name ______________________ Class ______________________ Date ________

Section 12-3 **Practice**

Concept Check: How You Breathe

Complete the cycle diagram to show the process of breathing.

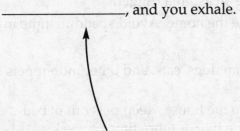

1. Rib muscles and diaphragm contract, making the chest cavity ______________.

2. The pressure of the air inside the lungs ______________.

3. Air rushes into the chest, and you ______________.

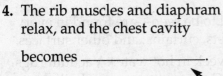

4. The rib muscles and diaphram relax, and the chest cavity becomes ______________.

5. The air is squeezed out of the ______________, and you exhale.

6. Describe the breathing process in your own words.

____

____

____

____

____

____

____

____

Name ______________________ Class ________________ Date ______

Section 12-3

Enrich

Community Involvement: Asthma and Indoor Triggers

Our ancestors spent most of their time outdoors hunting, farming, or moving from place to place. Today, most Americans spend much of their time indoors. In fact, some estimates show that we spend as much as 90 percent of our lives inside buildings. For some people with asthma, the most common triggers of an asthma attack might not be pollen or substances in outdoor air, but rather particles and gases that are found in indoor air.

How can asthma sufferers reduce their exposure to indoor triggers? Here are some suggestions for actions to reduce exposure to some common asthma triggers in the home.

Tobacco smoke People with asthma don't have to smoke to be affected by tobacco smoke. Secondhand smoke can be an asthma trigger.

Take action: Allow no one to smoke inside the home. Avoid spending time in the homes of smokers.

Pet dander The dander, or skin flakes, from dogs, cats, and other indoor pets can be an asthma trigger.

Take action: Don't bring any new pets into the house. Keep pets out of bedrooms. Vacuum rugs, carpets, and furniture two or more times a week.

Dust mites Dust mites—tiny animals too small to be seen—are found in every home in dust and on mattresses, blankets, carpets, curtains, and other surfaces.

Take action: Wash sheets and blankets once a week in hot water. Vacuum rugs, carpets, and furniture to remove dust buildup. Cover mattresses and pillows during the day with dust-proof, zippered covers.

Mold Mold can grow indoors on any damp surface. The tiny spores released by molds can be asthma triggers.

Take action: Wash mold off of all surfaces, and dry those surfaces. Eliminate sources of moisture in the home. Fix leaky plumbing.

Use the information above to write a public service announcement (PSA) about reducing exposure to indoor asthma triggers. Use another sheet of paper if you need more space.

____

____

____

____

____

____

Name ______________________ Class ____________________ Date ________

Section 12-3

Quiz

Decide whether each statement is true or false. Write true *or* false *in the space provided.*

______ **1.** The respiratory system brings carbon dioxide from the outside environment into the body.

______ **2.** On the way to the lungs, air passes through the bronchi before passing through the larynx.

______ **3.** Oxygen and carbon dioxide are exchanged in the alveoli.

______ **4.** The breathing process is controlled by the actions of muscles in your ribs and chest.

______ **5.** Excess weight strains the cardiovascular system, but not the respiratory sytem.

Write the letter of the correct answer in the space provided.

______ **6.** a dome-shaped muscle that lies below the lungs

______ **7.** an infection that involves inflammation of the mucous membranes lining the bronchi

______ **8.** tiny sacs in the lungs where gases are exchanged

______ **9.** the passageway that leads from the larynx to the lungs

______ **10.** a piece of tissue that prevents food from entering the trachea

a. alveoli
b. diaphragm
c. epiglottis
d. trachea
e. asthma
f. bronchitis

Name ______________________ Class ____________________ Date ________

Chapter 12 **Test**

Write the letter of the correct answer in the space provided.

______ **1.** Oxygen-rich blood is carried from the lungs to the
a. right atrium.
b. right ventricle.
c. left atrium.
d. left ventricle.

______ **2.** The rate at which your heart muscles contract is regulated by the
a. capillaries.
b. alveoli.
c. epiglottis.
d. pacemaker.

______ **3.** Which component of blood contains hemoglobin?
a. plasma
b. red blood cells
c. white blood cells
d. platelets

______ **4.** Which carrier in your blood is known as "good cholesterol"?
a. platelet
b. low-density lipoprotein
c. high-density lipoprotein
d. plasma

______ **5.** The breathing process is controlled by actions of
a. the arteries, capillaries, and veins.
b. plasma and platelets.
c. the heart and lung muscles.
d. muscles in the ribs and chest.

Decide whether each statement is true or false. Write true *or* false *in the space provided.*

______ **6.** Oxygen and dissolved nutrients diffuse through capillary walls and into your body's cells.

______ **7.** Blood pressure readings are recorded as systolic pressure over diastolic pressure.

______ **8.** A person with type AB blood can receive a transfusion with type B blood.

______ **9.** Hypertension is known as the "silent killer" because most people have no symptoms.

______ **10.** When your diaphram flattens, you exhale.

Name ______________________ Class __________________ Date ______

Chapter 12: Test *(continued)*

Write the letter of the correct answer in the space provided.

______ **11.** chamber of the heart that pumps blood from the heart

______ **12.** cells in the blood that contribute to the clotting process

______ **13.** tiny sacs in the lungs where gases are exchanged

______ **14.** chamber of the heart that receives blood from blood vessels

______ **15.** part of blood that transports dissolved substances

a. atrium
b. platelets
c. plaque
d. ventricle
e. alveoli
f. plasma

Write the word that best completes each sentence in the space provided.

16. Another term for high blood pressure is ________________.

17. A condition in which an artery wall hardens and thickens due to plaque buildup is ________________.

18. A disorder that involves the inflammation of respiratory passageways and difficulty breathing is ________________.

Use complete sentences to answer the following questions.

19. What are three functions of the cardiovascular system?

____

____

____

____

____

____

20. What are three ways to maintain cardiovascular health?

____

____

____

____

____

____

Name ______________________ Class ______________________ Date ______

Chapter 13

Personal Inventory

Fitness Activities

The chart below rates the effect various activities have on areas of fitness. Most of the activities improve fitness in some areas more than others.

In the chart, circle any physical activities that you participate in. Then, answer the questions that follow.

Fitness Ratings of Physical Activities				
Activity	**Cardiorespiratory Endurance**	**Muscular Strength**	**Muscular Endurance**	**Flexibility**
Ballet	high	moderate	moderate	high
Baseball/Softball	low	low	low	moderate
Basketball	high	low	moderate	moderate
Bicycling	high	moderate	high	low
Football	moderate–high	moderate	moderate	moderate
Gymnastics	low	high	high	high
Hiking	high	low	moderate	moderate
Running (at least 6 mph)	high	low	high	moderate
Skating	moderate–high	low	moderate–high	moderate
Soccer	high	moderate	moderate	moderate
Swimming	high	moderate	high	moderate
Volleyball	moderate	low	moderate	moderate
Walking (brisk)	high	low	high	moderate
Weight Lifting	low	high	high	moderate

1. List the activities that you circled that were rated "high" in at least one area of fitness.

____

____

2. How could you change your activities so you have at least one high-rated activity in each area of fitness?

____

____

Name______________________ Class__________ Date__________ M T W T F

Section 13-1

The Importance of Physical Activity

Lesson Plan

Section Objectives

- **Explain** some of the physical, psychological, and social benefits of physical activity.
- **Define** the five components of fitness.
- **Describe** five types of physical activity.

Time
2 periods
1 block

Local Standards

Vocabulary physical activity • endorphins • physical fitness • body composition • aerobic exercise • anaerobic exercise • isometric exercise • isotonic exercise • isokinetic exercise

1. FOCUS

Warm-Up: Myth/Fact Ask students to share fitness myths and explain why they are false.

Targeted Resources

- ❑ Transparency W42

2. TEACH

Building Health Skills Have students make a poster showing benefits of exercise that are especially important to teens. L3

Differentiated Instruction Ask students to find pictures showing benefits of exercise and explain which benefit(s) each picture represents. EL

Visual Learning: Figure 3 Ask students to add activities to the activity pyramid in the figure and identify everyday activities that are also cardiorespiratory, flexibility, or muscular training activities. L2

Cultural Connection Have volunteers discuss examples of active pastimes from their cultures and the types of physical activities they involve. L3

Targeted Resources

- ❑ RN Note Taking Guide 13-1 L3 EL
- ❑ ARN Note Taking Guide 13-1 L2
- ❑ Transparency and Worksheet 33
- ❑ TR Practice 13-1
- ❑ TR Enrich 13-1 L4
- ❑ Audio Summary 13-1 L1 L2 EL
- ❑ Health Links: Updates on the health benefits of sports

3. ASSESS

Evaluate Understanding The assignments listed in the Teacher's Edition can help you assess students' mastery of the section content.

Reteach Ask students to list components of fitness and types of physical activity. Then, ask them to match the components with the type(s) of activity that build them. L2

Targeted Resources

- ❑ TR Section 13-1 Quiz
- ❑ CTB Chapter 13

KEY

L1 Special Needs	L4 Gifted and Talented
L2 Less Proficient Readers	EL English Language Learners
L3 All Students	

Name ______________________ Class ________________ Date ________

Section 13-1 **Practice**

Role-Playing: No More Excuses

People who do not exercise regularly often have excuses. If you were trying to convince a friend to start exercising, what excuses for not exercising might the friend give? What convincing reasons for exercising could you give?

Brainstorm excuses teens might give for not exercising. Then brainstorm reasons for exercising. Record your ideas in the chart.

Excuses for NOT Exercising	Reasons for Exercising

Plan a role-play in which a teen tries to convince a friend to exercise. Base your role-play on the excuses and reasons in the chart. Record your plan below.

Plan for Role-Play:

Name ____________________ Class ______________ Date ______

Section 13-1 **Enrich**

Community Involvement: Exercise in the Community

Most communities have facilities for exercising. People might be able to lift weights at a fitness club, run at the high school track, or swim at a community center. What facilities for exercise are available in your community?

Contact your local Parks and Recreation Department and use a telephone directory and other sources to find information to complete the chart below. Use an extra sheet of paper if you need more space. Use your completed chart to make a brochure that contains all the information people need to use these exercise facilities in your community.

Exercise Facilities in Your Community

Name and Address of Facility	Contact Information	Activities Available	Days/ Hours	Costs

Name ____________________ Class ____________________ Date ________

Section 13-1 Quiz

Write the letter of the correct answer in the space provided.

______ **1.** Physical activity helps maintain weight by
a. raising cholesterol levels in the blood.
b. decreasing endorphin levels in the brain.
c. lowering the basal metabolic rate of the body.
d. increasing the amount of energy the body uses at rest.

______ **2.** Which component of physical fitness lets you lift a low-weight barbell many times?
a. flexibility
b. muscular strength
c. muscular endurance
d. cardiorespiratory endurance

______ **3.** Which activity is the best choice for building cardiorespiratory endurance?
a. volleyball
b. sit-ups
c. rowing
d. martial arts

______ **4.** An example of an anaerobic exercise is
a. running.
b. sprinting.
c. swimming.
d. brisk walking.

______ **5.** A pull-up is a(an)
a. aerobic exercise.
b. isotonic exercise.
c. isometric exercise.
d. isokinetic exercise.

Decide whether each statement is true or false. Write true *or* false *in the space provided.*

______ **6.** Exercise reduces your risk of osteoporosis by increasing muscle mass.

______ **7.** Physical activity can improve a bad mood.

______ **8.** Weight is the best indicator of a person's fitness.

______ **9.** Anaerobic exercise builds cardiorespiratory endurance.

______ **10.** Isokinetic exercises require specialized fitness machines.

Name______________________ Class__________ Date__________ M T W T F

Section 13-2

Setting Goals for Lifelong Fitness Lesson Plan

Section Objectives

- **Develop** a plan for achieving lifelong fitness.
- **Describe** the three phases of exercise.

Vocabulary lifelong fitness • FITT formula • target heart rate • cross-training

Time
2 periods
1 block

Local Standards

1. FOCUS

Warm-Up: Health Stats Ask students to explain why fewer teens are physically active as they get older.

Targeted Resources

- ❑ Transparency W43

2. TEACH

Building Health Skills Have small groups of students research the availability of specific activities in their community and have them share their findings with the class. L3

Differentiated Instruction Help students with physical disabilities find appropriate exercises and incorporate them into their fitness plans. L1

Visual Learning: Figure 6 Help students apply the FITT formula to their fitness goals. L3

Journal Writing Have students make charts in their journals to monitor progress toward their fitness goals. L3

Class Discussion Reinforce the importance of monitoring progress in a fitness program. L2

Targeted Resources

- ❑ RN Note Taking Guide 13-2 L3 EL
- ❑ ARN Note Taking Guide 13-2 L2
- ❑ Transparency and Worksheet 34
- ❑ TR Practice 13-2
- ❑ TR Enrich 13-2 L4
- ❑ Audio Summary 13-2 L1 L2 EL
- ❑ Health Links: Updates on physical fitness

3. ASSESS

Evaluate Understanding The assignments listed in the Teacher's Edition can help you assess students' mastery of the section content.

Reteach Use the headings and subheadings to create a section outline. Have students complete the outline by adding important details. L2

Targeted Resources

- ❑ TR Section 13-2 Quiz
- ❑ CTB Chapter 13

KEY

L1 Special Needs	L4 Gifted and Talented
L2 Less Proficient Readers	EL English Language Learners
L3 All Students	

Name ______________ Class ______________ Date ______

Section 13-2 **Practice**

Skill-Building Activity: Developing a Fitness Plan

Read the following description of Marcia's fitness goals. Then create a fitness schedule for Marcia.

Marcia took a fitness test at school and received the following results.

Flexibility Test	**Cardiorespiratory Endurance**
Marcia: 1 inch	Marcia: 14-min mile
Average: 4.5 inches	Average: 10:30-min mile

What type of fitness plan will help Marcia improve her flexibility and cardiorespiratory endurance? Some of Marcia's favorite activities are dancing, bicycling, and inline skating. She has about 45 minutes a day to devote to exercise. She also knows that she bores easily, so variety is important. Make sure to list the type of activities she should perform each day and the amount of time she should devote to them.

Week 1

Monday: ______________________________

Tuesday: ______________________________

Wednesday: ______________________________

Thursday: ______________________________

Friday: ______________________________

Saturday: ______________________________

Sunday: ______________________________

Week 2

Monday: ______________________________

Tuesday: ______________________________

Wednesday: ______________________________

Thursday: ______________________________

Friday: ______________________________

Saturday: ______________________________

Sunday: ______________________________

Name ______________________ Class ________________ Date ________

Section 13-2 **Enrich**

Family Involvement: Activities for Lifelong Fitness

Keeping active throughout life is an important long-term fitness goal. You may be more likely to achieve this goal if you adopt physical activities now that you can continue to enjoy as you grow older.

Are your parents or guardians, grandparents, or other relatives physically active? If not, do you know other adults who are physically active? What types of activities do they engage in? Do you think you might enjoy any of the activities?

With a parent's or guardian's permission, interview one or more active adults about their physical activities. Then answer the questions below in the spaces provided.

1. What physical activities do they enjoy? Which fitness components are improved by each of the activities?

2. Which of the activities do you think you would enjoy? How would the activities help keep you fit?

3. How could you engage in the activities with family members and help motivate each other to stay active?

Name ______________________ Class ____________________ Date ________

Section 13-2

Quiz

Decide whether each statement is true or false. Write true *or* false *in the space provided.*

______ **1.** Reaching your target heart rate is related to the intensity of your workout.

______ **2.** Muscle strengthening exercises should be done every day to see results.

______ **3.** Exercising only on weekends can make you prone to injury.

______ **4.** As you become more fit, you should see an increase in your resting heart rate.

______ **5.** You can use the "talk test" to monitor the intensity of your workout.

Write the letter of the correct answer in the space provided.

______ **6.** Which activity would be the best choice for a lifelong fitness program?
a. sprinting
b. gymnastics
c. brisk walking
d. snowboarding

______ **7.** Wanting to be able to run an eight-minute mile is an example of a
a. fitness plan.
b. fitness program.
c. long-term fitness goal.
d. short-term fitness goal.

______ **8.** In the FITT formula, what do the two Ts stand for?
a. time and type
b. time and target
c. type and target
d. type and training

______ **9.** Which resting heart rate usually indicates a good level of fitness?
a. over 100 beats per minute
b. under 98 beats per minute
c. over 72 beats per minute
d. under 72 beats per minute

______ **10.** When you exercise, you should always stretch
a. before you cool down.
b. before you warm up.
c. after you cool down.
d. during the workout.

Name____________________ Class__________ Date__________ M T W T F

Section 13-3 Physical Activity and Safety Lesson Plan

Section Objectives

- **List** five safety considerations related to physical activity.
- **Evaluate** the risks of using substances to enhance performance.
- **Identify** ways to avoid overtraining and prevent sports-related injuries.

Vocabulary dehydration • dietary supplement • overtraining

Time
2 periods
1 block

Local Standards

1. FOCUS

Warm-Up: Quick Quiz Discuss consequences of not following safe exercise practices and why teens might not follow the practices.

Targeted Resources
- ❑ Transparency W44

2. TEACH

Differentiated Instruction Have students point out examples in pictures of people exercising safely or unsafely. **L1**

Class Discussion Help students understand the pros and cons of sports drinks. **L2**

Differentiated Instruction Guide students in making a concept map of the information on exercising safely. **L2**

Addressing Misconceptions Address the misconception that athletes need protein supplements. Have students calculate an athlete's protein needs to see if the needs can be met with a proper diet. **L3**

Building Media Literacy Have students name criteria for evaluating the reliability of magazine articles on training, and ask volunteers to find and share articles meeting the criteria. **L4**

Targeted Resources
- ❑ RN Note Taking Guide 13-3 **L3** **EL**
- ❑ ARN Note Taking Guide 13-3 **L2**
- ❑ TR Practice 13-3
- ❑ TR Enrich 13-3 **L4**
- ❑ Audio Summary 13-3 **L1** **L2** **EL**
- ❑ PHSchool.com: More on exercise safety

3. ASSESS

Evaluate Understanding The assignments listed in the Teacher's Edition can help you assess students' mastery of the section content.

Reteach Students make an illustrated "do" and "don't" poster that describes how to be safe while exercising. **L2**

Targeted Resources
- ❑ TR Section 13-3 Quiz
- ❑ CTB Chapter 13

KEY

L1 Special Needs	**L4** Gifted and Talented
L2 Less Proficient Readers	**EL** English Language Learners
L3 All Students	

Name ______________________ Class ______________________ Date ________

Section 13-3

Practice

Group Activity: Playing Safe

Physical activities have different safety concerns. For example, weather is an important safety issue for outdoor activities like skiing but not for indoor activities like wrestling. Safety equipment is especially important for activities like skateboarding but less important for activities like walking.

As a group, brainstorm safety issues for each of the physical activities listed in the table.

Safety Guidelines for Different Physical Activities

Physical Activity	Safety Equipment	Your Surroundings	Weather Considerations	Proper Water and Food
Weight lifting				
Bicycling				
Baseball/ Softball				
Swimming				
Football				

Discuss the importance of medical care and proper water and food intake for physical activity and safety.

____

____

____

____

Name ______________________ Class ____________________ Date ______

Enrich

Consumer Skills: Exercising Control

Every year Americans spend millions of dollars on exercise equipment. Some people make good use of the equipment they purchase. However, a lot of equipment ends up collecting dust in a corner. Many consumers may impulsively buy a product after seeing an advertisement. Later, they realize it will not give them the instant results they hoped for.

Choose an ad for fitness equipment, accessories, or clothing from a magazine or newspaper. Then answer the following questions.

1. What product is being advertised? What aspect of fitness could be improved with use of this product?

____

____

____

2. What details does the ad give about the product? Does the ad promise results within a specific amount of time?

____

____

____

3. How is the product presented in the ad? For example, is a model using or wearing the product?

____

____

4. Who do you think would be influenced to buy this product?

____

____

5. Based on what you have learned about achieving physical fitness, rewrite this ad copy to make it as truthful as possible.

____

____

____

____

____

Name ______________________ Class ________________ Date ______

Section 13-3 **Quiz**

Decide whether each statement is true or false. Write true *or* false *in the space provided.*

______ **1.** Sports drinks do *not* have calories.

______ **2.** You should wear loose-fitting pants when bicycling.

______ **3.** Replacing the water lost in sweat prevents dehydration.

______ **4.** Anabolic steroids can cause enlarged breasts and infertility in males.

______ **5.** Unlike prescription medications, dietary supplements are not rigorously tested.

Write the letter of the correct answer in the space provided.

______ **6.** The best safety equipment to use for an activity is
- **a.** the most expensive kind of equipment available.
- **b.** the kind of equipment designed for that particular activity.
- **c.** the same kind of equipment that is used by professionals.
- **d.** the kind of equipment that is suitable for a variety of activities.

______ **7.** A stress fracture can be the result of
- **a.** a strain.
- **b.** a sprain.
- **c.** overuse of a bone.
- **d.** tendonitis.

______ **8.** Which statement about anabolic steroids is *not* true?
- **a.** All of the negative effects disappear when a person stops taking them.
- **b.** They are prescribed for people with muscle disorders.
- **c.** They have physical and psychological effects.
- **d.** They are artificial forms of testosterone.

______ **9.** How can you avoid overtraining?
- **a.** always exercise within your comfort level
- **b.** do only one type of exercise
- **c.** exercise at a higher intensity
- **d.** exercise more often

______ **10.** Overuse of a joint may cause
- **a.** nausea.
- **b.** fatigue.
- **c.** vomiting.
- **d.** tendonitis.

Name ______________________ Class __________________ Date ______

Chapter 13 Test

Write the letter of the correct answer in the space provided.

______ **1.** Which component of fitness includes strong heart muscles?
- **a.** muscular endurance
- **b.** stretching
- **c.** body composition
- **d.** cardiorespiratory endurance

______ **2.** What is the key difference between an isometric and an isotonic exercise?
- **a.** Isometric exercises require fitness machines; isotonic exercises require no special equipment.
- **b.** Isotonic exercises improve muscular strength; isometric exercises improve endurance.
- **c.** Isotonic exercises involve movement through a joint's range of motion; isometric exercises require little movement.
- **d.** Isometric exercises require more repetitions; isotonic exercises require heavier weights.

______ **3.** What is the first stage in planning a fitness program?
- **a.** developing your plan
- **b.** defining your goals
- **c.** monitoring your progress
- **d.** choosing your activities

______ **4.** Which of the following is a long-term fitness goal?
- **a.** having the endurance to play a best-of-five-set tennis match
- **b.** maintaining the ability to stay physically active throughout life
- **c.** walking 10,000 steps per day
- **d.** increasing lean tissue mass

______ **5.** What should you do if you stop noticing progress from your fitness program?
- **a.** Quit the program; you must have reached your goal.
- **b.** Overhaul your routine, and try all new exercises.
- **c.** Slightly increase the intensity or the time of your workout.
- **d.** Continue the same program. If it worked before, it should keep working.

Write the letter of the correct answer in the space provided.

______ **6.** amount of fat tissue compared to lean tissue

______ **7.** intense exercise that lasts for a short time

______ **8.** period of mild exercise following a workout

______ **9.** excessive loss of water from the body

______ **10.** first sign of overtraining

- **a.** fatigue
- **b.** cool-down
- **c.** dehydration
- **d.** cross-training
- **e.** body composition
- **f.** anaerobic exercise

Name ______________________ Class __________________ Date ______

Chapter 13: Test *(continued)*

Decide whether each statement is true or false. Write true *or* false *in the space provided.*

______ **11.** Exercise may help lower blood cholesterol levels.

______ **12.** Flexibility can vary from joint to joint in the same person.

______ **13.** The intensity of exercise refers to how long each exercise session lasts.

______ **14.** You should not feel pain during stretching exercises.

______ **15.** Dark-colored clothing keeps you cooler when you exercise on hot, sunny days.

Write the word that best completes each sentence in the space provided.

16. Physical activity benefits your body, your ______________, and your social interactions.

17. You should follow the warm-up and cool-down periods of an exercise session with ______________.

18. Exercising too intensely or for too long without enough time for recovery is called ______________.

Use complete sentences to answer the following questions.

19. Describe three steps in planning a fitness program.

20. List five safety considerations related to physical activity, and give an example of each.

Name ______________________ Class ______________ Date ________

Chapter 14 Personal Inventory

Personal Care Habits

Good personal care habits promote good physical and emotional health. Taking good care of your teeth, eyes, ears, skin, hair, and nails and getting enough sleep are all habits that can help you look and feel your best.

Read the list below. Place a checkmark by each statement that describes your current personal care habits. After reading the chapter, set a goal to include more of these habits in your everyday routine.

______ **1.** I brush my teeth at least twice a day.

______ **2.** I eat a healthy diet.

______ **3.** I floss my teeth once a day.

______ **4.** I wear a mouthguard when I play contact sports.

______ **5.** I see a dentist at least once a year.

______ **6.** I wear sunscreen when I am outdoors.

______ **7.** I examine my moles from time to time to look for changes.

______ **8.** I keep my hair clean and well-groomed.

______ **9.** I avoid sharing combs, brushes, and hats.

______ **10.** I keep my nails trimmed and clean.

______ **11.** I wear goggles around machinery and harmful substances.

______ **12.** I wear sunglasses that provide UV protection.

______ **13.** I get regular eye exams.

______ **14.** I avoid exposure to loud noises.

______ **15.** I see my doctor if I have ear pain or difficulty hearing.

______ **16.** I get about 9 hours of sleep each night.

______ **17.** I go to bed and wake up at about the same times each day.

______ **18.** I avoid exercising just before going to bed.

Goal: ____

____

____

____

____

____

Name_______________________ Class__________ Date__________ M T W T F

Section 14-1

Your Teeth and Gums — Lesson Plan

Section Objectives

- **List** the functions of teeth and gums.
- **Identify** two structural problems of the teeth and mouth.
- **Describe** ways to prevent teeth and gum problems.

Vocabulary enamel • cementum • dentin • pulp • malocclusion • orthodontist • halitosis • plaque • tartar • periodontal disease

Time
1 period
1/2 block

Local Standards

1. FOCUS

Warm-Up: Quick Quiz Use the Quick Quiz to stimulate students' thinking about caring for their teeth.

Targeted Resources

- ❑ Transparency W45

2. TEACH

Visual Learning: Figure 1 Have students examine the shape and structure of teeth. L2

Teacher Demo Help students visualize structural problems of the teeth and jaws using a three-ring binder as a model. L1

Building Health Skills Have students use Nutrition Facts labels to find information about the sugar content of snack foods and foods that they think are healthy. L3

Cooperative Learning Have students make posters that teach younger children about proper oral care. L2

Differentiated Instruction Ask English language learners to work with a partner to create and use flashcards to review the vocabulary terms in the section. EL

Targeted Resources

- ❑ RN Note Taking Guide 14-1 L3 EL
- ❑ ARN Note Taking Guide 14-1 L2
- ❑ Transparencies and Worksheets 35, 36
- ❑ TR Practice 14-1
- ❑ TR Enrich 14-1 L4
- ❑ Audio Summary 14-1 L1 L2 EL
- ❑ Health Links: Updates on caring for your teeth

3. ASSESS

Evaluate Understanding The assignments listed in the Teacher's Edition can help you assess students' mastery of the section content.

Reteach Have students review and give a verbal summary of the diagrams and illustrations in the section. L2

Targeted Resources

- ❑ TR Section 14-1 Quiz
- ❑ CTB Chapter 14

KEY

L1 Special Needs	L4 Gifted and Talented
L2 Less Proficient Readers	EL English Language Learners
L3 All Students	

Name ______________________ Class ____________________ Date ________

Section 14-1 **Practice**

Concept Check: The Structure of Teeth

People have several different types of teeth, each with a different shape and function. But all teeth have the same basic structure.

Review the diagram below. Write in the correct number for each term.

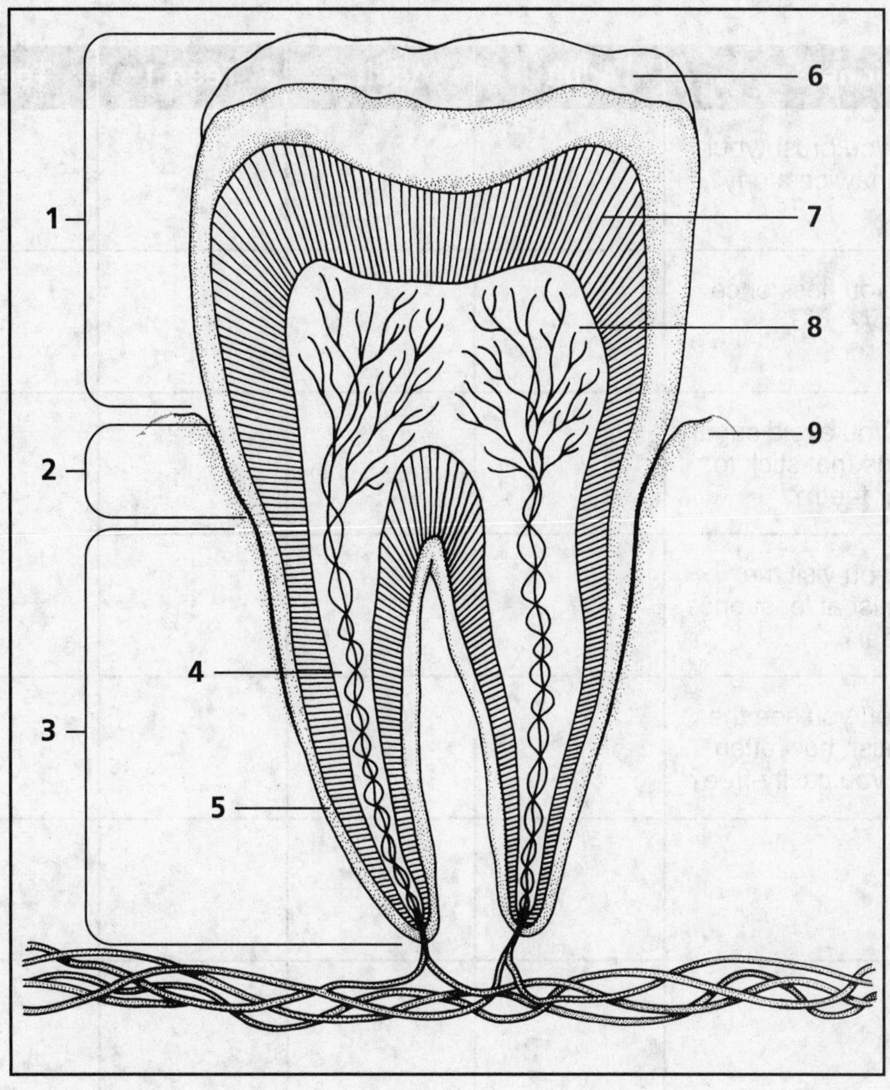

_____ enamel

_____ crown

_____ cementum

_____ dentin

_____ neck

_____ pulp

_____ root

_____ gum

_____ root canal

Name ______________________ Class __________________ Date ________

Community Involvement: Evaluating Oral Health Habits

Do people in your community follow guidelines for oral health? To find out, ask two adults and two people your own age to complete this survey. Add two questions of your own. Use the following scale for responses: 1 = always; 2 = sometimes; 3 = never.

Questions	Adult 1	Adult 2	Teen 1	Teen 2
1. Do you brush your teeth twice a day?				
2. Do you floss once a day?				
3. Do you avoid sugary foods that stick to your teeth?				
4. Do you visit the dentist at least once a year?				
5. When you see the dentist, how often are you cavity-free?				
6.				
7.				

After you have completed the survey, compare your results with those of your classmates. Summarize below your findings about the oral health habits of people in your community.

____

____

____

____

Name ______________________ Class ____________________ Date ________

Section 14-1

Quiz

Write the letter of the correct answer in the space provided.

______ **1.** Which term refers to the soft tissue found in the center of each tooth?
a. gum
b. pulp
c. dentin
d. cementum

______ **2.** Which type of tooth cuts food into bite-sized pieces?
a. premolar
b. incisor
c. molar
d. canine

______ **3.** Which term describes bad breath, which can be caused by poor oral hygiene?
a. plaque
b. tartar
c. halitosis
d. periodontal disease

______ **4.** Which is *not* one of the three main parts of a tooth?
a. gum
b. crown
c. neck
d. root

Decide whether each statement is true or false. Write true *or* false *in the space provided.*

______ **5.** An overbite and an underbite are examples of malocclusion.

______ **6.** Cementum is the part of a tooth that contains blood vessels.

______ **7.** The function of molars is to crush and grind food.

______ **8.** An orthodontist specializes in repairing cavities and treating gum disease.

______ **9.** Plaque that is not removed from teeth within 48 hours forms dentin.

______ **10.** Gingivitis is the first stage of periodontal disease.

Name________________________ Class__________ Date__________ M T W T F

Section 14-2

Your Skin, Hair, and Nails Lesson Plan

Section Objectives

- **Identify** the functions of the skin.
- **Describe** behaviors that can keep your skin healthy.
- **Explain** the functions of your hair and nails and how to care for them.

Vocabulary epidermis • keratin • melanin • dermis • pore • follicle • sebaceous gland • melanoma • acne • dermatologist • eczema

Time
2 periods
1 block

Local Standards

1. FOCUS

Warm-Up: Myth/Fact Have students share their writing. Assemble a list of common misconceptions. Ask students to look for information about these misconceptions as they read the section.

Targeted Resources
- ❑ Transparency W46

2. TEACH

Visual Learning: Figure 4 Have students use the diagram to identify the compounds of each layer of skin. L2

Differentiated Instruction Have students discuss the key words of the ABCD rule with a partner. Students should record a definition for each term using a symbol or short summarizing phrase. EL

Building Media Literacy Help students develop a survey with questions about hair care products. Students should incorporate questions about how ads influence buying decisions. L3

Class Discussion Have students examine tips for nail care and relate the care of the nails to the health of the skin. L1

Targeted Resources
- ❑ RN Note Taking Guide 14-2 L3 EL
- ❑ ARN Note Taking Guide 14-2 L2
- ❑ Transparency and Worksheet 37
- ❑ TR Practice 14-2
- ❑ TR Enrich 14-2 L4
- ❑ Audio Summary 14-2 L1 L2 EL
- ❑ PHSchool.com: More on acne

3. ASSESS

Evaluate Understanding The assignments listed in the Teacher's Edition can help you assess students' mastery of the section content.

Reteach Have students work as a class to complete a table that contains tips for skin care, hair care, and nail care. L2

Targeted Resources
- ❑ TR Section 14-2 Quiz
- ❑ CTB Chapter 14

KEY

L1 Special Needs	L4 Gifted and Talented
L2 Less Proficient Readers	EL English Language Learners
L3 All Students	

Name ______________________ Class ____________________ Date ______

Section 14-2 **Practice**

Vocabulary Activity: Word Scramble

Your skin, hair, and nails all serve important functions to the body. By taking good care of your skin, hair, and nails, you can look and feel your best.

Use the clues to unscramble each term below. Write the correct answer on the line provided.

1. eaintrk	a protein in skin	______________
2. mezcae	a skin disorder	______________
3. redsim	one of the layers of skin	______________
4. beaesoucs ladgn	a structure that secretes oil	______________
5. getotdraloism	a doctor who treats skin problems	______________
6. pmdieeris	the outermost layer of skin	______________
7. rope	a tiny opening in the skin	______________
8. lamnine	a protein produced in the epidermis	______________
9. iceflllo	a structure in the dermis	______________
10. lammneoa	a form of skin cancer	______________
11. nace	a common teen skin problem	______________
12. trsaw	hardened growths on the skin	______________
13. wnrmirgo	red, scaly patches on the skin	______________
14. frfnduad	occurs when cells on the scalp are shed too fast	______________
15. lbiso	infected hair follicles filled with pus	______________

Name ______________________ Class ____________________ Date ______

Section 14-2

Enrich

Consumer Skills: Evaluating Sunscreens

Sunscreen is one way of protecting your skin from the damaging rays of the sun. Sunscreens with the highest SPF provide the longest protection. SPF refers to UVB-ray protection, but some sunscreens also contain substances that block UVA rays. The sunscreen's label should inform you about its active ingredients and from which rays the sunscreen will protect you. This activity will help you evaluate which of the many sunscreen products is right for you.

Compare five different brands of sunscreen to find the best value. (To find the unit cost, divide the product price by the number of fluid ounces or milliliters.)

Brand	SPF	UVA Protection Yes/No	Active Ingredient	Price	Unit Cost

1. Which product do you think is the best value? Explain.

____

____

2. What other factors than those in the table influenced your choice of sunscreen?

____

____

____

3. Which SPF do you typically use? Why?

____

____

Name ______________________ Class __________________ Date ________

Section 14-2 Quiz

Write the letter of the correct answer in the space provided.

_____ **1.** hardened growths on skin caused by a virus

_____ **2.** infections of the hair follicles caused by bacteria

_____ **3.** clusters of watery blisters near the mouth caused by a virus

_____ **4.** red, scaly ring-shaped patches on the skin caused by a fungus

_____ **5.** burning, itchy skin on the feet caused by a fungus

a. cold sores
b. boils
c. athlete's foot
d. moles
e. warts
f. ringworm

Write the letter of the correct answer in the space provided.

_____ **6.** When you are cold, how does your skin keep heat in your body?
a. Sweat glands produce perspiration.
b. Blood vessels in the skin widen.
c. Sebaceous glands increase oil production.
d. Blood vessels in the skin narrow.

_____ **7.** Which term is a dark pigment produced in the epidermis?
a. keratin
b. melanin
c. melanoma
d. eczema

_____ **8.** Which of the following methods will *not* protect your skin from damage due to overexposure to the sun?
a. a base tan
b. wearing long sleeves
c. sunscreen with an SPF of 15 or higher
d. wearing a hat

_____ **9.** Your acne might become worse if you
a. eat greasy foods.
b. are experiencing stress.
c. wash your face twice a day.
d. use benzoyl peroxide.

_____ **10.** What substance makes your nails tough and hard?
a. melanin
b. dermis
c. keratin
d. epidermis

Name________________________ Class__________ Date__________ M T W T F

Section 14-3

Your Eyes and Ears — Lesson Plan

Section Objectives

- **Explain** how your eyes allow you to see.
- **Identify** two ways to keep your eyes healthy.
- **Explain** how your ears allow you to hear and maintain your balance.
- **Identify** ways to keep your ears healthy.

Vocabulary cornea • pupil • iris • lens • retina • optometrist • eardrum • cochlea • semicircular canals • audiologist

Time
2 periods
1 block

Local Standards

1. FOCUS

Warm-Up: Advice Line Have students write and share their responses to the letter. Then have students discuss the importance of advocating for their own health.

Targeted Resources

- ❑ Transparency W47

2. TEACH

Active Learning Have students note and discuss the way in which their eyes respond to darkness. L2

Visual Learning: Figure 12 Have students use the figure to learn about various types of vision problems. L3

Building Health Skills Have students research free or low-cost vision screenings that are available in their community. L3

Differentiated Instruction Use models of the eye and ear to help students grasp the structure of these organs. L1

Building Health Skills Help students develop a plan to adjust to using headphones set at a safe volume. L3

Targeted Resources

- ❑ RN Note Taking Guide 14-3 L3 EL
- ❑ ARN Note Taking Guide 14-3 L2
- ❑ Transparencies and Worksheets 38, 39
- ❑ TR Practice 14-3
- ❑ TR Enrich 14-3 L4
- ❑ Audio Summary 14-3 L1 L2 EL
- ❑ Health Links: Updates on eye diseases

3. ASSESS

Evaluate Understanding The assignments listed in the Teacher's Edition can help you assess students' mastery of the section content.

Reteach Have students review the structure of the eye and ear using the diagrams in the section. L2

Targeted Resources

- ❑ TR Section 14-3 Quiz
- ❑ CTB Chapter 14

KEY

L1 Special Needs	L4 Gifted and Talented
L2 Less Proficient Readers	EL English Language Learners
L3 All Students	

Name ____________________ Class ________________ Date ______

Section 14-3 **Practice**

Group Activity: How the Ear Works

Sound waves, or vibrations, travel through many structures in the ear before reaching the brain as nerve impulses. The ear also helps you maintain balance. *As a group, fill in the table by describing the function of each structure.*

Structure		Function
Inner Ear	Ear canal	
	Eardrum	
Middle Ear	Hammer	
	Anvil	
	Stirrup	
	Auditory tube	
Outer Ear	Oval window	
	Cochlea	
	Auditory nerve	
	Semicircular canals	

Name ____________________ Class ______________ Date ________

Section 14-3 **Enrich**

Community Involvement: Help for the Hearing Impaired

Arrange to talk to the nurse or professional who conducts hearing tests in your school. Ask the questions listed below and add some of your own. After your interview, write a letter to students' parents or guardians explaining how the school hearing-test program works.

1. How often is the hearing of students tested? What is involved in a hearing test?

2. What are the most common causes of hearing impairment among students?

3. What are the typical treatments recommended for these problems?

4. Where can a hearing-impaired student learn sign language?

5. What should people without hearing difficulties know about people with hearing impairments?

6. Additional Question: ____________________

7. Additional Question: ____________________

Name ______________________ Class ______________________ Date ________

Section 14-3

Quiz

Write the letter of the correct answer in the space provided.

______ **1.** Which part of the ear regulates pressure allowing the eardrum to vibrate correctly?
   a. oval window
   b. auditory tube
   c. semicircular canal
   d. ear canal

______ **2.** Which structure contains the cells that are most likely to be damaged from loud noises?
   a. semicircular canals
   b. stirrup
   c. cochlea
   d. auditory tube

______ **3.** In which part of the eye are rods and cones found?
   a. retina
   b. cornea
   c. lens
   d. iris

______ **4.** When light strikes the retina, impulses are carried to the brain by the
   a. auditory nerve.
   b. cornea.
   c. lens.
   d. optic nerve.

______ **5.** Which eye disease is characterized by a buildup of pressure in the eye?
   a. macular degeneration
   b. cataracts
   c. detached retina
   d. glaucoma

Write the letter of the correct answer in the space provided.

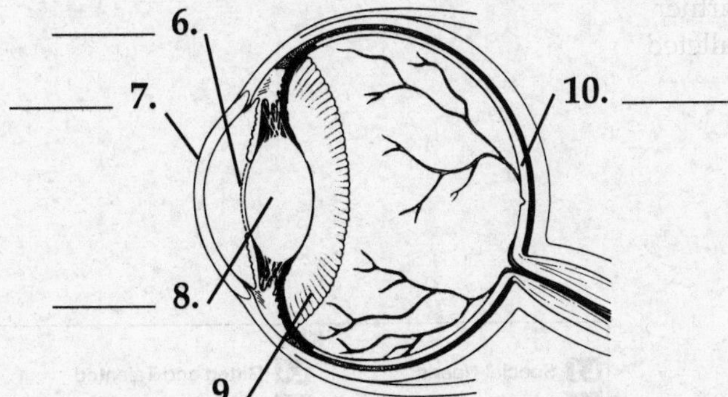

a. pupil
b. lens
c. cornea
d. retina
e. iris

Name________________________ Class__________ Date__________ M T W T F

Section 14-4

Sleep and Feeling Fit

Lesson Plan

Section Objectives

- **Describe** why sleep is important for health.
- **Explain** how circadian rhythms influence the sleep patterns of teens.

Vocabulary insomnia • sleep apnea • narcolepsy • circadian rhythm

Time
1 period
1/2 block

Local Standards

1. FOCUS

Warm-Up: Health Stats Use the statistics to challenge students to identify factors that contribute to the sleep habits of teens.

Targeted Resources
- ❑ Transparency W45

2. TEACH

Building Health Skills Have students make a poster that can be used to share information about the importance of sleep. L2

Writing and Health Ask students to create a public service announcement that describes one or more of the benefits of sleep. L3

Differentiated Instruction Have students use library and Internet resources to learn more about jet-lag. Ask students to prepare a presentation to share their findings with the class. L4

Cooperative Learning Assign small groups two or three tips for developing good sleep habits. Ask them to explain why the tips are helpful L2

Targeted Resources
- ❑ RN Note Taking Guide 14-4 L3 EL
- ❑ ARN Note Taking Guide 14-4 L2
- ❑ Transparency and Worksheet 40
- ❑ TR Practice 14-4
- ❑ TR Enrich 14-4 L4
- ❑ Audio Summary 14-4 L1 L2 EL
- ❑ PHSchool.com: More on teens and sleep

3. ASSESS

Evaluate Understanding The assignments listed in the Teacher's Edition can help you assess students' mastery of the section content.

Reteach Ask students to work with a partner to review the information found in the bulleted lists on each page of the section. L2

Targeted Resources
- ❑ TR Section 14-4 Quiz
- ❑ CTB Chapter 14

KEY

L1	Special Needs	L4	Gifted and Talented
L2	Less Proficient Readers	EL	English Language Learners
L3	All Students		

Name ____________ Class ____________ Date ________

Section 14-4

Practice

Skill-Building Activity: Healthy Sleep

Sleep is vital for good health. In fact, sleep is just as important to your body as air, water, and food. Developing good sleep habits can be important for lifelong health.

Answer the following questions about sleep. Then, fill in the chart with three tips for getting a good night's sleep that are not mentioned below.

1. Should you go to bed and get up at about the same time on weekends as you do during the week? Why or why not?

____

____

2. How can your food and drink choices affect your ability to sleep?

____

____

3. How can exercise positively affect your sleep? How can exercise negatively impact your sleep?

____

____

Tips for a Good Night's Sleep
1. ______________________________
2. ______________________________
3. ______________________________

Name ______________ Class ______________ Date ______

Section 14-4 **Enrich**

Class Debate: What Time Should School Start?

Most teens get far less sleep each night than they should. One reason teens get so little sleep is because puberty changes their circadian rhythm. Although teens tend to want to go to bed late at night and sleep late into the day, they must get up early for school.

As a group, take a position on whether your school should start later in the day so that students can get more sleep or if students should make other adjustments to their lives. Summarize your group's position and the arguments you'll use in the debate.

Position: ______________________________

Arguments: ______________________________

Name ______________________ Class ____________________ Date ________

Section 14-4

Quiz

Write the letter of the correct answer in the space provided.

______ **1.** Which describes NREM sleep?
- **a.** The eyes move rapidly.
- **b.** The body is in a deep state of relaxation.
- **c.** There is a high level of brain activity.
- **d.** The body's muscles are paralyzed.

______ **2.** Which does *not* occur during sleep?
- **a.** body temperature increases
- **b.** tissue damage is repaired
- **c.** heart rate decreases
- **d.** muscles relax

______ **3.** What is a circadian rhythm?
- **a.** a 24-hour cycle of behavior patterns
- **b.** the pattern of brain waves that occur during sleep
- **c.** a sleep disorder that causes breathing to stop during sleep
- **d.** a stage of NREM sleep in which the body is deeply relaxed

______ **4.** Which of the following would *not* disrupt your sleep patterns?
- **a.** watching television in bed
- **b.** having a candy bar before bed
- **c.** trying to make up lost sleep over the weekend
- **d.** opening your blinds as soon as you wake up

Decide whether each statement is true or false. Write true *or* false *in the space provided.*

______ **5.** As a teen you spend more time in NREM sleep than in REM sleep.

______ **6.** If you are tired in the afternoon you shouldn't deny yourself a long nap.

______ **7.** If you cannot fall asleep, the best thing to do is just stay in bed and keep trying.

Write the letter of the correct answer in the space provided.

______ **8.** difficulties falling asleep or staying asleep

______ **9.** a disorder that causes breathing to stop for periods of time during sleep

______ **10.** a disorder that causes sudden episodes of sleep or severe sleepiness

- **a.** insomnia
- **b.** REM sleep
- **c.** narcolepsy
- **d.** sleep apnea

Name ______________________ Class ___________________ Date ______

Chapter 14 Test

Write the letter of the correct answer in the space provided.

_____ **1.** What material covers a tooth's neck?
a. cementum
b. dentin
c. pulp
d. enamel

_____ **2.** What is the purpose of the oil secreted by sebaceous glands?
a. It produces melanin.
b. It protects the skin from UV rays.
c. It keeps hair and skin from becoming dry.
d. It fights acne.

_____ **3.** Which skin infection is caused by a fungus?
a. ringworm
b. warts
c. boils
d. cold sores

_____ **4.** Which part of the eye regulates the pupil's size?
a. cornea
b. iris
c. retina
d. lens

_____ **5.** Which vision problem is caused by an uneven curvature of the cornea or lens?
a. astigmatism
b. macular degeneration
c. farsightedness
d. nearsightedness

Write the letter of the correct answer in the space provided.

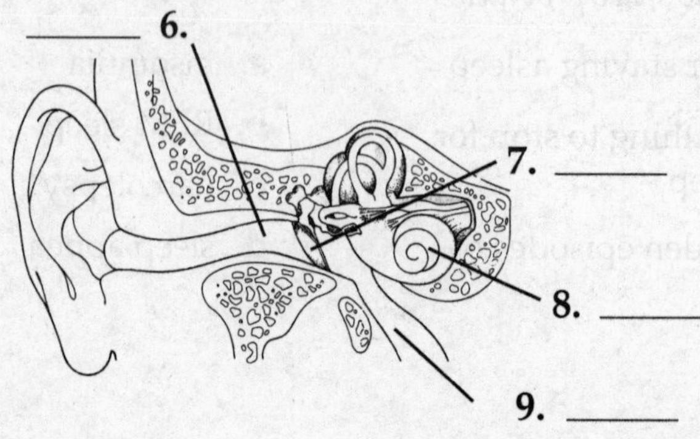

a. ear canal
b. stirrup
c. cochlea
d. auditory tube
e. eardrum

Name ______________________ Class ________________ Date ______

Chapter 14: Test *(continued)*

Decide whether each statement is true or false. Write true *or* false *in the space provided.*

_____ **10.** Temperature regulation is one of the skin's main functions.

_____ **11.** The oval window sends information to the brain about balance.

_____ **12.** Cone cells help people see in color.

_____ **13.** People who wash their hair every day can get head lice.

_____ **14.** People who are farsighted can clearly see items that are right in front of them.

Write the word that best completes each sentence in the space provided.

15. A specialist who corrects problems of the teeth and jaws is a(an) ____________________.

16. A professional who provides vision care is a(an) ____________________.

17. A professional who assesses hearing loss is a(an) ____________________.

18. A professional who treats skin problems is a(an) ____________________.

Use complete sentences to answer the following questions.

19. What are two reasons that adequate sleep is important the night before a test?

____

____

____

____

____

____

20. Explain the relationship between plaque, tartar, and periodontal disease.

____

____

____

____

____

____

Name ____________ Class ____________ Date ____________

Chapter 15

Personal Inventory

Attitudes About Alcohol

Both teenagers and adults hold many different attitudes about alcohol and its use. To look more closely at your own attitudes and behavior, complete these sentences.

Finish these sentences with your opinions

People drink alcohol when ____________

____

Controlling the use of alcohol is ____________

____

Getting drunk ____________

____

When it comes to alcohol, my friends ____________

____

Among my friends, the pressure to have a drink ____________

____

Running ads for alcohol on TV sports programs ____________

____

Describe what you would do in each of these situations.

I am at a party where a lot of beer, wine, and liquor is being served.

I would ____________

A good friend has been drinking a lot and is about to have another beer.

I would ____________

My friends are pressuring me to have "just one drink."

I would ____________

I am at a party where I know only a few people, and I am feeling uncomfortable.

I would ____________

Look over your responses. Are there any attitudes or behaviors you would change? If so, which ones?

____

____

Name________________________ Class__________ Date__________ M T W T F

Section 15-1

Alcohol Is a Drug — Lesson Plan

Section Objectives

- **Describe** how alcohol acts as a depressant in the body.
- **Identify** three major factors that influence underage drinking.

Vocabulary drug • depressant • fermentation • zero-tolerance policy

Time
1 period
1/2 block

Local Standards

1. FOCUS

Warm-Up: Quick Quiz Make sure students are aware that *no* responses to the quiz can endanger not only their health but also their lives. Call on students to share their ideas about ways to avoid drinking.

Targeted Resources

- ❑ Transparency W49

2. TEACH

Class Discussion Discuss why alcohol is classified as a drug and how it affects the body and brain. L2

Visual Learning: Figure 1 Help students interpret the numbers in the figure. Make sure they know that consuming large quantities of any kind of alcoholic drink can be deadly. L2

Addressing Misconceptions Address the misconception that the majority of teens regularly drink alcohol by having students review Youth Risk Behavior Surveillance System data from the CDC. L3

Differentiated Instruction Explain how the terms *drug* and *depressant* are used in this section. EL

Cultural Connection Discuss the role of alcohol in different religions, and ask students to share examples of religions that either use alcohol ritually or forbid its use. L3

Targeted Resources

- ❑ RN Note Taking Guide 15-1 L3 EL
- ❑ ARN Note Taking Guide 15-1 L2
- ❑ TR Practice 15-1
- ❑ TR Enrich 15-1 L4
- ❑ Audio Summary 15-1 L1 L2 EL
- ❑ Health Links: Updates on drunk driving

3. ASSESS

Evaluate Understanding The assignments listed in the Teacher's Edition can help you assess students' mastery of the section content.

Reteach Have small groups of students explain section content to one another, using the section objectives as a guide. L2

Targeted Resources

- ❑ TR Section 15-1 Quiz
- ❑ CTB Chapter 15

KEY

L1 Special Needs	L4 Gifted and Talented
L2 Less Proficient Readers	EL English Language Learners
L3 All Students	

Name ____________________ Class ____________________ Date ________

Section 15-1 **Practice**

Building Health Skills: Analyzing Influences on Teen Drinking

Teens may choose to drink or not to drink due to a variety of influences. Three of the most important influences on whether teens drink are peers, family, and the media.

Read each of the following examples. For each example, analyze the influences on the teen who is considering whether to drink. Identify the influences in the spaces provided.

1. Tasha has always admired Yolanda and was thrilled when Yolanda invited her to a party at her house. Now that she is at the party, Tasha sees that everyone is drinking beer, including Yolanda. Tasha isn't sure about drinking because her parents are opposed to it, but she really wants to fit in and for Yolanda to like her.

____

____

____

2. Zach has an uncle and an older brother who are problem drinkers, and Zach is determined not to end up like them. However, most of Zach's friends have started to drink, and they are putting pressure on Zach to join them.

____

____

____

3. Bryden thinks that the people in beer ads always look self-confident, relaxed, and outgoing. Bryden is very shy and wishes she were more outgoing. She wonders if she would be more self-confident in social situations if she drank a few beers first.

____

____

____

Select one of the three examples. If you were the teen in this example, how would you respond? What would influence you? How could you resist influences to drink?

____

____

____

____

Name ______________ Class ______________ Date ______

Consumer Skills: Alcohol Ads

Commercials and advertisements for beer are designed to be appealing. They often imply that in order to belong to a certain social group, you must drink a particular beer. They may also promise that if you drink that brand, you will have more fun, make more friends, and lead a more exciting life. Such advertising has become controversial over the last few years. Many people feel that it paints a misleading picture of drinking alcohol and that it is too often directed at underage people who may be overly influenced by the ads.

Identify three advertisements for alcohol in magazines or on TV. Analyze each advertisement in the spaces provided below.

Advertisement 1

Where you found the ad (e.g., during which TV program or in which magazine)

____

Name and type of alcoholic product ______________________________

Intended audience of the ad (e.g., men or women, age group, lifestyle)

____

What the ad emphasizes or seems to promise ______________________________

____

Advertisement 2

Where you found the ad ______________________________

Name and type of alcoholic product ______________________________

Intended audience of the ad ______________________________

What the ad emphasizes or seems to promise ______________________________

____

Advertisement 3

Where you found the ad ______________________________

Name and type of alcoholic product ______________________________

Intended audience of the ad ______________________________

What the ad emphasizes or seems to promise ______________________________

____

Name ______________________ Class ______________ Date ______

Section 15-1: **Enrich** *(continued)*

Answer the following questions in the spaces provided.

1. Which of the three advertisements did you personally find most appealing?

2. Look at your analysis of the ad you identified in question 1. What can you infer from this ad about the type of advertising that influences you?

3. Why is the advertisement you chose misleading?

4. How can you resist the influence of that ad and other ads like it?

Name ____________________ Class ____________________ Date ________

Section 15-1

Quiz

Write the letter of the correct answer in the space provided.

______ **1.** Why is alcohol classified as a drug?
- **a.** It causes changes in a person's body or behavior.
- **b.** It is legal for adults to buy and use.
- **c.** It increases the risk of violence.
- **d.** It can cause brain damage.

______ **2.** A depressant is a drug that causes
- **a.** increased alertness.
- **b.** faster reaction times.
- **c.** most body processes to speed up.
- **d.** brain and body reactions to slow down.

______ **3.** What is fermentation?
- **a.** a chemical that changes the body and brain
- **b.** the process that removes alcohol from beer
- **c.** the process that produces alcohol
- **d.** a depressant effect of alcohol

______ **4.** A zero-tolerance policy about underage drinking means that minors are
- **a.** prohibited from using large amounts of alcohol.
- **b.** not punished for an offense if they have zero previous offenses.
- **c.** punished for being caught with any amount of alcohol.
- **d.** not allowed to drink legally because they have zero tolerance for alcohol.

______ **5.** Which drink contains the most alcohol?
- **a.** 1.5-oz shot of liquor that is 40% alcohol
- **b.** 5-oz glass of wine that is 10% alcohol
- **c.** 12-oz bottle of beer that is 4% alcohol
- **d.** 24-oz can of beer that is 3% alcohol

Decide whether each statement is true or false. Write true *or* false *in the space provided.*

______ **6.** Alcohol is a depressant.

______ **7.** Alcohol is the second most widely abused drug among high school students.

______ **8.** Peers, family, and the media strongly influence teen drinking.

______ **9.** Teens who use alcohol are less likely to have alcohol problems later in life.

______ **10.** A teen may be sent to prison for drinking and driving.

Name________________________ Class__________ Date__________ M T W T F

Section 15-2

Alcohol's Effects on the Body Lesson Plan

Time
2 periods
1 block

Local Standards

Section Objectives

- **Summarize** the effects of intoxication on the body systems.
- **List** four factors that affect blood alcohol concentration.
- **Identify** three ways that intoxication may lead to death.

Vocabulary intoxication • blackout • blood alcohol concentration (BAC) • hangover • driving while intoxicated (DWI) • overdose • binge drinking

1. FOCUS

Warm-Up: Health Stats Ask students to describe a time when quick reactions helped them avoid an accident. Discuss what might have happened if their reaction time had been slowed by alcohol.

Targeted Resources
- ❑ Transparency W50

2. TEACH

Building Vocabulary Define the word parts *in–*, *toxic–*, and *–ation*, and have students use the definitions to define *intoxication*. L2

Teacher Demo Pour water through a filter at different rates to make an analogy to how the liver responds to different rates of alcohol consumption. L2

Visual Learning: Figure 5 Have students interpret the data in Figure 5 and relate it to the information in Figure 4. L3

Differentiated Instruction Have students do a simple hands-on activity with water and food coloring to help them understand the concept of blood alcohol concentration. L1

Building Health Skills Ask students what they would do if they were at a party where some teens were getting very drunk. L2

Targeted Resources
- ❑ RN Note Taking Guide 15-2 L3 EL
- ❑ ARN Note Taking Guide 15-2 L2
- ❑ Transparencies and Worksheets 41, 42
- ❑ TR Practice 15-2
- ❑ TR Enrich 15-2 L4
- ❑ Audio Summary 15-2 L1 L2 EL
- ❑ PHSchool.com: More on blood alcohol concentration

3. ASSESS

Evaluate Understanding The assignments listed in the Teacher's Edition can help you assess students' mastery of the section content.

Reteach Write the vocabulary terms on the board, and ask students to brainstorm facts about each term. L2

Targeted Resources
- ❑ TR Section 15-2 Quiz
- ❑ CTB Chapter 15

KEY

L1	Special Needs	L4	Gifted and Talented
L2	Less Proficient Readers	EL	English Language Learners
L3	All Students		

Name ______________________ Class ____________________ Date ________

Section 15-2 **Practice**

Group Activity: Effects of Intoxication on Body Systems

Intoxication affects many systems throughout the body. Four systems that are especially affected by intoxication are the nervous, cardiovascular, excretory, and digestive systems.

With a group, brainstorm the effects of intoxication on each of these four systems. List the effects in the spaces provided in the drawing below. If you need help, look at Figure 3 on page 381 in your text.

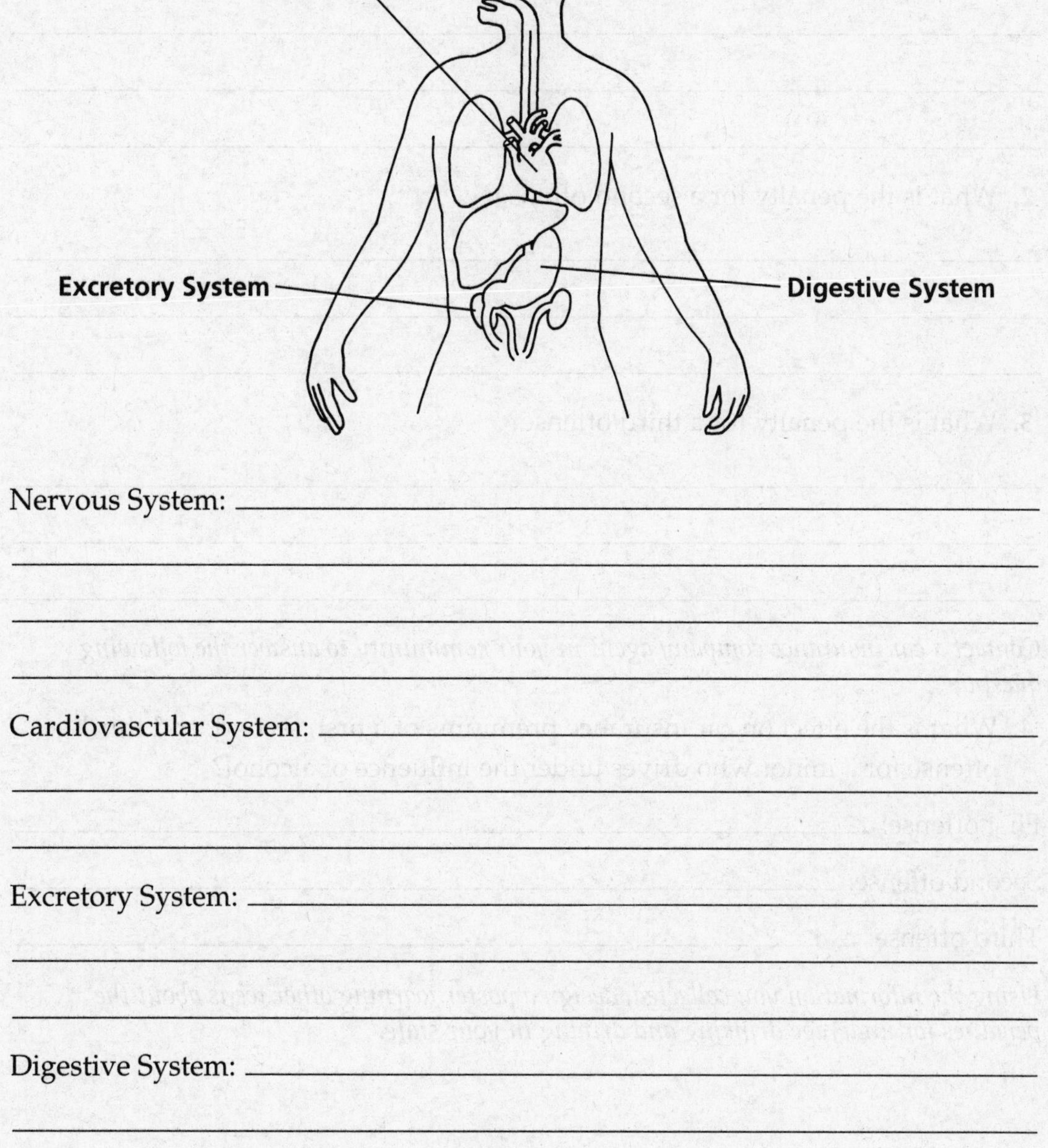

Nervous System: ____

____

____

____

Cardiovascular System: ____

____

____

Excretory System: ____

____

____

Digestive System: ____

____

Name ____________________ Class ____________________ Date ________

Community Involvement: Penalties for Drinking and Driving

States differ in their laws dealing with drinking and driving. All 50 states have zero tolerance laws for drivers under the age of 21, but states vary in their penalties for breaking the laws. Do you know the penalties in your state for a minor who drives under the influence of alcohol?

Contact your local police department or department of motor vehicles. Obtain and record answers to questions 1–3.

1. What is the penalty for a first offense for a minor who drives under the influence of alcohol?

____

____

____

2. What is the penalty for a second offense?

____

____

____

3. What is the penalty for a third offense?

____

____

____

Contact a car insurance company agent in your community to answer the following question.

4. What is the effect on car insurance premiums of a first, second, and third offense for a minor who drives under the influence of alcohol?

First offense: ____

Second offense: ____

Third offense: ____

Using the information you collected, design a poster warning other teens about the penalties for underage drinking and driving in your state.

Name ______________________ Class ______________________ Date __________

Section 15-2 Quiz

Write the letter of the correct answer in the space provided.

______ **1.** state in which a person is impaired by alcohol

______ **2.** period of time that a drinker cannot recall

______ **3.** amount of alcohol in a person's blood

______ **4.** taking so much of a drug that it leads to coma or death

______ **5.** consumption of excessive amounts of alcohol at one sitting

a. overdose

b. binge drinking

c. blackout

d. DWI

e. intoxication

f. BAC

Decide whether each statement is true or false. Write true *or* false *in the space provided.*

______ **6.** Intoxication causes core body temperature to increase.

______ **7.** Females generally have lower blood alcohol concentrations than males after drinking the same amount.

______ **8.** Alcohol is involved in about 40% of fatal motor vehicle crashes.

______ **9.** A person can die from binge drinking.

______ **10.** Combining alcohol with drugs such as sleeping pills can be fatal.

Name_______________________ Class__________ Date__________ M T W T F

Section 15-3 Long-Term Risks of Alcohol Lesson Plan

Section Objectives

- **Identify** five serious physical effects of long-term alcohol abuse.
- **Describe** the three stages of alcoholism.
- **List** in order three steps taken during recovery from alcoholism.

Time
2 periods
1 block

Local Standards

Vocabulary fetal alcohol syndrome • cirrhosis • alcoholism • tolerance • dependence • addiction • reverse tolerance • detoxification • withdrawal • rehabilitation

1. FOCUS

Warm-Up: Myth/Fact Call on volunteers to share their answers. Help dispel other misconceptions the students reveal by providing factual statements to counter the myths.

Targeted Resources
- ❑ Transparency W51

2. TEACH

Differentiated Instruction Ask groups of students to make graphic organizers showing the ways that long-term alcohol abuse may harm major organs. L2

Active Learning Have students trace their bodies on butcher paper and mark areas of the body affected by long-term alcohol abuse. L1

Building Media Literacy Ask students to search different types of media for more detailed definitions of terms relating to alcoholism and decide which type of media is most useful for this purpose. EL

Building Health Skills Ask students to make a brochure about Alateen for other teens. L3

Targeted Resources
- ❑ RN Note Taking Guide 15-3 L3 EL
- ❑ ARN Note Taking Guide 15-3 L2
- ❑ TR Practice 15-3
- ❑ TR Enrich 15-3 L4
- ❑ Audio Summary 15-3 L1 L2 EL
- ❑ Health Links: Updates on alcoholism

3. ASSESS

Evaluate Understanding The assignments listed in the Teacher's Edition can help you assess students' mastery of the section content.

Reteach Ask students to make an outline of the section using the headings, boldfaced sentences, and definitions. L2

Targeted Resources
- ❑ TR Section 15-3 Quiz
- ❑ CTB Chapter 15

KEY

L1 Special Needs	L4 Gifted and Talented
L2 Less Proficient Readers	EL English Language Learners
L3 All Students	

Name ______________________ Class __________________ Date ______

Section 15-3 **Practice**

Vocabulary Activity: Long-Term Risks of Alcohol

There are many long-term risks of alcohol use, including organ damage and alcoholism. In this section, you learned several terms about long-term risks of alcohol. Some of the terms are closely related and easy to confuse. Check your knowledge of these terms.

Match each definition in the left column with the correct term in the right column. Then write the number of each term in the appropriate box below. When you have filled in all the boxes, add up the numbers in each column, row, and two diagonals. All the sums should be the same.

Definition

A. condition in which less and less alcohol causes intoxication

B. liver disease caused by heavy drinking

C. symptoms that occur when a dependent person stops taking a drug

D. process of removing all alcohol from a person's body

E. condition characterized by a craving to use alcohol

F. state in which a drinker's body needs more alcohol to achieve the original effect

G. disease in which people can no longer control their use of alcohol

H. process of learning to cope with everyday life without alcohol

I. condition in which the brain develops a chemical need for alcohol

Term

1. cirrhosis

2. alcoholism

3. tolerance

4. dependence

5. addiction

6. reverse tolerance

7. detoxification

8. withdrawal

9. rehabilitation

			(diagonal) = ____
A ____	B ____	C ____	= ____
D ____	E ____	F ____	= ____
G ____	H ____	I ____	= ____
= ____	= ____	= ____	(diagonal) = ____

Name ______________________ Class ________________ Date ______

Section 15-3 **Enrich**

Class Debate: Should Alcohol Be Illegal?

Alcohol is the most widely used drug in the United States, and its costs to society are enormous. Some people think alcohol should be illegal for these and other reasons. Other people think that adults should be allowed to drink alcohol legally (as they can at present). They argue that attempts to prohibit alcohol in the past were not very successful and that making alcohol illegal would infringe on people's rights.

With a group, think of reasons why alcohol should and should not be legal for adults. You can also research the issue online or ask adults you know for their opinions. List arguments on both sides of the issue in the spaces provided below. Use an extra sheet of paper if necessary.

Reasons Why Alcohol Should Be Legal:

____

____

____

____

____

____

____

____

Reasons Why Alcohol Should Be Illegal:

____

____

____

____

____

____

____

____

Divide your group in half, and have each half argue one side of the issue. Present your debate to the class. After the debate, ask other students to state which side of the issue they agree with.

Name ________________ Class ________________ Date ______

Section 15-3

Quiz

Write the letter of the correct answer in the space provided.

______ **1.** disease in which a drinker's liver develops scar tissue	**a.** alcoholism
______ **2.** disease in which a drinker needs alcohol to function	**b.** absolute dependence
______ **3.** state in which fewer drinks are needed to cause the original effect	**c.** reverse tolerance
______ **4.** one of the stages of alcoholism	**d.** detoxification
______ **5.** one of the steps of recovery from alcoholism	**e.** cirrhosis
	f. tolerance

Write the letter of the correct answer in the space provided.

______ **6.** Alcohol is more damaging to teen brains than adult brains because teen brains are
- **a.** not as accustomed to alcohol.
- **b.** still developing.
- **c.** able to bounce back faster from injury.
- **d.** exposed to alcohol at a less critical time.

______ **7.** How much alcohol can a woman drink during pregnancy without risk of harming her baby?
- **a.** none
- **b.** one drink per day
- **c.** two drinks per day
- **d.** three drinks per week

______ **8.** Excessive drinking contributes to heart disease by causing
- **a.** decreased heart rate.
- **b.** decreased blood pressure.
- **c.** fatty deposits in the heart.
- **d.** liver failure.

______ **9.** Risk factors for becoming an alcoholic include
- **a.** being the child of an alcoholic.
- **b.** avoiding alcohol until age 21 or older.
- **c.** being exposed to negative attitudes toward drinking.
- **d.** being unable to obtain alcohol in the home.

______ **10.** Which support group is for friends and family members of alcoholics?
- **a.** Alcoholics Anonymous
- **b.** Al-Anon
- **c.** Alateen
- **d.** AA

Name____________________________ Class__________ Date__________ M T W T F

Section 15-4 Choosing Not to Drink Lesson Plan

Section Objectives

- **Evaluate** how refusal skills help you stick to your decision not to drink.
- **Identify** two benefits of avoiding situations where alcohol is present.

Vocabulary refusal skills

Time
1 period
1/2 block

Local Standards

1. FOCUS

Warm-Up: Advice Line Ask students to share what they wrote. Discuss why honest reasons make refusals more effective.

Targeted Resources

- ❑ Transparency W52

2. TEACH

Cooperative Learning Have English proficient students help English language learners formulate answers to the questions in the text under the heading "Prepare for Pressure." EL

Building Health Skills Have pairs of students write dialogues in which a teen uses refusal skills to resist peer pressure to drink. L3

Differentiated Instruction Have students read aloud refusal statements that they have had a chance to practice reading at home. L2

Building Health Skills Have students make posters showing other teens how to avoid high-pressure situations involving alcohol. L1

Targeted Resources

- ❑ RN Note Taking Guide 15-4 L3 EL
- ❑ ARN Note Taking Guide 15-4 L2
- ❑ TR Practice 15-4
- ❑ TR Enrich 15-4 L4
- ❑ Audio Summary 15-4 L1 L2 EL
- ❑ PHSchool.com: More on alcohol-free celebrations

3. ASSESS

Evaluate Understanding The assignments listed in the Teacher's Edition can help you assess students' mastery of the section content.

Reteach Have students demonstrate how to use refusal skills to turn down an alcoholic drink. Call on other students to point out specific ways the students said *no* convincingly. L2

Targeted Resources

- ❑ TR Section 15-4 Quiz
- ❑ CTB Chapter 15

KEY

L1 Special Needs	L4 Gifted and Talented
L2 Less Proficient Readers	EL English Language Learners
L3 All Students	

Name ______________________ Class __________________ Date ______

Section 15-4 Practice

Role-Playing: Avoiding Alcohol

You can avoid alcohol by using refusal skills when other people pressure you to drink. You can also avoid alcohol by staying away from high-pressure situations.

With a group, write a short role-play in which a teen avoids alcohol in one of the two ways stated above. Plan your role-play in the spaces provided below. You can use another sheet of paper if you need more space. Practice your role-play so you can present it to the class if your teacher asks you.

Title:

____

Characters:

____

____

Setting:

____

____

Overview of role-play:

____

____

____

____

Dialogue:

____

____

____

____

____

____

____

____

____

Name ______________________ Class ____________________ Date ______

Community Involvement: Safe Rides for Teens

Most teens know they should avoid riding with a driver who has been drinking. However, they may not know what to do if they find themselves in that situation. If you needed a ride home and the person you were depending on for the ride was drinking, would you know what to do? Do you have an alternative plan in place and the information you need to use it?

Use a local telephone directory and any other sources you need to find the information requested below. In the spaces provided, record any information that is relevant to your community.

Taxis:

Name of Company ______________ Name of Company ______________

Number to call to schedule a taxi ______________ Number to call to schedule a taxi ______________

Cost ______________ Cost ______________

Public Transportation

Bus:

Number to call for route information ______________

Locations of nearby bus stops

____

____

____

Cost ______________

Subway or Train:

Number to call for route information ______________

Locations of nearby stations

____

____

____

Cost ______________

Use the information above to make a brochure entitled, "Safe Rides for Teens." Include information about the dangers of riding with a driver who has been drinking. Leave spaces in the brochure for teens to add information about other drivers who might be able to give them a safe ride. Use a format like the one below.

Drivers I Know and Trust:

Name of driver ______________ Name of driver ______________

Telephone number(s) Telephone number(s)

______________ ______________

Name of driver ______________ Name of driver ______________

Telephone number(s) Telephone number(s)

______________ ______________

Name ____________________ Class ____________________ Date ________

Section 15-4 Quiz

Decide whether each statement is true or false. Write true *or* false *in the space provided.*

______ **1.** Abstinence is the best decision teens can make about alcohol.

______ **2.** Refusal skills are the skills needed to say *no*.

______ **3.** When you refuse to drink, you should always apologize for not drinking.

______ **4.** You should put yourself in situations where there is alcohol so you can practice refusal skills.

______ **5.** You should never get into a car with anyone who has been drinking.

Write the letter of the correct answer in the space provided.

______ **6.** Which choice states a correct relationship between age and alcohol?
- **a.** Underage drinking is legal.
- **b.** After age 21, everyone drinks.
- **c.** Few adults abstain from alcohol.
- **d.** Drinking is legal only at ages 21 and older.

______ **7.** Sticking to a decision to abstain from alcohol means
- **a.** never being in places where other people are drinking.
- **b.** being able to say *no* around people who are drinking.
- **c.** offending people who ask you to drink.
- **d.** trying to pressure other people not to drink.

______ **8.** How can you prepare for peer pressure to drink?
- **a.** Avoid thinking about alcohol.
- **b.** Think of reasons for not drinking.
- **c.** Go along with the crowd and pretend to drink.
- **d.** Hang out with peers who drink so you will get used to the pressure.

______ **9.** What activity should teens who abstain from alcohol avoid?
- **a.** going to parties where others are drinking
- **b.** organizing a school activity
- **c.** playing an instrument
- **d.** participating in a sport

______ **10.** If you find yourself dependent on a drinker for a ride home, you should
- **a.** ask someone for help.
- **b.** see if the drinker is drunk.
- **c.** try to sober up the drinker.
- **d.** worry about being rude to the drinker.

Name ______________________ Class ______________________ Date ________

Chapter 15 Test

Write the letter of the correct answer in the space provided.

_____ **1.** Advertisements for alcohol usually
  a. are meant to appeal to older adults.
  b. give detailed information about the products.
  c. warn about the negative side effects of alcohol.
  d. give false impressions about drinking.

_____ **2.** How does intoxication affect the cardiovascular system?
  a. It increases heart rate.
  b. It decreases blood pressure.
  c. It increases core body temperature.
  d. It decreases blood flow to the skin's surface.

_____ **3.** What happens in an alcohol overdose?
  a. reverse tolerance
  b. coma or death
  c. dependence
  d. withdrawal

_____ **4.** Inflammation of the liver that is caused by alcohol is called alcoholic
  a. cirrhosis.
  b. hepatitis.
  c. fatty liver.
  d. indigestion.

_____ **5.** What is the first step in an alcoholic's recovery?
  a. withdrawal
  b. detoxification
  c. complete dependence
  d. acknowledging the problem

Write the letter of the correct answer in the space provided.

_____ **6.** drug that slows brain and body reactions
_____ **7.** after-effects of drinking too much alcohol
_____ **8.** lack of control over the use of alcohol
_____ **9.** first stage of alcoholism
_____ **10.** not drinking at all

a. problem drinking
b. addiction
c. blackout
d. depressant
e. abstinence
f. hangover

Name ____________________ Class ____________________ Date ________

Chapter 15: **Test** *(continued)*

Decide whether each statement is true or false. Write true *or* false *in the space provided.*

______**11.** A person can die from drinking too much alcohol.

______**12.** Alcohol increases drinkers' natural fears.

______**13.** Drinking on an empty stomach decreases BAC.

______**14.** Long-term alcohol abuse destroys nerve cells in the brain.

______**15.** Alcoholism affects many other people besides the drinker.

Write the word that best completes each sentence in the space provided.

16. The process in which microorganisms produce alcohol is called

____________________.

17. The state in which a person's abilities are impaired by alcohol is called

____________________.

18. The condition in which the brain has a chemical need for alcohol is called

____________________.

Use complete sentences to answer the following questions.

19. Identify three major factors that influence underage drinking, and for each one, give an example of how it might be an influence.

____

____

____

____

____

____

____

20. Describe two ways of abstaining from alcohol.

____

____

____

____

____

Name ______________________ Class ____________________ Date ______

Chapter 16 Personal Inventory

Attitudes About Tobacco

In the United States, attitudes about tobacco use have become more negative over recent decades. Attitudes, in turn, influence whether people use tobacco. What are your attitudes about tobacco?

Complete the following sentences with your own opinions.

1. Using tobacco is ______________________________

2. I think that people start to use tobacco because ______________________________

3. The effects of tobacco on the body are ______________________________

4. Banning smoking in public places is ______________________________

5. Warning labels on cigarette packages are ______________________________

6. When someone near me lights up a cigarette, I ______________________________

7. When I am around people who are smoking, I ______________________________

8. When asked to choose a smoking or nonsmoking area, I ______________________________

9. When someone offers me tobacco, I ______________________________

10. When I am with someone who is trying to quit smoking, I ______________________________

Look over how you completed sentences 1–10. Then, answer the questions below.

11. Are you satisfied and comfortable with your attitudes about tobacco?

12. Are there any attitudes that you would like to change? If so, which ones?

Name____________________ Class________ Date________ M T W T F

Section 16-1

Teens and Tobacco — Lesson Plan

Section Objectives

- **Identify** three factors that influence teens' decisions about tobacco use.
- **Describe** the various forms of tobacco products.

Time
1 period
1/2 block

Local Standards

Vocabulary nicotine • smokeless tobacco • chewing tobacco • snuff

1. FOCUS

Warm-Up: Health Stats Ask students to explain the decline in teen smoking shown in the graph.

Targeted Resources

- ❑ Transparency W53

2. TEACH

Journal Writing Have students write a private journal entry examining their own views about tobacco use. L2

Differentiated Instruction Work with students to create a visual display showing influences on teen tobacco use. L1

Visual Learning: Figure 2 Ask students to explain what the graph shows and how a report on the dangers of smoking seems to have affected cigarette use. L3

Building Media Literacy Have students find articles about nicotine from different types of media, and discuss which examples seem most informative and reliable. L3

Cooperative Learning Have groups of students with different ability levels make charts comparing and contrasting smoked and smokeless tobacco. L2

Targeted Resources

- ❑ RN Note Taking Guide 16-1 L3 EL
- ❑ ARN Note Taking Guide 16-1 L2
- ❑ TR Practice 16-1
- ❑ TR Enrich 16-1 L4
- ❑ Audio Summary 16-1 L1 L2 EL
- ❑ Health Links: Updates on the anti-smoking campaign

3. ASSESS

Evaluate Understanding The assignments listed in the Teacher's Edition can help you assess students' mastery of the section content.

Reteach Ask students to make a concept map of section content using the headings and subheadings. L2

Targeted Resources

- ❑ TR Section 16-1 Quiz
- ❑ CTB Chapter 16

KEY

L1 Special Needs	L4 Gifted and Talented
L2 Less Proficient Readers	EL English Language Learners
L3 All Students	

Name ______________________ Class ____________________ Date ______

Section 16-1

Practice

Skill-Building Activity: Analyzing Influences on Tobacco Use

Friends, family, and the media greatly influence whether someone starts to use tobacco. Being aware of these influences can help you avoid tobacco use.

Read about the teens below. In the spaces provided, explain which factors—friends, family, and/or media—influenced each teen's decision about tobacco use.

1. At a party, a friend offered Tanya a cigarette. Tanya was tempted to smoke it to fit in. Then, she thought about how hard it was for her dad to quit smoking last year. She decided to say no.

____

____

____

2. Reggie thinks that the people in tobacco ads look cool. They are very attractive and seem to be having a great time. Many of the people in the ads look like athletes, so Reggie wonders if tobacco is as dangerous as he has heard. He thinks he will try a cigarette the next time a friend offers him one.

____

____

____

3. When Soledad wrote a paper on tobacco last year, she read many reports about how tobacco damages health. Soledad shared what she learned with her friend, Elyse, who was a smoker. Elyse decided to quit smoking when she realized how much harm it was doing to her body. Soledad supported Elyse's decision to quit and helped her overcome her addiction to nicotine.

____

____

____

4. Both of Farris's parents smoke cigarettes, and Farris always figured he would smoke as an adult. Recently, Farris saw an anti-smoking program on television that showed how dangerous it is to use tobacco. Now, Farris is determined not to smoke, and he is trying to convince his parents to quit smoking.

____

____

____

Name ______________________ Class ____________________ Date ________

Section 16-1 **Enrich**

Family Involvement: Family Influences on Tobacco Use

Family members may be an important influence on whether a teen starts to use tobacco. Older family members may have started using tobacco and become addicted to it before its dangers were well known. Later, they may have quit or wanted to quit but found it extremely difficult.

Interview an adult family member. Ask the questions below and record the answers.

Do you smoke? Why or why not?

____

____

If you smoke, do you want to quit? Why or why not?

____

____

When and how did you learn about the dangers of using tobacco?

____

____

What is your present attitude about tobacco use?

____

____

Has your attitude changed over time? If so, what changed it?

____

____

What advice would you give teens about using tobacco?

____

____

Review your family member's responses and answer the questions below.

1. Which of the responses surprised you? Explain.

____

____

2. How might this family member influence your decisions about tobacco use?

____

____

Name ______________________ Class __________________ Date ______

Section 16-1 Quiz

Write the letter of the correct answer in the space provided.

______ **1.** The percentage of teens who use tobacco
a. is significantly lower than it was in the 1990s.
b. doubles about every ten years.
c. has increased steadily for decades.
d. has never been calculated.

______ **2.** Three major influences on whether someone starts to use tobacco are
a. price, ads, and movies.
b. friends, family, and media.
c. television, radio, and magazines.
d. peers, movies, and media.

______ **3.** Tobacco laws have *not* prohibited tobacco companies from
a. advertising near schools.
b. supplying their products to be sold in pharmacies.
c. using cartoon characters in advertisements.
d. advertising on the radio.

______ **4.** What is nicotine?
a. a naturally occurring insecticide in tobacco leaves
b. a highly addictive chemical in tobacco products
c. an extremely poisonous substance in pure form
d. all of the above

______ **5.** Which of the following is considered a safe tobacco product?
a. cigar
b. *kretek*
c. snuff
d. none of the above

Decide whether each statement is true or false. Write true *or* false *in the space provided.*

______ **6.** Tobacco use is much more socially acceptable that it used to be.

______ **7.** Most people who become addicted to tobacco start using it in their teens.

______ **8.** Many teens who do not smoke credit their friends for helping them make good decisions.

______ **9.** Cigarettes are the most frequently used type of tobacco product.

______ **10.** Chewing tobacco is not addictive.

Name________________________ Class__________ Date__________ M T W T F

Section 16-2

Chemicals in Tobacco Products Lesson Plan

Section Objectives

- **Explain** how nicotine affects the body.
- **Identify** two other dangerous substances in tobacco smoke.
- **Examine** why using smokeless tobacco is not a safe alternative to smoking.

Time
1 period
1/2 block

Local Standards

Vocabulary stimulant • tar • carcinogen • carbon monoxide

1. FOCUS

Warm-Up: Myth/Fact Ask students where people get information about tobacco products, and discuss whether the sources provide accurate information.

Targeted Resources
- ❑ Transparency W54

2. TEACH

Visual Learning: Figure 4 Challenge students to describe symptoms smokers might experience due to nicotine's effects on each system in the figure. L2

Addressing Misconceptions Address the misconception that nicotine addiction is not as potent as addiction to other drugs. L2

Differentiated Instruction Help students focus on important facts about nicotine addiction by copying three summary sentences into their notebooks. L1

Building Health Skills Ask groups of students to create posters advocating for avoiding tobacco because of its short-term dangers. L3

Targeted Resources
- ❑ RN Note Taking Guide 16-2 L3 EL
- ❑ ARN Note Taking Guide 16-2 L2
- ❑ Transparency and Worksheet 43
- ❑ TR Practice 16-2
- ❑ TR Enrich 16-2 L4
- ❑ Audio Summary 16-2 L1 L2 EL
- ❑ Health Links: Updates on nicotine

3. ASSESS

Evaluate Understanding The assignments listed in the Teacher's Edition can help you assess students' mastery of the section content.

Reteach Have pairs of students demonstrate their knowledge of section objectives to one another. L2

Targeted Resources
- ❑ TR Section 16-2 Quiz
- ❑ CTB Chapter 16

KEY

L1 Special Needs	L4 Gifted and Talented
L2 Less Proficient Readers	EL English Language Learners
L3 All Students	

Name ____________________ Class ____________________ Date ________

Section 16-2

Practice

Group Activity: Tobacco Smoke and the Body

Tobacco smoke has many harmful effects on the body. It is especially harmful to the respiratory and cardiovascular systems. Three of the most harmful substances in tobacco smoke are nicotine, tar, and carbon monoxide.

As a group, complete the table about the harmful chemicals in tobacco smoke.

Substance	What It Is	Some Effects on the Body
Nicotine		
Tar		
Carbon Monoxide		

Use information from the table to write a 30-second public service announcement about the dangers of smoking. Use the lines below and another sheet of paper, if needed, to write a draft of your announcement.

____

____

____

____

____

____

____

____

____

____

Name ______________________ Class ________________ Date ________

Section 16-2 **Enrich**

***Community Involvement:* Letter to the Editor**

Tobacco companies spend billions of dollars each year trying to influence people to start smoking or keep smoking. Making people aware of the dangers of tobacco products is one way to help counter the influence of these ads.

In the spaces below, write a letter to the editor of a local newspaper urging community members to avoid tobacco because of its dangers. In your letter, describe the health effects of the three most dangerous substances in tobacco products.

(your address)

(date)

Dear Editor:

Sincerely,

Name ______________________ Class ______________________ Date ______

Section 16-2

Quiz

Write the letter of the correct answer in the space provided.

_____ **1.** drug that increases the activity of the nervous system

_____ **2.** dark, sticky substance that forms when tobacco burns

_____ **3.** any chemical or other substance that causes cancer

_____ **4.** poisonous gas produced when tobacco is burned

_____ **5.** the need for more of a drug to produce the same effect

a. tar
b. tolerance
c. oxygen
d. stimulant
e. carcinogen
f. carbon monoxide

Write the letter of the correct answer in the space provided.

_____ **6.** A short-term consequence of nicotine use is
a. increased heart rate.
b. decreased blood pressure.
c. increased blood flow to skin.
d. decreased risk of blood clotting.

_____ **7.** How does nicotine affect the respiratory system?
a. It increases muscle action in the airways.
b. It causes breathing to become shallow.
c. It increases some reflex actions.
d. It decreases mucus production.

_____ **8.** Short-term effects of tar include
a. brown stains on teeth.
b. increased blood pressure.
c. tooth decay.
d. drooling.

_____ **9.** How does carbon monoxide affect a smoker's blood?
a. It reduces the number of red blood cells in the blood.
b. It increases the amount of oxygen in the blood.
c. It reduces the blood's ability to transport oxygen.
d. It increases the amount of hemoglobin in the blood.

_____ **10.** Which term refers to symptoms in a tobacco user who goes without nicotine?
a. addiction
b. dependence
c. tolerance
d. withdrawal

Name________________________ Class__________ Date__________ M T W T F

Section 16-3 **Risks of Tobacco Use** **Lesson Plan**

Section Objectives

- **Describe** the long-term health risks of tobacco use.
- **Identify** the long-term risks of exposure to secondhand smoke.
- **Examine** how smoking by a pregnant woman can affect her baby.

Time
2 periods
1 block

Local Standards

Vocabulary chronic obstructive pulmonary disease (COPD) • chronic bronchitis • emphysema • leukoplakia • mainstream smoke • sidestream smoke • secondhand smoke

1. FOCUS

Warm-Up: Quick Quiz Explain why the only false statement in the quiz is not true.

Targeted Resources
- ❑ Transparency W55

2. TEACH

Building Health Skills Have students find recent, reliable facts about tobacco-related deaths and use the facts to create a brochure about the dangers of tobacco use. L3

Differentiated Instruction Read aloud difficult vocabulary terms, and have students make and use vocabulary flash cards. EL

Building Health Skills Have students make an intricate concept map that illustrates the relationship between smoking and cardiovascular disease risk factors. L4

Class Discussion Discuss how smoking causes cancer in organs other than the lung and mouth. L2

Building Health Skills Have students write a letter to the editor of a local newspaper encouraging smokers to protect other people from their secondhand smoke. L3

Visual Learning: Figure 10 Have students rewrite cigarette warning labels after reading the section on tobacco use and pregnancy. L1

Targeted Resources
- ❑ RN Note Taking Guide 16-3 L3 EL
- ❑ ARN Note Taking Guide 16-3 L2
- ❑ TR Practice 16-3
- ❑ TR Enrich 16-3 L4
- ❑ Audio Summary 16-3 L1 L2 EL
- ❑ PHSchool.com: More on secondhand smoke

3. ASSESS

Evaluate Understanding The assignments listed in the Teacher's Edition can help you assess students' mastery of the section content.

Reteach Ask students to write a paragraph addressing section objectives and using all the vocabulary terms. L2

Targeted Resources
- ❑ TR Section 16-3 Quiz
- ❑ CTB Chapter 16

KEY

L1 Special Needs	L4 Gifted and Talented
L2 Less Proficient Readers	EL English Language Learners
L3 All Students	

Name ______________________ Class ______________________ Date ________

Section 16-3

Practice

Vocabulary Activity: Tobacco Smoke and Its Dangers

Tobacco smoke causes many long-term risks to the body. People who smoke tobacco or who are exposed to tobacco smoke are more likely to develop certain diseases, including respiratory illnesses and cancers.

Complete the crossword puzzle below. Use section vocabulary terms about tobacco smoke and its dangers.

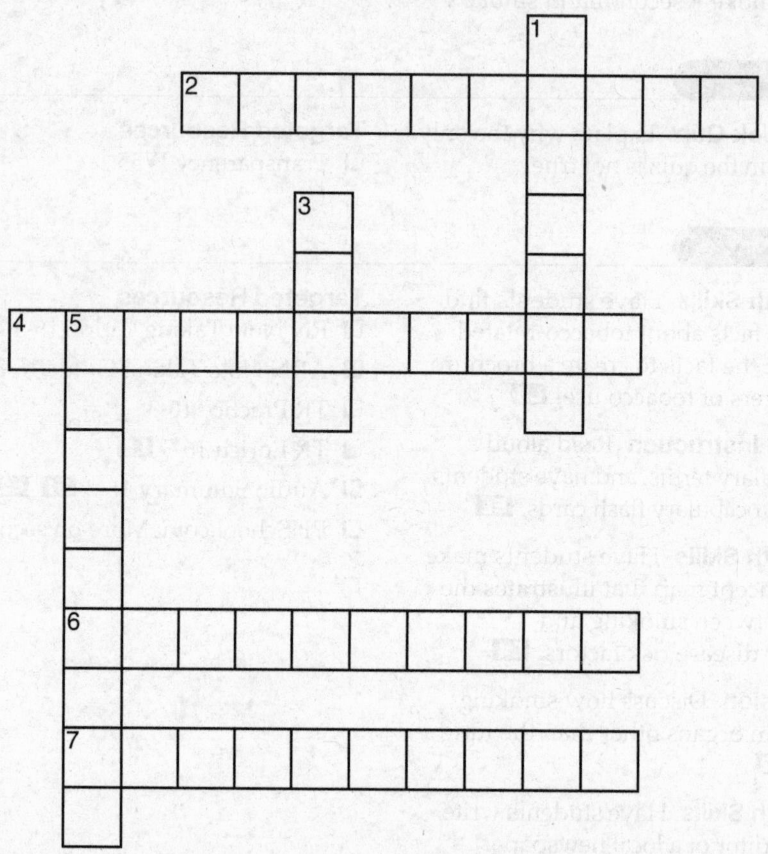

Clues Down

1. type of bronchitis that occurs in smokers
3. condition associated with loss of lung function
5. disease in which alveoli no longer function properly

Clues Across

2. smoke that includes mainstream and sidestream smoke
4. mouth sores in smokers that can become cancerous
6. smoke that goes into the air from burning tobacco
7. smoke exhaled into the air by smokers

Name ______________________ Class ____________________ Date ________

Section 16-3 **Enrich**

Class Debate: Should Smokers Be Denied Jobs?

Some companies not only ban smoking in the workplace. They also do not allow employees to smoke on their own time without risk of being fired, and they do not hire new employees who smoke. Many arguments have been made on both sides of this issue. For example, smokers argue that what they do on their own time should not influence whether they are hired or fired. Employers with such policies argue that smokers' healthcare costs are high. How do you feel about this issue? Do you think that employers should have the right to deny a qualified person a job because he or she smokes?

Use the questions below to help you consider the arguments for both sides of this issue. With your group, prepare an argument for each side of the debate and be prepared to represent either side during a class debate.

Position 1: Employers should be allowed to deny jobs to people who smoke.

Questions to Consider:

- What are some ways in which smoking might affect an individual's productivity, the amount of work accomplished during a specific period of time?
- In what ways could smoking impact the number of days a person works?

Debate Points:

____

____

____

____

____

Position 2: Employers should not be allowed to deny jobs to people who smoke.

Questions to Consider:

- Are people who smoke during non-work hours breaking the law?
- Should smokers be singled out when there are other health-related choices that people make that could also affect work performance?

Debate Points:

____

____

____

____

____

Name ______________________ Class ___________________ Date ______

Section 16-3

Quiz

Decide whether each statement is true or false. Write true *or* false *in the space provided.*

______ **1.** Tobacco use is the leading cause of preventable death in the United States.

______ **2.** Emphysema is a disorder in which artery walls thicken and harden.

______ **3.** Chronic bronchitis can be cured if a person stops smoking.

______ **4.** Sidestream smoke contains more tar and nicotine than mainstream smoke.

______ **5.** Secondhand smoke is a worse problem today than it was a few decades ago.

Write the letter of the correct answer in the space provided.

______ **6.** Permanent inflammation of the airways accompanied by excess mucus production is called
- **a.** stroke.
- **b.** leukoplakia.
- **c.** emphysema.
- **d.** chronic bronchitis.

______ **7.** Tobacco use can lead to weakened blood vessels because it
- **a.** decreases blood cholesterol.
- **b.** raises blood pressure.
- **c.** thins artery walls.
- **d.** lowers heart rate.

______ **8.** Smoke that is exhaled from smokers' lungs is called
- **a.** environmental smoke.
- **b.** secondhand smoke.
- **c.** mainstream smoke.
- **d.** sidestream smoke.

______ **9.** Children exposed to secondhand smoke are more likely to have
- **a.** asthma.
- **b.** allergies.
- **c.** recurring ear infections.
- **d.** all of the above.

______ **10.** When a woman smokes during pregnancy, how does it affect the baby?
- **a.** The baby grows faster.
- **b.** The baby gets more oxygen.
- **c.** The baby has a slower heart rate.
- **d.** After birth, the baby has a higher risk for sudden infant death syndrome.

Name____________________ Class__________ Date__________ M T W T F

Section 16-4

Saying No to Tobacco — Lesson Plan

Section Objectives

- **Examine** how refusal skills will help you stick with your decision not to use tobacco.
- **Describe** the benefits of quitting tobacco use.
- **Identify** the most important factor for successfully quitting tobacco.

Vocabulary nicotine substitute

Time
1 period
1/2 block

Local Standards

1. FOCUS

Warm-Up: Advice Line Ask students to share advice they would give a teen about avoiding tobacco use.

Targeted Resources
- ❑ Transparency W56

2. TEACH

Cooperative Learning Have pairs of students write and present dialogues in which a teen refuses tobacco. L3

Differentiated Instruction Have students who speak the same language practice using refusal skills for tobacco, first in their own language and then in English. EL

Visual Learning: Figure 11 Have students make a timeline of the information presented in the figure. L1

Building Health Skills Ask students to develop an action plan for a person with the goal of quitting smoking. L3

Class Discussion Discuss ways that a person can develop a strong personal commitment to quit smoking. L2

Targeted Resources
- ❑ RN Note Taking Guide 16-4 L3 EL
- ❑ ARN Note Taking Guide 16-4 L2
- ❑ Transparency and Worksheet 44
- ❑ TR Practice 16-4
- ❑ TR Enrich 16-4 L4
- ❑ Audio Summary 16-4 L1 L2 EL
- ❑ PHSchool.com: More on quitting tobacco use

3. ASSESS

Evaluate Understanding The assignments listed in the Teacher's Edition can help you assess students' mastery of the section content.

Reteach Call on students to list benefits of quitting tobacco and tips for quitting. L2

Targeted Resources
- ❑ TR Section 16-4 Quiz
- ❑ CTB Chapter 16

KEY

L1 Special Needs	L4 Gifted and Talented
L2 Less Proficient Readers	EL English Language Learners
L3 All Students	

Name ______________________ Class ______________ Date ________

Section 16-4 **Practice**

***Role-Playing:* Refusing Tobacco**

During your teens, it is likely that people will offer you cigarettes or other tobacco products. Knowing how to refuse such offers politely yet firmly will help you avoid tobacco use now and in the future. You may want to review pages 378-379 of the Student Edition where refusal skills are discussed before completing this activity.

Suppose that a friend offers you a cigarette. Explain in the table how you would handle the situation using refusal skills. Work with a partner to complete the table.

Refusal Guidelines	What You Would Say or Do
Give a reason for your refusal.	
Use body language to reinforce what you say.	
Show your concern for others.	
Provide alternatives.	
Take a definite action.	

With your partner, write a role-play in which a teen uses refusal skills to turn down an offer of a cigarette from a peer. Use what you wrote in the table as the basis for your role-play. Record the dialogue on a separate piece of paper. Be prepared to present the role-play to the class.

Name ____________________ Class ____________________ Date ____________

Section 16-4 **Enrich**

Consumer Skills: Choosing Help to Quit Tobacco

Most communities have a range of resources to help people who are trying to quit using tobacco. Clinics, hospitals, health departments, and organizations such as the American Lung Association may offer workshops, classes, support groups, or other types of help for people trying to quit.

Find two community resources for people who are trying to quit tobacco use. Learn about each resource and fill in the table below with the information requested.

Factor	Resource A: ____________	Resource B: ____________
Success rate		
Type of help offered		
Cost		
Follow-up support		
Other comment(s):		

Review the information in the table. Then, answer the questions below in the spaces provided.

1. What are the pros and cons of Resource A?

____

____

2. What are the pros and cons of Resource B?

____

____

3. Which, if either, resource would you recommend to a friend or family member who is trying to quit tobacco use? Explain.

____

____

Name ______________________ Class ____________________ Date ________

Section 16-4

Quiz

Write the letter of the correct answer in the space provided.

______ **1.** Which statement is true about teens and smoking in the United States?
- **a.** Fewer than one out of four teens smoke.
- **b.** More than two out of three teens smoke.
- **c.** A growing majority of teens chooses to smoke.
- **d.** It is easier to quit if you start smoking in your teens.

______ **2.** Which change occurs in a smoker's body within two days of quitting?
- **a.** Risk of heart disease is reduced by half.
- **b.** Risk of oral cancer is reduced by half.
- **c.** Risk of sudden heart attack decreases.
- **d.** Risk of stroke returns to normal.

______ **3.** What happens to the risk of mouth and throat cancer after a smoker quits?
- **a.** The risk decreases in the first few days.
- **b.** The risk increases for several years.
- **c.** The risk decreases after five years.
- **d.** The risk remains the same.

______ **4.** The most important factor in successfully quitting tobacco is
- **a.** changing your daily routine.
- **b.** avoiding people who use tobacco.
- **c.** setting up a rewards system.
- **d.** having a strong personal commitment.

______ **5.** Nicotine substitutes
- **a.** contain more nicotine than cigarettes.
- **b.** do not contain nicotine.
- **c.** help reduce nicotine withdrawal symptoms.
- **d.** contain all the same chemicals as tobacco smoke.

Decide whether each statement is true or false. Write true *or* false *in the space provided.*

______ **6.** Nine out of ten smokers want to quit smoking.

______ **7.** The health benefits of quitting tobacco begin immediately.

______ **8.** Psychological symptoms of nicotine withdrawal often last longer than physical symptoms.

______ **9.** Quitting "cold turkey" is a method of quitting smoking that works for everyone.

______ **10.** Nicotine substitutes should never be used along with tobacco products.

Name ______________________ Class ____________________ Date ________

Chapter 16 Test

Write the letter of the correct answer in the space provided.

______ **1.** Cigarette use in the United States has
- **a.** stayed the same since 1950.
- **b.** increased since 1980.
- **c.** declined since 1960.
- **d.** declined since 1940.

______ **2.** One way nicotine affects the nervous system is by
- **a.** mimicking neurotransmitters.
- **b.** decreasing its activity level.
- **c.** deactivating the brain's "reward pathway."
- **d.** reducing blood flow to the skin.

______ **3.** What part of the body is most affected by emphysema?
- **a.** blood vessels
- **b.** alveoli
- **c.** bronchi
- **d.** the heart

______ **4.** Pregnant women who smoke have higher rates of
- **a.** stillbirths.
- **b.** miscarriages.
- **c.** premature births.
- **d.** all of the above.

______ **5.** Which benefit of quitting tobacco occurs three months after quitting?
- **a.** Risk of oral cancer is cut in half.
- **b.** Risk of heart disease is cut in half.
- **c.** Lung function improves.
- **d.** Risk of stroke returns to the risk of a nonsmoker.

Write the letter of the correct answer in the space provided.

______ **6.** very addictive chemical in tobacco products

______ **7.** gas that replaces oxygen in the blood of smokers

______ **8.** white patches in the mouths of some tobacco users

______ **9.** smoke that goes from a cigarette directly into the air

______ **10.** another name for environmental tobacco smoke

- **a.** nicotine
- **b.** leukoplakia
- **c.** carbon monoxide
- **d.** sidestream smoke
- **e.** tar
- **f.** secondhand smoke

Name ______________________ Class __________________ Date ______

Chapter 16: **Test** *(continued)*

Decide whether each statement is true or false. Write true *or* false *in the space provided.*

______ **11.** Tobacco in cigars usually contains less nicotine than tobacco in cigarettes.

______ **12.** Carbon monoxide in tobacco smoke causes paralysis of cilia lining the airways.

______ **13.** Smokeless tobacco has many of the same dangerous chemicals as tobacco smoke.

______ **14.** Most people who don't smoke as teens never start to smoke.

______ **15.** Secondhand smoke exposure is not linked to sudden heart attacks.

Write the word or phrase that best completes each sentence in the space provided.

16. Three examples of cancer that are associated with tobacco use besides lung cancer are ______________, ______________, and ______________.

17. The dark, sticky substance that forms when tobacco burns is called ______________.

18. The disorder in which alveoli can no longer function properly is ______________.

Use complete sentences to answer the following questions.

19. Describe the effects of tobacco use on the cardiovascular system.

____

____

____

____

____

____

20. Identify four tips that can help a person cope with withdrawal symptoms.

____

____

____

____

____

____

Name ______________________ Class ______________________ Date __________

Chapter 17

Personal Inventory

Over-the-Counter Drugs

Over-the-counter drugs are medicines you can buy without a prescription from a doctor. They include medicines such as aspirin. Most people use over-the-counter drugs at some time in their life, and many people use them often. Have you ever used over-the-counter drugs? How much do you know about them?

Each of the terms listed below describes a type of medicine that has a specific effect on the body. Next to each term, list this effect. If necessary, use a dictionary. Then write the name of an over-the-counter drug that has this effect (if you know one).

Type of Medicine	Effect of this Type of Medicine on the Body	Over-the-Counter Drug With this Effect
Analgesic		
Antacid		
Antihistamine		
Antiseptic		
Decongestant		
Expectorant		

Complete the following statements with your own thoughts and feelings.

1. People use over-the-counter drugs to ______________________

____

2. Television and magazine ads for over-the-counter drugs are ______________________

____

3. Stores that sell over-the-counter drugs should ______________________

____

4. Taking over-the-counter drugs with alcohol is ______________________

____

Name____________ Class________ Date________ M T W T F

Section 17-1 Legal and Illegal Drugs — Lesson Plan

Section Objectives

- **Define** drug abuse and distinguish it from both appropriate use and misuse.
- **Describe** how psychoactive drugs affect the brain.
- **Summarize** the risks of drug abuse.

Time
3 periods
1½ blocks

Local Standards

Vocabulary medicine • over-the-counter drug • prescription drug • illegal drug • drug misuse • drug abuse • psychoactive drug • side effect • drug antagonism • drug synergism

1. FOCUS

Warm-Up: Myth/Fact Call on students to identify myths teens might believe about medicines or drugs.

Targeted Resources
- ❑ Transparency W57

2. TEACH

Cooperative Learning Pair students with differing ability levels, and have the pairs make a concept map of facts about drug use. L2

Differentiated Instruction Make a display of over-the-counter and prescription medicine bottles and packages to reinforce the major concepts about drug use. L1

Class Discussion Discuss drug overdose as a danger of tolerance, and ask students to explain why tolerance might lead to overdose. L3

Building Vocabulary Discuss the meanings of the prefixes *syn/sym* and *anti*. Then have students choose the correct meanings of *synergism* and *antagonism*, based on familiar words with the same prefixes. EL

Visual Learning: Figure 5 Ask students to calculate the percentage by which juvenile drug violations decreased between 1995 and 2000 and to suggest possible reasons for the decrease. L2

Targeted Resources
- ❑ RN Note Taking Guide 17-1 L3 EL
- ❑ ARN Note Taking Guide 17-1 L2
- ❑ Transparency and Worksheet 45
- ❑ TR Practice 17-1
- ❑ TR Enrich 17-1 L4
- ❑ Audio Summary 17-1 L1 L2 EL
- ❑ Health Links: Updates on drug interactions

3. ASSESS

Evaluate Understanding The assignments listed in the Teacher's Edition can help you assess students' mastery of the section content.

Reteach Have students use the section vocabulary terms in sentences. For each term, call on a student to read his or her sentence. L2

Targeted Resources
- ❑ TR Section 17-1 Quiz
- ❑ CTB Chapter 17

KEY
L1 Special Needs
L2 Less Proficient Readers
L3 All Students
L4 Gifted and Talented
EL English Language Learners

Name ______________________ Class ____________________ Date ______

Section 17-1 **Practice**

Concept Check: How Drugs Affect the Brain

The reward pathway in the brain is activated when you engage in pleasurable activities, such as eating a tasty treat. The reward pathway is also activated by addictive drugs.

The drawing below represents the brain's reward pathway. Label the structures in the drawing with the following terms: pleasure signal, dopamine receptor, dopamine.

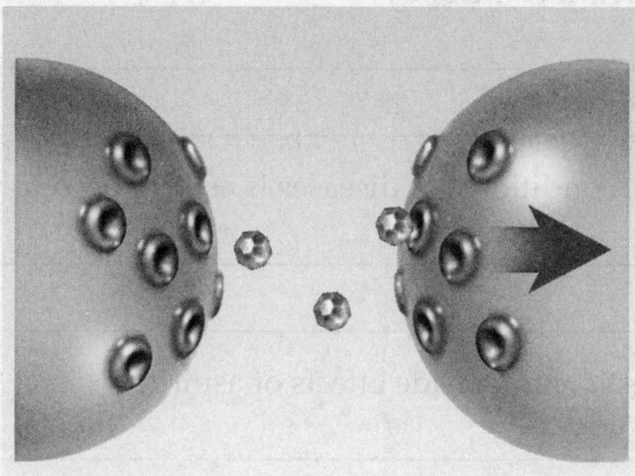

Answer the questions that follow in the spaces provided.

1. Describe the brain's reward pathway under normal conditions.

____

____

____

____

2. State what happens to the reward pathway when a person takes an addictive drug.

____

____

____

____

3. Explain how long-term drug use can affect the reward pathway.

____

____

____

Name ______________________ Class ______________________ Date ________

Section 17-1 **Enrich**

Research Project: Warnings About Aspirin

Aspirin is one of the most commonly used over-the-counter (OTC) drugs. You might think that such a widely used drug must be very safe, but is it really? How much do you know about aspirin?

Consult OTC drug reference books, reliable online sources, or a pharmacist for answers to the questions below. Record the answers in the spaces provided.

1. How does aspirin affect the body?

____

____

2. What symptoms, conditions, or diseases is aspirin used to treat?

____

____

3. What are the most common side effects of aspirin?

____

____

4. How does aspirin interact with other drugs?

____

____

____

5. Who should not take aspirin and why?

____

____

____

____

6. Review your answers to questions 3–5. Then write a warning statement about aspirin use.

____

____

____

____

____

Name ______________________ Class ______________________ Date ________

Section 17-1

Quiz

Write the letter of the correct answer in the space provided.

______ **1.** medicine sold without a doctor's written order

______ **2.** medicine sold only with a doctor's written order

______ **3.** incorrectly taking a medicine by mistake

______ **4.** incorrectly taking a medicine on purpose

______ **5.** unwanted symptom caused by a drug

a. side effect
b. illegal drug
c. prescription drug
d. drug misuse
e. over-the-counter drug
f. drug abuse

Decide whether each statement is true or false. Write true *or* false *in the space provided.*

______ **6.** Psychoactive drugs trigger activity along the reward pathway in the brain.

______ **7.** Drug antagonism occurs when drugs interact to produce a greater effect.

______ **8.** Drugs can pass through a mother's breast milk and harm a nursing baby.

______ **9.** Drug users who share needles can become infected with HIV.

______ **10.** Drug abuse affects only the abusers themselves.

Name________________________ Class__________ Date__________ M T W T F

Section 17-2 Factors Affecting Drug Abuse Lesson Plan

Section Objective

- **Evaluate** how family, friends, and personal factors can influence an individual's decisions about drugs.

Vocabulary protective factor

Time
1 period
1/2 block

Local Standards

1. FOCUS

Warm-Up: Quick Quiz Discuss why yes responses to the quiz can help protect students from drug abuse. Ask students to share other factors that protect against drug use.

Targeted Resources
- ❑ Transparency W58

2. TEACH

Active Learning Have students create a chart on the family, social, and personal risk factors for teen drug abuse. L2

Cultural Connection Have students research and report on the International Olympic Committee's regulations prohibiting the use of certain drugs by olympic athletes. L3

Differentiated Instruction Help students rephrase difficult words in more familiar terms. EL

Building Health Skills Have groups of students make collages of drug-free role models, and discuss how the role models can help teens avoid drugs. L1

Journal Writing Ask students to write a private journal entry about ways they could strengthen protective factors over which they have control. L3

Targeted Resources
- ❑ RN Note Taking Guide 17-2 L3 EL
- ❑ ARN Note Taking Guide 17-2 L2
- ❑ TR Practice 17-2
- ❑ TR Enrich 17-2 L4
- ❑ Audio Summary 17-2 L1 L2 EL
- ❑ PHSchool.com: More on signs of drug dependency

3. ASSESS

Evaluate Understanding The assignments listed in the Teacher's Edition can help you assess students' mastery of the section content.

Reteach Ask students to use the headings and subheadings to make a concept map of the section. L2

Targeted Resources
- ❑ TR Section 17-2 Quiz
- ❑ CTB Chapter 17

KEY

L1 Special Needs	L4 Gifted and Talented
L2 Less Proficient Readers	EL English Language Learners
L3 All Students	

Name ______________________ Class ________________ Date ______

Section 17-2

Practice

Role-Playing: Protective Factors and Teen Drug Abuse

Three categories of factors help protect teens from using drugs: social factors, family factors, and personal factors. The Student Edition describes specific protective factors in each of these three categories.

As a group, select two specific protective factors from the text. Then plan a role-play about a teen who is pressured to use drugs. The role-play should show how the protective factors help the teen resist drugs. Record your description and plan in the spaces provided.

Situation: ____

____

____

____

Role-Play: ____

____

____

____

____

____

____

____

____

____

Practice your role-play, and present it to the class. Challenge the class to identify the protective factors you demonstrated with your role-play. Summarize your classmates' responses here.

____

____

____

____

____

Name ______________________ Class ____________________ Date ________

Section 17-2 **Enrich**

Family Involvement: Factors Affecting Drug Abuse

When your parents and grandparents were teens, they probably had different risk factors and protective factors for drug abuse than you have today. For example, they may have been under more or less peer pressure to use drugs than you are, or drug use may have been more or less acceptable than it is now. How do you think factors affecting drug abuse have changed in recent years?

Interview a family member from a different generation about factors affecting drug abuse that may have influenced him or her as a teen. Include the following questions in your interview. If you add questions, record the questions and answers on another sheet.

1. When you were a teen, did you have friends or other peers who used drugs?

____

2. What role models were popular when you were a teen? Did the role models use drugs?

____

3. As teens, how do you think the majority of people in your generation viewed drug use?

____

____

4. What was your own attitude toward drug use when you were a teen?

____

____

5. What factors do you think shaped your attitude toward drug use as a teen?

____

____

6. What, if any, cultural values helped to protect you from drug use as a teen?

____

____

Based on the answers to the interview questions, how do you think factors affecting drug abuse have changed since your family member was a teen? Record your response on the lines below or on a separate sheet of paper.

____

____

____

Name ______________________ Class ______________________ Date ________

Section 17-2 Quiz

Write the letter of the correct answer in the space provided.

______ **1.** Teens who feel distant from family members are

a. usually more likely to abuse drugs.
b. protected from drug abuse.
c. less influenced by their peers.
d. not influenced by family risk factors.

______ **2.** What type of risk factor for drug abuse is competitive pressure?

a. personal factor
b. family factor
c. social factor
d. protective factor

______ **3.** Which choice is a personal risk factor for drug abuse?

a. having low self-esteem
b. having a low level of stress
c. having parents who do not use drugs
d. believing that drug abuse is unacceptable

______ **4.** Protective family factors include

a. weak family bonds.
b. clear family rules.
c. weak bonds to school.
d. alienation from parents.

______ **5.** A commitment to success in academics is

a. a protective factor against drug abuse.
b. a personal risk factor for drug abuse.
c. a social risk factor for drug abuse.
d. unrelated to risk of drug abuse.

Decide whether each statement is true or false. Write true *or* false *in the space provided.*

______ **6.** Drug use is often influenced by a combination of factors.

______ **7.** Poor family relationships are a risk factor for teen drug abuse.

______ **8.** Use of drugs by role models is a protective factor against drug use.

______ **9.** Teens who feel good about themselves are more likely to use drugs.

______ **10.** Teens are less likely to use drugs when they have supportive friends.

Name__________________ Class__________ Date__________ M T W T F

Section 17-3 Commommonly Abused Drugs Lesson Plan

Section Objectives

- **Compare** the effects of depressants, stimulants, and hallucinogens on the body.
- **Describe** the effects of marijuana.
- **Name** three classes of drugs of increasing concern in recent years.

Vocabulary depressant • barbiturates • opiate • heroin • stimulant • amphetamines • methamphetamine • cocaine • hallucinogen • marijuana • club drugs • inhalant

Time
2 periods
1 block

Local Standards

1. FOCUS

Warm-Up: Health Stats Call on volunteers to share factors they think are responsible for the increase in prescription drug abuse.

Targeted Resources

- ❑ Transparency W59

2. TEACH

Visual Learning: Figure 10 Ask students to explain how the side effects of depressant drugs might affect daily activities. L2

Differentiated Instruction Direct students to works of fiction and non-fiction that give an anti-drug message, and have students write a book report. L4

Active Learning Help students with the correct pronunciation of the words for the classes and kinds of drugs used in the section. EL

Building Health Skills Assign students to access information about drug-related mental illnesses from different sources, and discuss which sources are most informative. L3

Addressing Misconceptions Stress the dangers of anabolic steroid use to address the misconception that steroids are less dangerous than other drugs. L3

Targeted Resources

- ❑ RN Note Taking Guide 17-3 L3 EL
- ❑ ARN Note Taking Guide 17-3 L2
- ❑ Transparencies and Worksheets 46, 47, 48
- ❑ TR Practice 17-3
- ❑ TR Enrich 17-3 L4
- ❑ Audio Summary 17-3 L1 L2 EL
- ❑ PHSchool.com: More on commonly abused drugs

3. ASSESS

Evaluate Understanding The assignments listed in the Teacher's Edition can help you assess students' mastery of the section content.

Reteach Ask students to use information in the figures to create true-false quizzes, and have partners try to solve each other's quiz. L2

Targeted Resources

- ❑ TR Section 17-3 Quiz
- ❑ CTB Chapter 17

KEY

L1 Special Needs
L2 Less Proficient Readers
L3 All Students
L4 Gifted and Talented
EL English Language Learners

Name ______________________ Class ____________________ Date ________

Section 17-3

Practice

Vocabulary Activity: Commonly Abused Drugs

In this section, you learned about many categories of drugs and specific names of drugs that are abused. They include:

> marijuana, stimulants, amphetamines, club drugs, LSD, opiates, inhalants, hallucinogens, anabolic steroids, GHB, PCP, cocaine, depressants, ketamine, methamphetamine, barbiturates, rohypnol, CNS depressants, psilocybin

Use the terms above to complete the concept map.

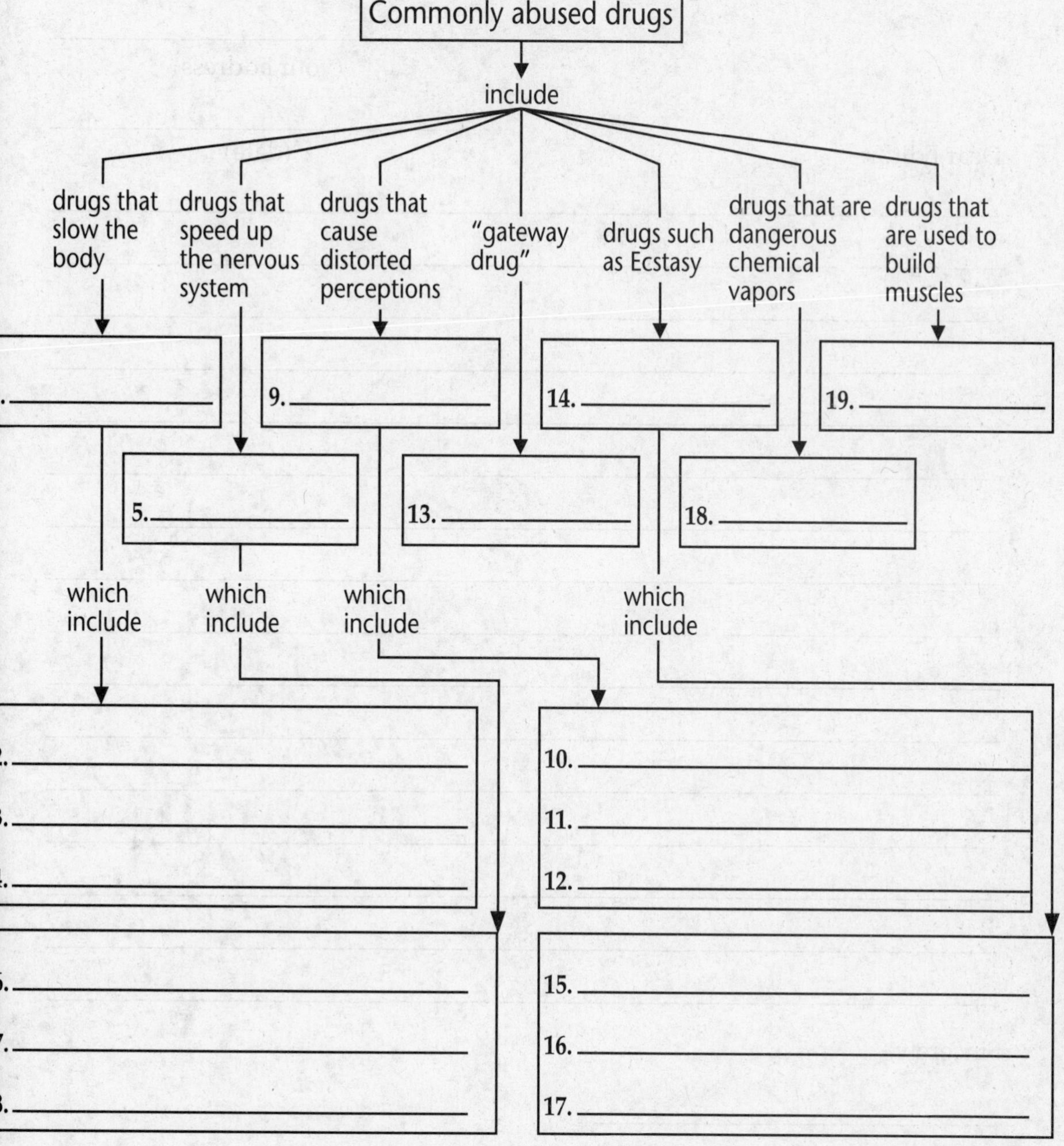

Name ______________ Class ______________ Date ______

Community Involvement: Dangers of Commonly Abused Drugs

Teens who are unaware of the dangers of commonly abused drugs, may be more likely to use the drugs. Local media, such as hometown newspapers, can be used to warn teens in the community about the dangers of drug abuse.

Write a letter to the editor of a local newspaper describing the dangers of one commonly abused drug. Use the facts to try to persuade the editor to print future articles about the dangers of drug abuse. Write your letter in the spaces provided below.

____

____

(your address)

____

(date)

Dear Editor:

____

____

____

____

____

____

____

____

____

____

____

____

____

____

____

____

Sincerely,

____

Name ____________________ Class ____________________ Date ________

Section 17-3

Quiz

Write the letter of the correct answer in the space provided.

______	1. any drug that slows body functions	a. marijuana
______	2. any drug that speeds up the central nervous system	b. stimulant
______	3. any drug that causes a distorted sense of reality	c. anabolic steroid
______	4. drug that is often a gateway to other drugs	d. depressant
______	5. drug that is used to make muscles bigger	e. inhalant
		f. hallucinogen

Write the letter of the correct answer in the space provided.

______ **6.** Drugs made from poppy seed pods are called
- **a.** CNS depressants.
- **b.** stimulants.
- **c.** opiates.
- **d.** amphetamines.

______ **7.** Which drug may cause severe tooth and gum disease in long-term users?
- **a.** LSD
- **b.** PCP
- **c.** ketamine
- **d.** methamphetamine

______ **8.** An example of a hallucinogen is
- **a.** ecstasy.
- **b.** alcohol.
- **c.** heroin.
- **d.** psilocybin.

______ **9.** Which drug may act as a stimulant, depressant, or hallucinogen?
- **a.** barbiturate
- **b.** marijuana
- **c.** cocaine
- **d.** anabolic steroid

______ **10.** A CNS depressant associated with date rape is
- **a.** LSD.
- **b.** cocaine.
- **c.** rohypnol.
- **d.** ecstasy.

Name________________________ Class__________ Date__________ M T W T F

Section 17-4

Choosing to Be Drug Free — Lesson Plan

Section Objectives

- **Identify** three treatment options for people who abuse drugs.
- **Name** three steps you can take to stay drug free.

Vocabulary therapeutic community

Time
2 periods
1 block

Local Standards

1. FOCUS

Warm-Up: Advice Line Call on students to share ways to help a friend who abuses drugs.

Targeted Resources

- ❑ Transparency W60

2. TEACH

Visual Learning: Figure 17 Describe scenarios that incorporate specific signs of drug abuse, and have students try to identify the signs. L2

Cooperative Learning Ask students to present role-plays in which a teen helps a friend with a drug abuse problem. L3

Active Learning Have interested students learn about a local therapeutic community and share their findings with the class. L3

Teacher Demo Role-play a call to a drug-abuse hotline and suggest options for help in the local community. L2

Building Health Skills Ask groups of students to make illustrated posters demonstrating ways that teens can stay drug free. L3

Differentiated Instruction Have students practice speaking assertively the refusal statements that come most easily to them. EL

Targeted Resources

- ❑ RN Note Taking Guide 17-4 L3 EL
- ❑ ARN Note Taking Guide 17-4 L2
- ❑ TR Practice 17-4
- ❑ TR Enrich 17-4 L4
- ❑ Audio Summary 17-4 L1 L2 EL
- ❑ Health Links: Updates on treating drug abuse

3. ASSESS

Evaluate Understanding The assignments listed in the Teacher's Edition can help you assess students' mastery of the section content.

Reteach Call on students to contribute to a list of ways to treat drug abuse and ways to stay drug free. L2

Targeted Resources

- ❑ TR Section 17-4 Quiz
- ❑ CTB Chapter 17

KEY

- L1 Special Needs
- L2 Less Proficient Readers
- L3 All Students
- L4 Gifted and Talented
- EL English Language Learners

Name ______________________ Class ____________________ Date ________

Section 17-4 **Practice**

Skill-Building Activity: Help for Drug Abuse

People who abuse drugs are likely to show warning signs of drug abuse, such as lying or withdrawing from normal activities. If you had a friend who was abusing drugs, would you recognize the warning signs? If you did recognize the signs, would you know how to act as an advocate for your friend?

Read the story below about two friends, Stacia and Corinne. As you read, look for warning signs of drug abuse.

Stacia is worried about her friend, Corinne. Corinne always used to be a lot of fun, but lately she has been acting very grouchy. Until recently, Corinne was an excellent student. Now she forgets to do her homework and sometimes falls asleep in class. As a result, Corinne's grades are slipping, although she doesn't seem to care. Corinne also used to spend hours in front of the mirror. Now, she looks as though she barely bothers to comb her hair.

Every time Stacia asks Corinne what is wrong, Corinne denies there is a problem. Stacia is growing more concerned about Corinne, but she doesn't know what is wrong or what to do.

Answer the questions below in the spaces provided.

1. What are signs that Corinne might be abusing drugs?

____

____

____

____

2. If Corinne continues to deny there is a problem, what could happen to her?

____

____

____

____

3. What should Stacia do to act as an advocate for her friend?

____

____

____

____

Name ______________________ Class ________________ Date ______

Section 17-4 **Enrich**

Consumer Skills: Health Insurance for Substance Abuse Treatment

Although some substance abuse treatment (for alcohol or other drug) is free or low-cost, it can be very expensive. Many health insurance plans provide at least partial coverage for substance abuse treatment, but plans vary in what they cover and how much they pay.

You can learn about different health insurance plans by contacting a behavioral health insurance company. Working adults may also have brochures from their company health insurance plans that provide coverage information.

Obtain and compare information about three different health insurance plans that provide coverage for drug abuse treatment. Record the information about each plan below.

Name of Insurance Company	Type(s) of Substance Abuse Treatment	% Paid, Duration or No. of Visits (for each type of treatment)

Answer the questions below in the spaces provided.

1. Evaluate the information in the table. Which plan offers the best support for substance abuse treatment?

____

2. State the criteria you used to make your decision, and explain why you used those criteria.

____

____

____

____

Name ______________________ Class ____________________ Date ______

Section 17-4

Quiz

Decide whether each statement is true or false. Write true *or* false *in the space provided.*

______ **1.** Lying is a behavioral sign of possible drug abuse.

______ **2.** All drug treatment programs are very expensive.

______ **3.** Detoxification may cause withdrawal symptoms.

______ **4.** Long-term methadone use is harmless to the body.

______ **5.** Denying your problems can help you stay drug free.

Write the letter of the correct answer in the space provided.

______ **6.** What is the first step in treating a drug abuse problem?
- **a.** detoxification
- **b.** supervised medication
- **c.** acknowledging the problem
- **d.** exploring treatment options

______ **7.** What is the purpose of a therapeutic community?
- **a.** learning to live without drugs
- **b.** identifying drug abusers
- **c.** drug replacement
- **d.** detoxification

______ **8.** Replacement drugs are used by former drug abusers as a
- **a.** way to get "high."
- **b.** way to prevent cravings.
- **c.** type of behavioral therapy.
- **d.** treatment for detoxification.

______ **9.** When you refuse drugs, you should
- **a.** never give reasons.
- **b.** give reasons only if asked.
- **c.** clearly state your personal reasons.
- **d.** give reasons your peers want to hear.

______ **10.** What is a healthy alternative to drug use?
- **a.** helping other people
- **b.** avoiding social activities
- **c.** withdrawing from youth groups
- **d.** spending all your free time studying

Name ______________________ Class ______________ Date ________

Chapter 17

Test

Write the letter of the correct answer in the space provided.

_____ **1.** Aspirin is an example of a(an)
a. illegal drug.
b. over-the-counter drug.
c. prescription drug.
d. replacement drug.

_____ **2.** What happens after repeated use of a psychoactive drug?
a. Brain cells lose dopamine receptors.
b. The brain produces more and more dopamine.
c. The brain's natural pleasure signal gets stronger.
d. Brain cells become better at processing dopamine.

_____ **3.** A risk factor for drug abuse is
a. having good role models.
b. spending quality time with family.
c. being unable to cope with stress.
d. having friends who respect you.

_____ **4.** Which type of drug is ketamine?
a. club drug
b. over-the-counter drug
c. inhalant
d. anabolic steroid

_____ **5.** Detoxification usually
a. takes place in a hospital.
b. includes supervised medication.
c. involves the use of replacement drugs.
d. follows treatment in a therapeutic community.

Write the letter of the correct answer in the space provided.

_____ **6.** legal drug that helps the body fight injury or illness

_____ **7.** factor that helps teens resist pressure to use drugs

_____ **8.** strong stimulant

_____ **9.** highly addictive opiate drug made from morphine

_____ **10.** treatment center where former drug abusers live together

a. heroin
b. risk factor
c. medicine
d. protective factor
e. methamphetamine
f. therapeutic community

Name ______________________ Class __________________ Date ______

Chapter 17: Test *(continued)*

Decide whether each statement is true or false. Write true *or* false *in the space provided.*

______**11.** Drug addiction changes the structure and function of the brain.

______**12.** Combining alcohol and sleep medicine causes drug synergism.

______**13.** Having strong risk factors in your life helps you stay drug free.

______**14.** Frequent use of marijuana may damage short-term memory.

______**15.** Seeking help from others increases the risk of drug abuse.

Write the word that best completes each sentence in the space provided.

16. Drug use by teens is influenced by family, social, and ______________ factors.

17. Drugs classified as hallucinogens include LSD, PCP, and ______________.

18. Methadone prevents withdrawal symptoms from ______________.

Use complete sentences to answer the following questions.

19. Compare the effects of depressants and stimulants, and give an example of each.

20. Identify three ways you can stay drug free.

Name ____________ Class ____________ Date ____________

Chapter 18

Personal Inventory

Habits for a Healthy Reproductive System

What habits do you practice to keep your reproductive system healthy? You may already practice some good reproductive health habits, but you may not be aware of others.

Complete the appropriate sections of the following inventory. Use your answers to identify ways you can improve your reproductive health habits.

For Both Males and Females:

1. I think sexual abstinence means ____________

2. Sexual abstinence is important for my health because ____________

For Males:

3. When I lift heavy objects, I avoid injury by ____________

4. If I found a sore in my genital area, I would ____________

5. True or false? I do regular self-exams for testicular cancer. ____________

For Females:

3. I can reduce my risk of toxic shock syndrome by ____________

4. If I noticed an unusual discharge from my vagina, I would ____________

5. True or false? I do regular self-exams for breast cancer. ____________

Name______________________ Class__________ Date__________ M T W T F

Section 18-1

Endocrine System — Lesson Plan

Section Objectives

- **Decribe** the general roles of the endocrine system.
- **Identify** the glands of the endocrine system.

Vocabulary endocrine gland • hormone • hypothalamus • pituitary gland • puberty

Time
1 period
1/2 block

Local Standards

1. FOCUS

Warm-Up: Health Stats Have students observe and suggest causes for gender differences in height.

Targeted Resources

- ❑ Transparency W61

2. TEACH

Active Learning Demonstrate with a role-play how an endocrine hormone acts as a chemical messenger. L2

Class Discussion Discuss how the relationship between a conductor and an orchestra is similar to the relationship between endocrine glands and the body. EL

Differentiated Instruction Ask students to make and label a drawing of the endocrine system. L1

Visual Learning: Figure 2 Have pairs of students make endocrine gland flashcards based on the figure and use the cards to learn the functions of the glands. L2

Building Health Skills Ask students to use reference books to find out if tiredness can be a symptom of a thyroid problem and what type of doctor treats endocrine problems. Discuss how to find a local doctor of that type. L3

Targeted Resources

- ❑ RN Note Taking Guide 18-1 L3 EL
- ❑ ARN Note Taking Guide 18-1 L2
- ❑ Transparency and Worksheet 49
- ❑ TR Practice 18-1
- ❑ TR Enrich 18-1 L4
- ❑ Audio Summary 18-1 L1 L2 EL
- ❑ PHSchool.com: More on endocrine glands

3. ASSESS

Evaluate Understanding The assignments listed in the Teacher's Edition can help you assess students' mastery of the section content.

Reteach Play a quiz game in which you describe the functions of the endocrine glands and students try to name the glands. L2

Targeted Resources

- ❑ TR Section 18-1 Quiz
- ❑ CTB Chapter 18

KEY

L1 Special Needs
L2 Less Proficient Readers
L3 All Students
L4 Gifted and Talented
EL English Language Learners

Name ______________________ Class ________________ Date ______

Section 18-1 **Practice**

Role-Playing: The Endocrine System

The endocrine system controls most body functions. For example, an endocrine gland called the thyroid gland controls how the body uses food for energy. Within the endocrine system, the hypothalamus and pituitary glands have special roles. They control the other glands of the system, including the thyroid gland.

With a group of at least five other students, role-play how the endocrine system works, using the thyroid gland as an example. Use the spaces below, plus extra paper if needed, to organize your role-play. Practice your role-play with your group so you are prepared to present it to the class if your teacher asks you.

Cast:

Three students in your group should play the roles of the hypothalamus, pituitary gland, and thyroid gland. Three other students should play the roles of hormones produced by these three glands.

Hypothalamus: ____________ Releasing hormone: ____________

Pituitary gland: ____________ Pituitary hormone: ____________

Thyroid gland: ____________ Thyroid hormone: ____________

Props:

You can use signs or other objects to show which roles students are playing.

____

____

____

____

Overview:

Describe any actions and dialogue you will use to show how the glands and hormones work.

____

____

____

____

____

____

____

Name ______________________ Class ____________________ Date ______

Section 18-1 **Enrich**

***Research Project:* Endocrine Hormone Replacement**

Endocrine hormone deficiencies can cause serious, life-long problems. But sometimes deficient hormones can be replaced with synthetic versions. For example, if the pituitary gland does not produce enough growth hormone in childhood, growth will be extremely slow and the child will be very short. Injecting the child with synthetic growth hormone during childhood results in a nearly normal growth rate and adult height. Several other endocrine hormone deficiencies can also be treated with hormone replacement.

Answer the following questions in the spaces provided.

1. What is hormone replacement?

____

____

____

2. Describe how hormone replacement is used to treat growth hormone deficiency.

____

____

____

3. Thyroid hormone deficiency, or hypothyroidism, is a relatively common endocrine problem. Based on the functions of the thyroid gland described in the text, predict how the body might be affected by not having enough thyroid hormone.

____

____

____

4. Find at least two reliable Web sites with information about hypothyroidism. What are the symptoms of this problem? Were your predictions correct?

____

____

____

5. Based on your online sources, how is hormone replacement used to treat hypothyroidism?

____

____

____

Name ______________________ Class ________________ Date ______

Section 18-1 **Quiz**

Write the letter of the correct answer in the space provided.

_____ **1.** How do endocrine glands differ from other body glands such as sweat glands?
a. Endocrine glands have ducts.
b. Endocrine glands affect only nearby structures.
c. Endocrine glands release chemicals into tiny tubes.
d. Endocrine glands release chemicals into the bloodstream.

_____ **2.** What are hormones?
a. parts of the body that are targeted by endocrine glands
b. minerals that are needed for proper bone formation
c. substances that are needed for muscle and nerve activity
d. substances that are released by endocrine glands

_____ **3.** Which endocrine gland is part of *both* the nervous and endocrine systems?
a. pituitary gland
b. hypothalamus
c. adrenal gland
d. pancreas

_____ **4.** What does the thyroid gland control?
a. other endocrine glands
b. sugar levels in the blood
c. calcium levels in the blood
d. the body's response to stress

_____ **5.** What is puberty?
a. a period in early childhood when growth is very fast
b. a period in adolescence when a person becomes sexually mature
c. a period in childhood when the immune system develops
d. a period in adolescence when the nervous system stops growing

Decide whether each statement is true or false. Write true *or* false *in the space provided.*

_____ **6.** The endocrine system regulates many body functions.

_____ **7.** Endocrine hormones act as chemical messengers.

_____ **8.** The pituitary gland controls the hypothalamus.

_____ **9.** Adrenal gland hormones affect the kidneys.

_____ **10.** Only females have reproductive glands.

Name____________________ Class__________ Date__________ M T W T F

Section 18-2

The Male Reproductive System Lesson Plan

Section Objectives

- **Describe** three functions of the male reproductive system.
- **Identify** five ways to keep the male reproductive system healthy.

Vocabulary sperm • fertilization • testes • testosterone • scrotum • penis • semen • ejaculation • infertility

Time
1 period
1/2 block

Local Standards

1. FOCUS

Warm-Up: Myth/Fact Discuss reasons why there are so many myths about the reproductive system. Discuss how the myths could affect the health of teenagers.

Targeted Resources

- ❑ Transparency W62

2. TEACH

Differentiated Instruction Show students how to organize the material on the male reproductive system in a simple table so they can see the main points without distracting details. L2

Visual Learning: Figure 4 Have students create a flowchart of the pathway of sperm, as described in the figure. L3

Teacher Demo Use a microscope to demo a slide showing sperm. L1

Building Media Literacy Have students find and report on different types of print media that discuss how to keep the male reproductive system healthy. Discuss whether certain types of print media seem more appropriate for this kind of information. L3

Cooperative Learning Ask groups of students to create brochures explaining how to care for the male reproductive system. L3

Targeted Resources

- ❑ RN Note Taking Guide 18-2 L3 EL
- ❑ ARN Note Taking Guide 18-2 L2
- ❑ Transparencies and Worksheets 50, 51
- ❑ TR Practice 18-2
- ❑ TR Enrich 18-2 L4
- ❑ Audio Summary 18-2 L1 L2 EL
- ❑ Health Links: Updates on male reproductive health

3. ASSESS

Evaluate Understanding The assignments listed in the Teacher's Edition can help you assess students' mastery of the section content.

Reteach Have students brainstorm facts about each vocabulary term and record the facts in their notebooks. L2

Targeted Resources

- ❑ TR Section 18-2 Quiz
- ❑ CTB Chapter 18

KEY

L1 Special Needs
L2 Less Proficient Readers
L3 All Students
L4 Gifted and Talented
EL English Language Learners

Name ______________________ Class ______________________ Date ________

Section 18-2 **Practice**

Vocabulary Activity: Structures of the Male Reproductive System

Structures of the male reproductive system include the testis, penis, vas deferens, urethra, epididymis, seminal vesicle, prostate gland, and bulbourethral gland. Each structure plays a different role in reproduction.

On the lines below write the names and functions of the numbered structures in the drawing. You can look at Figure 3 in your textbook if you need help.

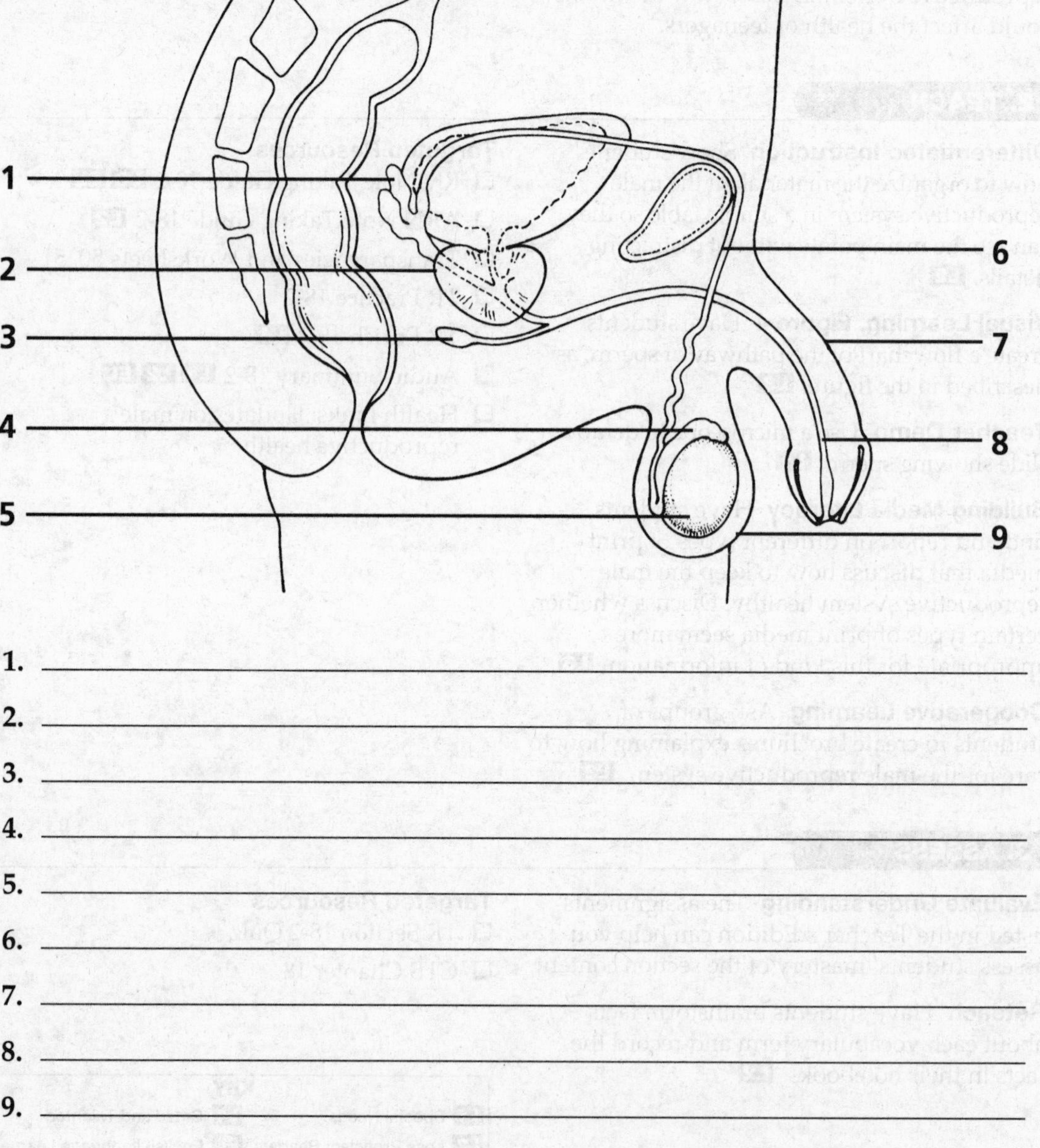

1. ____

2. ____

3. ____

4. ____

5. ____

6. ____

7. ____

8. ____

9. ____

Name ______________________ Class ____________________ Date ________

Section 18-2 **Enrich**

Family Involvement: Gender and Health Care

Cultural attitudes about health care may influence whether people have recommended medical checkups or do regular self-exams. In the U.S., men are much less likely than women to go to the doctor for either treatment or routine testing. According to a recent survey, one of the main reasons men avoid the doctor is the belief that "real" men should "tough it out" when it comes to their health. Men are also less likely than women to do self-exams. A recent study found that three in four men do not even know how to perform a testicular self-exam.

Interview an adult male relative and an adult female relative individually about their health-care attitudes and behaviors. Include questions about how often and why they see a doctor, when they had their last routine checkup, and whether they do regular self-exams. Also, ask how they feel about going to the doctor and doing self-exams.

After you conduct the interviews, answer the following questions in the spaces provided. You may keep your answers private, if you wish.

1. Describe health-care attitudes and behaviors of the two people you interviewed.

Male: ____

____

____

Female: ____

____

____

2. How are the health-care attitudes and behaviors of the two people different? How are they the same?

____

____

____

____

3. Describe how any differences in health-care attitudes and behaviors might affect health.

____

____

____

____

Name ____________________ Class ____________________ Date ________

Section 18-2
Quiz

Write the letter of the correct answer in the space provided.

______	**1.** male reproductive cell	**a.**	testosterone
______	**2.** male sex hormone	**b.**	infertility
______	**3.** mixture of sperm cells and fluids	**c.**	sperm
______	**4.** release of semen from the penis	**d.**	fertilization
______	**5.** condition of being unable to reproduce	**e.**	ejaculation
		f.	semen

Decide whether each statement is true or false. Write true *or* false *in the space provided.*

______ **6.** Sperm are produced by the scrotum.

______ **7.** Sperm mature in the vas deferens.

______ **8.** The seminal vesicles carry semen out of the body.

______ **9.** A hernia can be caused by lifting heavy objects.

______ **10.** Most cases of testicular cancer occur in older men.

Name____________________________ Class___________ Date___________ M T W T F

Section 18-3

The Female Reproductive System Lesson Plan

Section Objectives

- **Describe** three functions of the female reproductive system.
- **Summarize** the stages of the menstrual cycle.
- **Identify** five ways to keep the female reproductive system healthy.

Time
2 periods
1 block

Local Standards

Vocabulary ova • ovaries • estrogen • progesterone • ovulation • fallopian tubes • uterus • vagina • menstrual cycle • menopause • Pap smear • mammogram

1. FOCUS

Warm-Up: Advice Line Discuss why it is normal for boys and girls to prefer seeing a doctor of the same gender after puberty.

Targeted Resources
- ❑ Transparency W63

2. TEACH

Differentiated Instruction Guide students in using the diagrams in the section to learn the names of the structures and functions of the female reproductive system. EL

Building Vocabulary Explain that the terms *menstrual cycle* and *menstruation* come from a word meaning "month." Ask students how the two terms are related to *month.* L2

Cultural Connection Raise students' awareness of cultural "coming of age" traditions associated with the onset of menstruation. L3

Active Learning Have students use a monthly calendar to show the stages and events of the menstrual cycle. L2

Cooperative Learning Have same-gender groups express the five habits for female reproductive system health as lists of "Do's" and "Don'ts." L1

Targeted Resources
- ❑ RN Note Taking Guide 18-3 L3 EL
- ❑ ARN Note Taking Guide 18-3 L2
- ❑ Transparencies and Worksheets 52, 53
- ❑ TR Practice 18-3
- ❑ TR Enrich 18-3 L4
- ❑ Audio Summary 18-3 L1 L2 EL
- ❑ PHSchool.com: More on the menstrual cycle

3. ASSESS

Evaluate Understanding The assignments listed in the Teacher's Edition can help you assess students' mastery of the section content.

Reteach Have students draw and label on poster board the female reproductive system and the menstrual cycle. L2

Targeted Resources
- ❑ TR Section 18-3 Quiz
- ❑ CTB Chapter 18

KEY

L1 Special Needs	L4 Gifted and Talented
L2 Less Proficient Readers	EL English Language Learners
L3 All Students	

Name ______________ Class ______________ Date ______

Section 18-3

Practice

Skill-Building Activity: Advocating Mammograms

Breast cancer is relatively common in females. The key to curing breast cancer is early detection. Breast cancer can be detected with self-exams, physical exams by a doctor, and mammograms. Mammograms are breast X-rays that screen females for breast cancer. Doctors recommend that women have an annual mammogram starting at about age 40.

Write a letter to persuade a female relative who is 40 or older to have annual mammograms. Include facts you know about breast cancer in your letter. Use the following form to draft your letter.

____

(your address)

____

(date)

Dear ______________________,

____

____

____

____

____

____

____

____

____

____

____

____

____

____

____

Sincerely,

____

Name ______________________ Class ______________________ Date __________

Section 18-3 **Enrich**

Cultural Connection: Puberty Rituals

Puberty is a time of major physical changes that mark the beginning of a child's transition to adulthood. Most cultures recognize this important time of life with rituals, such as the Christian communion, Hispanic *quinceañera,* or Jewish *bar mitzvah* or *bat mitzvah.* Are you familiar with puberty rituals from your own or another culture? If not, adults in your family may be.

Ask adult family members and friends the questions below about puberty rituals in a particular culture. You may use an extra sheet of paper if you need more space for responses.

1. With which culture (including your own) are you most familiar?

____

2. In this culture, what rituals, including religious ceremonies, occur when children reach the age of puberty?

____

3. Are the rituals for boys, girls, or both?

____

4. What happens during the rituals?

____

____

____

____

5. What, if any, new rights or responsibilities are given to people that have gone through the rituals?

____

____

____

____

6. Have the rituals changed over the past few generations? If so, how have they changed?

____

____

____

After the interviews, share what you learned with the class. Then, help lead a class discussion on how different cultures recognize puberty.

Name ______________________ Class ____________________ Date ______

Section 18-3 **Quiz**

Write the letter of the correct answer in the space provided.

______	**1.** female reproductive gland	**a.** vagina
______	**2.** release of an egg from an ovary	**b.** menstruation
______	**3.** organ where a fertilized egg develops	**c.** ovary
______	**4.** structure that is also called the birth canal	**d.** menopause
______	**5.** time of life when ovaries stop releasing eggs	**e.** ovulation
		f. uterus

Write the letter of the correct answer in the space provided.

______ **6.** Where does fertilization usually occur?
- **a.** ovary
- **b.** uterus
- **c.** vagina
- **d.** fallopian tube

______ **7.** What happens during the first stage of the menstrual cycle?
- **a.** ovulation
- **b.** menopause
- **c.** fertilization
- **d.** menstruation

______ **8.** Caring for the female reproductive system includes all of the following *except*
- **a.** sexual abstinence.
- **b.** menstruation.
- **c.** self-exams.
- **d.** cleanliness.

______ **9.** What does a Pap smear detect?
- **a.** ovarian cysts
- **b.** breast cancer
- **c.** endometriosis
- **d.** cancer of the cervix

______**10.** When should females start having yearly reproductive system checkups?
- **a.** when they reach age 18
- **b.** when they reach puberty
- **c.** when they become pregnant
- **d.** when they become sexually active

Name_______________________ Class__________ Date__________ M T W T F

Section 18-4

Heredity

Lesson Plan

Section Objectives

- **Explain** how genetic information passes from one generation to the next.
- **Identify** the causes of genetic disorders.
- **Compare** the role of genes, environment, and behavior in affecting a person's risk for disease.

Vocabulary heredity • chromosome • gene • genetic disorder

Time
1 period
1/2 block

Local Standards

1. FOCUS

Warm-Up: Quick Quiz Guide students in inferring that different people have different forms of the same trait because they inherit different forms of genes from their parents.

Targeted Resources

- ❑ Transparency W64

2. TEACH

Building Vocabulary Have students look up *dominant* and *recessive* in a dictionary and use the words in context. EL

Cooperative Learning Ask students who know about Punnett squares to use one to explain the inheritance of traits. L3

Visual Learning: Figure 13 Use a series of questions to guide students in comparing and contrasting the genetic disorders listed in the figure. L2

Building Health Skills Have students research and report on risk factors for diseases with a genetic link. Then discuss the relative influences of heredity, environment, and behavior on risk of the diseases. L4

Differentiated Instruction Make spider diagrams to show students the difference between genetic disorders and diseases with a genetic link. L1

Targeted Resources

- ❑ RN Note Taking Guide 18-4 L3 EL
- ❑ ARN Note Taking Guide 18-4 L2
- ❑ Transparency and Worksheet 54
- ❑ TR Practice 18-4
- ❑ TR Enrich 18-4 L4
- ❑ Audio Summary 18-4 L1 L2 EL
- ❑ Health Links: Updates on genetic disorders

3. ASSESS

Evaluate Understanding The assignments listed in the Teacher's Edition can help you assess students' mastery of the section content.

Reteach Divide the class into small groups, and have members of each group demonstrate their knowledge of section objectives to one another. L2

Targeted Resources

- ❑ TR Section 18-4 Quiz
- ❑ CTB Chapter 18

KEY	
L1 Special Needs	L4 Gifted and Talented
L2 Less Proficient Readers	EL English Language Learners
L3 All Students	

Name ______________________ Class ______________ Date ________

Section 18-4

Practice

Group Activity: Genes and Traits

Genes determine many of your physical traits. Most traits are affected by several different genes and have complicated inheritance patterns. However, a few traits are determined very simply. For example, people who inherit the dominant form of the "hairline gene" from one or both parents have a widow's peak. In contrast, people who inherit the recessive form of the gene from both parents have a smooth hairline.

Use markers to color in the squares. Use a dark color to represent the dominant form of the "hairline gene" and a light color to represent the recessive form. Then answer the question at the bottom.

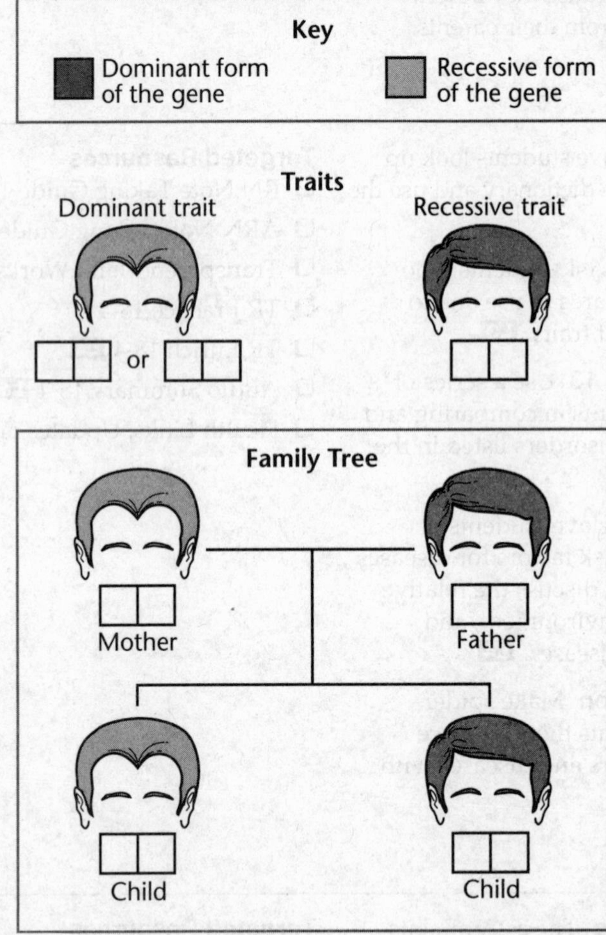

How do you know which combination of genes is correct for the two people with a widow's peak in the family tree?

____

____

____

Name ______________________ Class ______________ Date ______

Section 18-4

Enrich

Community Involvement: Genetic Disorders

Many organizations help people deal with genetic disorders. One of the most active organizations is the March of Dimes Birth Defects Foundation. Write a letter to the local chapter of this foundation, or another relevant organization of your choice, requesting information about what the foundation does, how it raises money for its efforts, and how young people can become involved. You can find local contact information in the white pages of your telephone directory or online. Use the following form to draft your letter.

____

____

(your address)

____

(date)

March of Dimes Birth Defects Foundation

____

(local chapter's address)

Dear Director:

____

____

____

____

____

____

____

____

____

____

____

____

Thank you for your assistance.

Sincerely,

____

Name ______________________ Class ____________________ Date ________

Section 18-4 **Quiz**

Decide whether each statement is true or false. Write true *or* false *in the space provided.*

______ **1.** A normal human fertilized egg contains 23 chromosomes.

______ **2.** Most traits are controlled by a single gene.

______ **3.** A dominant trait appears whenever its gene is present.

______ **4.** Breast cancer is a disease with a genetic link.

______ **5.** The risk of a genetic disorder depends mainly on environment and behavior.

Write the letter of the correct answer in the space provided.

______ **6.** What does every chromosome contain?
a. genes
b. sex cells
c. biological traits
d. chromosomal disorders

______ **7.** If you have attached earlobes, how many recessive genes for this trait do you have?
a. two
b. one
c. none
d. one or two

______ **8.** Which genetic disorder causes problems with blood clotting?
a. hemophilia
b. phenylketonuria
c. Down Syndrome
d. Duchenne muscular dystrophy

______ **9.** Which genetic disorder is caused by an abnormal number of chromosomes?
a. cystic fibrosis
b. Down syndrome
c. Tay-Sachs disease
d. Huntington's disease

______ **10.** What is gene therapy?
a. using drugs to treat the symptoms of genetic disorders
b. testing blood to detect abnormal genes
c. using surgery to remove unhealthy genes
d. giving healthy genes to people with defective genes

Name ____________________ Class ____________________ Date ________

Chapter 18 Test

Write the letter of the correct answer in the space provided.

_____ **1.** Which endocrine gland controls other endocrine glands?
- **a.** pancreas
- **b.** thymus
- **c.** pituitary gland
- **d.** parathyroid gland

_____ **2.** What does the pancreas regulate?
- **a.** sugar levels in the blood
- **b.** calcium levels in the blood
- **c.** reproduction and metabolism
- **d.** development of the immune system

_____ **3.** Which hormones control sperm production?
- **a.** LH, progesterone, FSH
- **b.** testosterone, FSH, estrogen
- **c.** testosterone, LH, progesterone
- **d.** LH, FSH, testosterone

_____ **4.** What happens on days 14–15 of an average menstrual cycle?
- **a.** An egg matures in an ovary.
- **b.** An ovary releases an egg.
- **c.** An egg enters the uterus.
- **d.** The uterus sheds its lining.

_____ **5.** Which of the following is a genetic disorder?
- **a.** colon cancer
- **b.** cystic fibrosis
- **c.** high blood pressure
- **d.** Alzheimer's disease

Write the letter of the correct answer in the space provided.

_____ **6.** substance released by endocrine glands

_____ **7.** structures where sperm are produced

_____ **8.** name for female reproductive cells

_____ **9.** shedding of the uterine lining

_____ **10.** tiny structures you inherit from your parents

- **a.** testes
- **b.** menstruation
- **c.** hormone
- **d.** chromosomes
- **e.** ovaries
- **f.** ova

Decide whether each statement is true or false. Write true *or* false *in the space provided.*

_____ **11.** The endocrine system controls many of the body's daily activities.

_____ **12.** The union of sperm and egg is called ejaculation.

_____ **13.** Toxic shock syndrome is caused by bacteria.

_____ **14.** Heredity is the transmission of biological traits from parent to child.

_____ **15.** A recessive trait appears only when the dominant form of the gene is present.

Name ______________________ Class ________________ Date ________

Chapter 18: **Test** *(continued)*

Write the word that best completes each sentence in the space provided.

16. Puberty starts when the ______________________ signals the pituitary to produce LH and FSH.

17. The only way to eliminate the risk of sexually transmitted infections is sexual ______________________.

18. An X-ray of the breast that can help detect breast cancer is a(an) ______________________.

Use complete sentences to answer the following questions.

19. Describe three functions of the male reproductive system.

____

____

____

____

____

____

20. Summarize the stages of the menstrual cycle.

____

____

____

____

____

____

____

____

Name ______________________ Class ______________ Date ______

Chapter 19

Personal Inventory

Becoming a Parent

Becoming a parent is a huge responsibility. Yet, many people do not consider their feelings about being a parent and taking on the responsibilities of parenthood before they become a parent.

To explore your own feelings about parenthood, complete these statements.

1. To me, a family is ____

____

2. When it comes to planning a family—or just letting it happen—I think married couples should ______________________________________

____

3. I think the nicest thing about having a baby would be ______________

____

4. When a woman is pregnant, she should ____________________________

____

____

5. What I know about childbirth is _________________________________

____

____

6. After a baby is born, the parents' responsibilities are _______________

____

____

7. Babies are able to ____

but they cannot yet ____

____

8. Toddlers can ____

but they cannot yet ____

____

9. Young children are able to ______________________________________

but they cannot yet ____

____

Name__________________ Class__________ Date__________ M T W T F

Section 19-1

Development Before Birth Lesson Plan

Section Objectives

- **Summarize** the events that occur during the first week after fertilization.
- **Describe** the structures that protect and nourish the embryo and fetus.

Vocabulary zygote • embryo • blastocyst • implantation • amniotic sac • placenta • umbilical cord • fetus

Time
1 period
1/2 block

Local Standards

1. FOCUS

Warm-Up: Quick Quiz Use the Quick Quiz to begin a discussion on the factors that a married couple should consider before having children.

Targeted Resources

- ❑ Transparency W65

2. TEACH

Active Learning Have students construct a time line that highlights the events in the development of an embryo. L3

Visual Learning: Figure 1 Use the diagram for a discussion on the development of a fertilized egg. L2

Differentiated Instruction Depending on students' English competency, assign either beginning-level or intermediate-level vocabulary terms and have them make flashcards. EL

Teacher Demo Use the motion of balls suspended in water and air to demonstrate how amniotic fluid cushions an embryo. L3

Active Learning Help students find and compare classroom objects that are similar in size to an eight-week embryo, a six-month fetus, and a newborn baby. L1

Targeted Resources

- ❑ RN Note Taking Guide 19-1 L3 EL
- ❑ ARN Note Taking Guide 19-1 L2
- ❑ Transparency and Worksheet 55
- ❑ TR Practice 19-1
- ❑ TR Enrich 19-1 L4
- ❑ Audio Summary 19-1 L1 L2 EL
- ❑ PHSchool.com: More on development before birth

3. ASSESS

Evaluate Understanding The assignments listed in the Teacher's Edition can help you assess students' mastery of the section content.

Reteach Have students use the figures in the section to describe the stages in the development of a human embryo and fetus. L2

Targeted Resources

- ❑ TR Section 19-1 Quiz
- ❑ CTB Chapter 19

KEY

L1 Special Needs
L2 Less Proficient Readers
L3 All Students
L4 Gifted and Talented
EL English Language Learners

Name ______________________ Class ______________________ Date ________

Section 19-1 **Practice**

Vocabulary Activity: The Embryo and Surrounding Structures

After the embryo implants in the uterus, it continues to develop. Several other structures grow along with the embryo. These structures protect the embryo and help nourish it.

Fill in the blanks in the drawing below with the names of the numbered structures. You can look at Figure 2 in the Student Edition, if you need help.

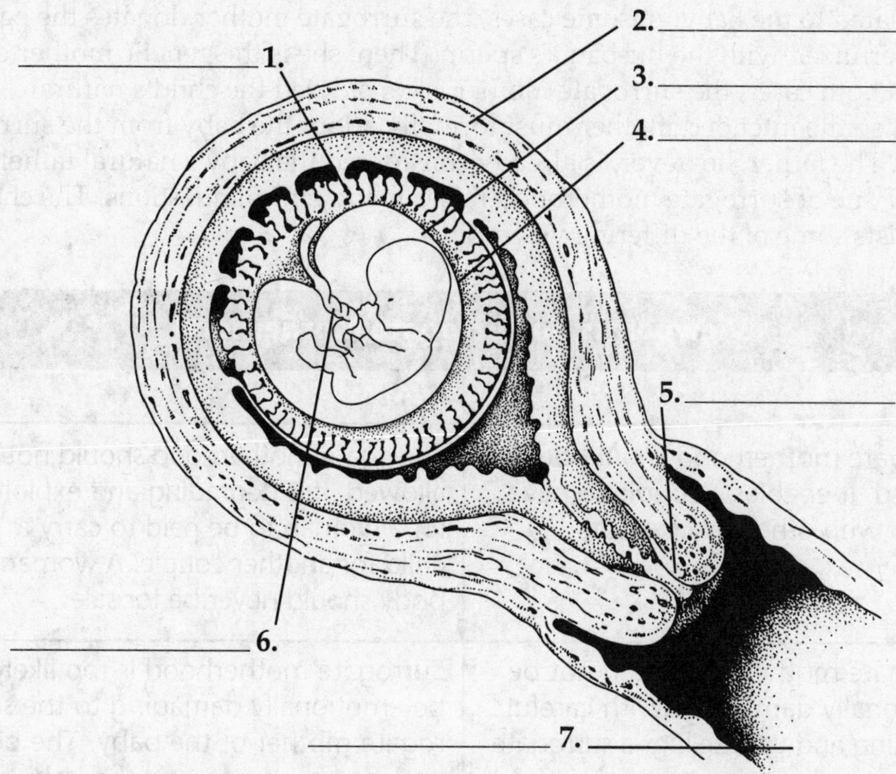

Describe the function of the following structures from the diagram above.

8. Structure 1: ____

____

9. Structure 4: ____

____

10. Structure 6: ____

____

Name ______________________ Class ____________________ Date ________

Class Debate: Surrogate Motherhood

About 10 percent of married couples in the United States are unable to have children of their own because the husband, the wife, or both are infertile. Infertility is caused by many different factors, and many medical advances have been made to address these factors.

An option for some couples is to hire a surrogate mother to carry the child for them. In many cases, the surrogate mother is implanted with the couple's embryo that was fertilized in a laboratory. The surrogate mother is not genetically related to the baby. In some cases, the surrogate mother donates the egg that is fertilized with the husband's sperm. Then, she is the genetic mother of the baby. In both cases, the surrogate mother is considered the child's natural mother, so the intended mother must formally adopt the baby from the surrogate mother. The father, however, is already considered the baby's natural father.

The issue of surrogate motherhood raises many ethical questions. The chart below lists some of the differing viewpoints.

Viewpoints on Surrogate Motherhood

Pros	Cons
Surrogate motherhood should be allowed. It enables a couple to have a child who otherwise cannot.	Surrogate motherhood should not be allowed. It is degrading and exploitive for a woman to be paid to carry a child for another couple. A woman's body should never be for sale.
Surrogate motherhood need not be emotionally damaging. With careful screening and counseling, a surrogate mother can be prepared to give up the baby.	Surrogate motherhood is too likely to be emotionally damaging to the surrogate mother or the baby. The bond between a woman and the baby she carries is too strong to be broken.
Contracts for surrogate motherhood should be made legally binding. There should be specific laws to enforce the terms of the surrogate contract.	Contracts for surrogate motherhood should be made illegal. A woman should not be allowed to enter into a contract to give birth to and then sell her baby.
A surrogate mother should not be allowed to change her mind. A contract is a legal agreement and should not be broken.	A surrogate mother should be allowed to change her mind. There should be a period of time during which she can decide to keep the baby.

Name ______________________ Class ________________ Date ______

Section 19-1: **Enrich** *(continued)*

Answer the following questions to clarify your own position on this difficult issue. Be prepared to defend your position in a class debate.

1. Do you feel that married couples who cannot have children should be able to hire a surrogate mother? Explain.

____

____

____

____

2. Do you think that a surrogate mother should have the right to change her mind about giving up her child? Explain your answer.

____

____

____

____

3. Suppose you were the judge in a surrogate motherhood case. What factors would you consider in deciding who should have the child?

____

____

____

____

____

Review your answers to questions 1 to 3 to help you answer the next question.

4. Do you feel that surrogate motherhood should be legal? Why or why not?

____

____

____

____

____

Name ______________________ Class ____________________ Date ______

Section 19-1 Quiz

Write the letter of the correct answer in the space provided.

______ **1.** The fertilized egg is called a(an)
a. zygote.
b. embryo.
c. blastocyst.
d. fetus.

______ **2.** During implantation,
a. sperm are deposited into the vagina.
b. sperm fertilize an egg.
c. the blastocyst attaches to the wall of the uterus.
d. the embryo is surrounded by the amniotic sac.

______ **3.** Which is a function of the amniotic fluid?
a. holds sperm
b. nourishes the embryo
c. protects the zygote
d. cushions the embryo

______ **4.** Which is a structure containing blood vessels that carry nutrients and oxygen from the mother to the embryo?
a. cervix
b. umbilical cord
c. amniotic sac
d. blastocyst

______ **5.** From the third month until birth, the growing baby is called a(an)
a. zygote.
b. embryo.
c. fetus.
d. newborn.

Decide whether each statement is true or false. Write true *or* false *in the space provided.*

______ **6.** Only one sperm can fertilize an egg.

______ **7.** The fertilized egg stays in the fallopian tube for several months.

______ **8.** The placenta prevents dangerous substances from passing from the mother to the embryo.

______ **9.** By the end of eight weeks, the head of an embryo is small in proportion to its body.

______ **10.** The fetus begins to move and kick during the third to sixth month of development.

Name_________________________ Class__________ Date__________ M T W T F

Section 19-2

A Healthy Pregnancy Lesson Plan

Section Objectives

- **Identify** four behaviors that are essential for a healthy pregnancy.
- **Explain** the importance of prenatal care throughout pregnancy.

Vocabulary prenatal care • obstetrician • trimester • ultrasound • chorionic villus sampling • amniocentesis • ectopic pregnancy • miscarriage • preeclampsia • gestational diabetes

Time
2 periods
1 block

Local Standards

1. FOCUS

Warm-Up: Myth/Fact Assess students' preconceptions about what pregnant women should and shouldn't do. Address any misconceptions while teaching the section.

Targeted Resources
- ❑ Transparency W66

2. TEACH

Differentiated Instruction Have students create a word web that summarizes the behaviors essential for a healthy pregnancy. L2

Building Health Skills Have students write an e-mail to an imaginary older relative who is newly pregnant in which they advocate for the avoidance of an environmental hazard. L3

Cooperative Learning Have student groups produce a list of questions that a woman might ask her doctor during a prenatal visit. L3

Using Visuals: Figure 5 Use the lists of things to expect at routine prenatal visits to begin a discussion on the importance of prenatal care. L2

Differentiated Instruction Work with students to create a notebook or bulletin board display of the terms used to describe monitoring tools and possible complications during pregnancy. EL

Targeted Resources
- ❑ RN Note Taking Guide 19-2 L3 EL
- ❑ ARN Note Taking Guide 19-2 L2
- ❑ TR Practice 19-2
- ❑ TR Enrich 19-2 L4
- ❑ Audio Summary 19-2 L1 L2 EL
- ❑ Health Links: Updates on pregnancy care

3. ASSESS

Evaluate Understanding The assignments listed in the Teacher's Edition can help you assess students' mastery of the section content.

Reteach Have students create a poster describing behaviors that ensure a healthy pregnancy. L2

Targeted Resources
- ❑ TR Section 19-2 Quiz
- ❑ CTB Chapter 19

KEY

L1 Special Needs	L4 Gifted and Talented
L2 Less Proficient Readers	EL English Language Learners
L3 All Students	

Name ______________________ Class ______________________ Date ____________

Role-Playing: Staying Healthy During Pregnancy

Prenatal care and healthy behaviors are essential to staying healthy during pregnancy, as well as increasing the chances of having a healthy baby. Behaviors that are important for a healthy pregnancy include proper nutrition, exercise, and the avoidance of drugs and environmental hazards. Regular prenatal visits can help prevent or effectively manage complications such as preeclampsia or gestational diabetes.

With another student, role-play a situation in which one person is advocating for healthful behaviors to a pregnant friend or relative who is practicing unhealthful behaviors. Use the spaces below to organize your role-play.

Title of Role Play: ______________________

Characters: ______________________

Setting: ______________________

____

Props: ______________________

____

Describe any actions and dialogue you will use to convince the pregnant woman to change her unhealthful behaviors. Practice your role-play, and be prepared to present it if asked.

Script: ______________________

____

____

____

____

____

____

____

____

____

____

____

____

Name ______________________ Class __________________ Date ________

Section 19-2 **Enrich**

Consumer Skills: Prenatal Tests

Doctors have a number of tests for assessing the health of a fetus and the mother. During a visit, the doctor advises the pregnant woman of the tests that are most appropriate, given her medical history and genetic risk factors. Certain tests, like ultrasound, have become routine because they give the doctor a great deal of information about the fetus and do not pose a health risk. Other tests carry more risk or are high-cost and are therefore recommended only when their benefits are likely to outweigh their risks or cost.

Use the Internet or library resources to complete the table below. You may wish to expand your table on a separate sheet of paper to include other tests.

renatal Test	When It Is Done	Who Needs It	Accuracy of Test	Risks of Test
ltrasound				
lpha-Fetoprotein creen				
mniocentesis				
horionic Villus ampling				

1. List the sources you used. ______________________________

2. Call an insurance company or look in your family's health insurance plan to find out which tests are covered by insurance.

3. If a 25-year-old woman with no history of genetic disorders, birth defects, or sexually transmitted diseases is pregnant with her first child, which of the prenatal tests above would likely be recommended? Explain.

Name ______________________ Class ____________________ Date ______

Section 19-2 Quiz

Write the letter of the correct answer in the space provided.

______ 1. test in which a doctor removes a piece of the placenta

______ 2. occurs when the blastocyst implants in the fallopian tube

______ 3. test in which a doctor removes amniotic fluid

______ 4. high-frequency sound waves used to create an image of the fetus

______ 5. characterized by high blood sugar levels

a. ultrasound
b. chorionic villus sampling
c. amniocentesis
d. ectopic pregnancy
e. miscarriage
f. gestational diabetes

Write the letter of the correct answer in the space provided.

______ 6. Which is *not* a behavior essential for a healthy pregnancy?
a. getting enough folic acid
b. avoiding exercise
c. avoiding alcohol
d. avoiding cigarette smoke

______ 7. Which substance is safe for a pregnant woman?
a. lead
b. cat litter
c. X-rays
d. calcium

______ 8. Prenatal care is important because it
a. causes complications.
b. reduces the number of doctor visits.
c. increases the chances of having a healthy baby.
d. requires amniocentesis.

______ 9. A trimester is
a. about three months long.
b. the length of an entire pregnancy.
c. how frequently a woman should visit her doctor.
d. the time when an ultrasound is performed.

______10. Which is *not* a characteristic of preeclampsia?
a. high blood pressure
b. chromosomal abnormalities
c. high levels of protein in urine
d. swollen wrists and ankles

Name____________________ Class__________ Date__________ M T W T F

Section 19-3

Childbirth — Lesson Plan

Section Objectives

- **Identify** the three stages of the birth process.
- **Describe** four complicating factors that may arise at birth.

Vocabulary certified nurse-midwife • labor • postpartum period • stillbirth • cesarean section • premature birth • low birthweight • multiple birth

Time
2 periods
1 block

Local Standards

1. FOCUS

Warm-Up: Health Stats Use the graphs to discuss the effects of smoking on a baby's birthweight.

Targeted Resources
- ❑ Transparency W67

2. TEACH

Visual Learning: Figure 6 Use the illustrations to review what happens during the three stages of the birth process. L2

Building Health Skills Have students make a poster or brochure that describes the types of birthing facilities available in their local community. L4

Class Discussion Lead a discussion on changes that the newborn and the mother make during the postpartum period. L2

Cooperative Learning Have student groups make a poster describing a complication at birth, its causes, and how to prevent it, if possible. L3

Building Health Skills Have groups prepare a brochure that advocates ways to prevent low birthweight. L3

Visual Learning: Figure 9 Use the diagram to explain how identical and fraternal twins develop. L2

Targeted Resources
- ❑ RN Note Taking Guide 19-3 L3 EL
- ❑ ARN Note Taking Guide 19-3 L2
- ❑ Transparencies and Worksheets 56, 57
- ❑ TR Practice 19-3
- ❑ TR Enrich 19-3 L4
- ❑ Audio Summary 19-3 L1 L2 EL
- ❑ PHSchool.com: More on the birth process

3. ASSESS

Evaluate Understanding The assignments listed in the Teacher's Edition can help you assess students' mastery of the section content.

Reteach Have student pairs create a concept map of section concepts and vocabulary. L2

Targeted Resources
- ❑ TR Section 19-3 Quiz
- ❑ CTB Chapter 19

KEY

L1	Special Needs	L4	Gifted and Talented
L2	Less Proficient Readers	EL	English Language Learners
L3	All Students		

Name ______________________ Class ______________________ Date ________

Section 19-3 **Practice**

Concept Check: The Birth Process

Childbirth is a process that involves various stages and events. Described below are several events that occur during the three stages of birth.

Cut out the boxes and arrange them in the order in which they would generally occur during birth.

1. The umbilical cord is clamped and cut.	**6. The uterus begins a series of contractions.**
2. The baby's heel is pricked for a blood sample.	**7. Eye drops are put in the baby's eyes to prevent infection.**
3. The cervix becomes wide enough that the baby can pass through.	**8. The contractions are only a few seconds apart.**
4. The amniotic sac breaks.	**9. The baby's mouth and nose are suctioned to make breathing easier.**
5. The placenta is delivered.	**10. The baby is pushed out through the cervix and vagina.**

Name ____________________ Class ____________________ Date __________

Section 19-3 **Enrich**

***Family Involvement:* Learning About Childbirth**

To find out about the process of childbirth, interview three couples with children. If possible, try to select one couple who has had children in the past 10 years, one couple whose children were born between 10 and 20 years ago, and one couple whose children were born more than 20 years ago. Ask them the following questions about their childbirth experiences. Add one question of your own.

1. In what type of facility was your child born (for example, hospital, birthing center, home)?

   Couple 1: ____________________

   Couple 2: ____________________

   Couple 3: ____________________

2. What type of medical intervention was used during the childbirth process (for example, medications, instruments, surgical procedures)?

   Couple 1: ____________________

   Couple 2: ____________________

   Couple 3: ____________________

3. What role did the father play in the childbirth process?

   Couple 1: ____________________

   Couple 2: ____________________

   Couple 3: ____________________

4. What type of childbirth training did you have during the pregnancy?

   Couple 1: ____________________

   Couple 2: ____________________

   Couple 3: ____________________

5. Question: ____________________

   Couple 1: ____________________

   Couple 2: ____________________

   Couple 3: ____________________

Review the answers provided by the couples. Then, using a separate sheet of paper, write a short essay describing how the childbirth process has changed over the years.

Name ______________________ Class __________________ Date ______

Section 19-3

Quiz

Write the letter of the correct answer in the space provided.

______ **1.** a surgical method of birth

______ **2.** when a newborn weighs less than 5.5 pounds

______ **3.** the delivery of more than one baby

______ **4.** occurs when a fetus dies and is expelled from the body

______ **5.** delivery of a live baby before the 37th week of pregnancy

a. stillbirth
b. cesarean section
c. premature birth
d. labor
e. low birthweight
f. multiple birth

Write the letter of the correct answer in the space provided.

______ **6.** If a couple chooses to have their baby at home, the delivery usually involves
a. an obstetrician.
b. special medical equipment.
c. a certified nurse-midwife.
d. a cesarean section.

______ **7.** Which occurs during labor?
a. The placenta is pushed out of the uterus.
b. The baby is born.
c. The doctor cuts the umbilical cord.
d. Contractions of the uterus get stronger.

______ **8.** During the postpartum period,
a. the afterbirth is delivered.
b. the mother experiences hormonal changes.
c. the baby is pushed out of the uterus.
d. the umbilical cord is cut.

______ **9.** Which is *not* a risk factor for having a baby with low birthweight?
a. smoking during pregnancy
b. teenage pregnancy
c. exercising during pregnancy
d. dieting during pregnancy

______ **10.** When two different sperm fertilize two eggs,
a. fraternal twins result.
b. identical twins result.
c. twins of different sexes always result.
d. twins of the same sex always result.

Name____________________ Class__________ Date__________ M T W T F

Section 19-4

Childhood

Lesson Plan

Section Objectives

- **Describe** the changes that children undergo during early childhood.
- **Identify** key areas of development that occur during middle and late childhood.

Vocabulary pre-adolescence

Time
1 period
1/2 block

Local Standards

1. FOCUS

Warm-Up: Advice Line Use the Warm-Up activity to lead students in using their own experiences with toddlers to understand childhood behavior.

Targeted Resources

- ❑ Transparency W68

2. TEACH

Cultural Connection Discuss similarities in the first words uttered by students with different cultural and language backgrounds. L3

Visual Learning: Figure 10 Use the photographs and charts in Figure 10 to begin a discussion on the changes that children undergo during early childhood. L2

Differentiated Instruction Have groups order various pictures of infants, toddlers, and young children and identify which are walking and which have achieved other milestones. L1

Cooperative Learning Assign groups to make a poster that depicts the changes in physical growth, mental abilities, or social abilities that children in middle and late childhood experience. L3

Targeted Resources

- ❑ RN Note Taking Guide 19-4 L3 EL
- ❑ ARN Note Taking Guide 19-4 L2
- ❑ TR Practice 19-4
- ❑ TR Enrich 19-4 L4
- ❑ Audio Summary 19-4 L1 L2 EL
- ❑ Health Links: Updates on growth and development

3. ASSESS

Evaluate Understanding The assignments listed in the Teacher's Edition can help you assess students' mastery of the section content.

Reteach Instruct student pairs to make a table that summarizes the developmental changes that children undergo from birth to age 12. L2

Targeted Resources

- ❑ TR Section 19-4 Quiz
- ❑ CTB Chapter 19

KEY

L1	Special Needs	L4	Gifted and Talented
L2	Less Proficient Readers	EL	English Language Learners
L3	All Students		

Name ______________________ Class ____________________ Date ________

Section 19-4

Practice

Concept Check: An Early Childhood Time Line

On the time line below, list some of the important mental and physical changes that occur in each stage of a child's development. Two examples are given.

Birth → **18 months** → **3 years**

Birth – 18 months	18 months – 3 years
Newborn directs its gaze	
Learns to smile after about a month	

3 years → **6 years** → **12 years**

3 years – 6 years	6 years – 12 years

Name ______________________ Class ______________________ Date __________

Section 19-4 **Enrich**

Community Involvement: Babysitting Responsibilities

Finding a responsible babysitter can sometimes be difficult. The questionnaire below can help parents find out about the skills of prospective babysitters. Add another question that you think is important for parents to ask. Then pretend that you are applying for a babysitting job and complete the questionnaire.

1. What are the three biggest responsibilities of a babysitter?

____

____

____

2. What skills must a babysitter have? How should a babysitter obtain these skills?

____

____

____

____

3. What information would you need from a parent before babysitting?

____

____

____

4. How would you handle a six-year-old child who refuses to go to bed?

____

____

5. What would you do if a child cut his finger and it won't stop bleeding?

____

____

6. Question: ____

____

____

____

Find out about babysitter training courses offered in your school or community. On a separate sheet of paper, record the names and telephone numbers of organizations offering such courses.

Name ______________________ Class ____________________ Date ________

Section 19-4 Quiz

Decide whether each statement is true or false. Write true *or* false *in the space provided.*

______ **1.** Babies and young children are like miniature adults.

______ **2.** Toddlers tend to play alongside others their own age.

______ **3.** Children between the ages of three and six have a lot of energy.

______ **4.** Children in middle childhood have a decreased appetite.

______ **5.** Best friends are important to children in late childhood.

Write the letter of the correct answer in the space provided.

______ **6.** Which is *not* a physical skill that newborns are usually born with?
- **a.** nursing
- **b.** crying
- **c.** smiling
- **d.** gazing at you

______ **7.** At what age do most children learn to talk?
- **a.** from birth to 18 months
- **b.** from 18 months to 3 years
- **c.** from 3 years to six years
- **d.** in middle childhood

______ **8.** Which is characteristic of most children between the ages of 3 and 6?
- **a.** learning to behave in a group
- **b.** taking on chores at home
- **c.** losing baby teeth
- **d.** playing alongside, but not with, others

______ **9.** Pre-adolescence is
- **a.** another name for late childhood.
- **b.** the stage of development after adolescence.
- **c.** defined as the period between ages 6 and 8.
- **d.** the period between adolescence and adulthood.

______ **10.** Which is *not* a key area of development during middle and late childhood?
- **a.** physical growth
- **b.** mastering new skills
- **c.** making friends
- **d.** learning to share

Name ______________________ Class ______________________ Date ________

Chapter 19 Test

Write the letter of the correct answer in the space provided.

______ **1.** From the third month until birth, the developing baby is called a(an)
a. zygote.
b. fetus.
c. embryo.
d. blastocyst.

______ **2.** Which complication during pregnancy occurs when the blastocyst implants in the fallopian tube?
a. gestational diabetes
b. preeclampsia
c. miscarriage
d. ectopic pregnancy

______ **3.** Which occurs first during childbirth?
a. implantation
b. delivery of the baby
c. labor
d. delivery of the afterbirth

______ **4.** In the first week after fertilization, the fertilized egg
a. undergoes many cell divisions.
b. implants in the uterus.
c. develops into a fetus.
d. forms inside the placenta.

______ **5.** Which does *not* play a role in nourishing the developing embryo and fetus?
a. substances from the mother's blood
b. cervix
c. umbilical cord
d. placenta

______ **6.** Which should be avoided during pregnancy?
a. exercise
b. folic acid
c. mercury
d. iron

______ **7.** Which prenatal test is used to check the position of the fetus in the uterus?
a. ultrasound
b. chorionic villus sampling
c. cesarean section
d. amniocentesis

Name ________________ Class ________________ Date ______

Chapter 19: **Test** *(continued)*

Write the letter of the correct answer in the space provided.

______ 8. Child learns to talk.

______ 9. Child learns to play with others.

______ 10. Child has many interests and hobbies.

______ 11. Child learns to sit and crawl.

______ 12. Child cries for help.

______ 13. Child becomes less self-centered.

a. birth to eighteen months

b. eighteen months to three years

c. three to six years

d. seven to twelve years

Write the word that best completes each sentence in the space provided.

14. Late childhood, the ages between 9 and 12, is also called ____________.

15. The first six weeks after birth during which many changes occur in the mother and the newborn is called the ____________ period.

16. A pregnancy is divided into three periods of time called ____________.

17. The process in which a blastocyst attaches itself to the wall of the uterus is called ____________.

18. Twins that develop from two different fertilized eggs are ____________ twins.

Use complete sentences to answer the following questions.

19. Explain the importance of prenatal care during pregnancy.

20. Describe four possible complicating factors at birth.

Name ____________ Class ____________ Date ______

Chapter 20

Personal Inventory

Changes During Adolescence

Adolescence is a time of physical, mental, and emotional changes. To identify your thoughts and ideas about the changes of adolescence, finish these sentences.

1. To me, the changes of adolescence seem ____________

2. One thing about the physical changes of adolescence that I would like to know more about is ____________

3. I think that the mental changes of adolescence include ____________

4. One thing about emotional changes during adolescence that I would like to know more about is ____________

5. Two things that I think adolescents should be responsible for are ____________

6. Three influences on the behavior of adolescents are ____________

7. I think that becoming more independent means ____________

Name________________________ Class__________ Date__________ M T W T F

Section 20-1

Adolescence: A Time of Change Lesson Plan

Section Objectives

- **List** three main categories of physical changes that occur during adolescence.
- **Describe** three mental changes that adolescents experience.
- **Summarize** the emotional changes of adolescence.

Vocabulary adolescence • reproductive maturity • secondary sex characteristics

Time
2 periods
1 block

Local Standards

1. FOCUS

Warm-Up: Advice Line Have students write about and share strategies for reassuring a friend who has questions about the physical changes that occur during adolescence.

Targeted Resources
- ❑ Transparency W69

2. TEACH

Building Health Skills Ask students to assess the reliability of various sources of information about the physical changes of adolescence. L3

Differentiated Instruction Have students work in pairs to develop a graphic organizer for the material in the section. L2

Differentiated Instruction Have students investigate the derivation of *early bloomers, late bloomers, and other idioms.* EL

Class Discussion Have a class discussion using everyday examples to clarify the mental changes that occur during adolescence. L2

Active Learning Have students choose a magazine photograph that they think represents an important emotional aspect of adolescence. L1

Targeted Resources
- ❑ RN Note Taking Guide 20-1 L3 EL
- ❑ ARN Note Taking Guide 20-1 L2
- ❑ Transparency and Worksheet 58
- ❑ TR Practice 20-1
- ❑ TR Enrich 20-1 L4
- ❑ Audio Summary 20-1 L1 L2 EL
- ❑ PHSchool.com: More on adolescence

3. ASSESS

Evaluate Understanding The assignments listed in the Teacher's Edition can help you assess students' mastery of the section content.

Reteach Instruct students to review the section material by writing one summary sentence for each figure in the section. L2

Targeted Resources
- ❑ TR Section 20-1 Quiz
- ❑ CTB Chapter 20

KEY

L1 Special Needs	L4 Gifted and Talented
L2 Less Proficient Readers	EL English Language Learners
L3 All Students	

Name ______________________ Class ______________________ Date ________

Section 20-1 **Practice**

Group Activity: Growing and Changing

Adolescence is a time of many physical changes. Sometimes these changes can be a source of concern or stress. Being supportive of your peers as they experience the changes of adolescence is an important part of being a good friend.

Imagine that some friends are concerned about the physical changes they are experiencing. With a group, brainstorm a thoughtful and supportive response to each of their concerns.

1. "My skin and hair have become so oily!"

____

____

____

____

____

2. "My mother and father are fairly tall, but I'm still so short. In fact, most of my classmates are taller than I am."

____

____

____

____

____

3. "I feel so clumsy, and sometimes my arms and legs ache."

____

____

____

____

4. "I'm hungry all the time. I can't seem to pass a vending machine without buying a candy bar."

____

____

____

____

Name ______________________ Class ____________________ Date ________

Section 20-1 **Enrich**

Consumer Skills: Evaluating Advertising Claims

Some of the physical changes that occur during adolescence can make teens feel insecure about their appearance. There are many reliable, safe, and useful products on the market that can help teens deal with changes such as oily hair and pimples. There are other products marketed to teens that make impossible claims or are unsafe to use. For example, over-the-counter products that claim to help people gain muscle mass, lose weight rapidly, or grow taller are usually fraudulent, and may be dangerous.

With a group, gather health-care product advertisements from magazines that are aimed at teens. Evaluate the advertisements, and then answer the questions below.

1. For what type of product did your group find the most advertisements?

____

2. List some of the claims made by the advertisements.

____

____

____

3. Which of the claims that you listed above seem to be reasonable and reliable? Explain your response.

____

____

____

4. Which of the claims that you listed above seem misleading or fraudulent? Explain your response.

____

____

____

5. Do you think that most health-care products marketed to teens make them feel more or less confident about their body? Give specific examples to support your response.

____

____

____

____

____

Name ______________________ Class ____________________ Date ______

Section 20-1

Quiz

Write the word or phrase that best completes each sentence in the space provided.

1. The period of gradual change between ages 12 and 19 is called ______________________.

2. The ability to produce children, called ______________________ ______________________, is the result of puberty.

3. Increased muscle strength, appearance of body hair, and increased perspiration are all examples of ______________________ ______________________.

Decide whether each statement is true or false. Write true *or* false *in the space provided.*

______ **4.** During adolescence, the need for food energy decreases.

______ **5.** Boys are usually taller than girls at the beginning of adolescence.

______ **6.** During adolescence the ability to think abstractly increases.

______ **7.** Teens are usually able to use reasoning to solve problems.

______ **8.** The human brain does not change after age 12.

______ **9.** Adolescents often search for meaning in life.

______ **10.** Most adolescents do not question their parents' values.

Name________________ Class__________ Date__________ M T W T F

Section 20-2

Adolescence and Responsibility Lesson Plan

Section Objectives

- **Identify** the responsibilities that adolescents have to themselves and others.

Vocabulary autonomy

Time
2 periods
1 block

Local Standards

1. FOCUS

Warm-Up: Quick Quiz Encourage students to write about steps that they can take to become more responsible.

Targeted Resources
- ❑ Transparency W70

2. TEACH

Cooperative Learning Have students work in small groups to discuss ways that teens can take increased responsibility for their actions and decisions. L3

Visual Learning: Figure 8 Ask students to describe the conflict depicted in the cartoon and relate this to the section content that describes how a teen's autonomy can sometimes cause friction in the family. L3

Differentiated Instruction Discuss with students the prefix *auto-* to clarify the meaning of the vocabulary term *autonomy.* EL

Cultural Connection Discuss with students the role that culture plays in a teen's responsibilities to his or her family. L3

Differentiated Instruction Guide students in planning and carrying out a simple project that demonstrates responsibility to the community. L1

Targeted Resources
- ❑ RN Note Taking Guide 20-2 L3 EL
- ❑ ARN Note Taking Guide 20-2 L2
- ❑ TR Practice 20-2
- ❑ TR Enrich 20-2 L4
- ❑ Audio Summary 20-2 L1 L2 EL
- ❑ Health Links: Updates on "coming of age"

3. ASSESS

Evaluate Understanding The assignments listed in the Teacher's Edition can help you assess students' mastery of the section content.

Reteach Instruct students to use a three-column table to organize information about teens' responsibilities to themselves, their families, and their communities. L2

Targeted Resources
- ❑ TR Section 20-2 Quiz
- ❑ CTB Chapter 20

KEY

L1 Special Needs	L4 Gifted and Talented
L2 Less Proficient Readers	EL English Language Learners
L3 All Students	

Name ______________________ Class ____________________ Date ______

Section 20-2 **Practice**

Role-Playing: Showing Responsibility

One of the changes associated with adolescence is an increased responsibility to yourself, your family, your friends, and your community. Sometimes your words demonstrate responsibility. For example, if you encourage your little sister to do her homework, you are showing responsibility to your family. Your actions can also demonstrate responsibility. Helping a classmate study for an exam shows responsibility to friends.

With a partner, choose one of the situations below. Write and perform a role-play that shows how an adolescent could show responsibility in the described situation. Use the provided lines to write the role-play.

A: A friend asks you to give her the answers during an exam.

B: Your mother asks you to take care of your younger brother, but you want to go shopping with your friends.

C: Your friends invite you to go skateboarding in a local parking lot, but there are signs saying, "No skateboarding."

Role-Play:

Name ______________________ Class ______________________ Date ________

Section 20-2 **Enrich**

Community Involvement: Letter to the Editor

Teens have an increased responsibility to their community. This responsibility can take many forms, from obeying laws to volunteering at community events.

On the lines below, write a letter to the editor of your local newspaper. Your letter should encourage adolescents to contribute to their community. In your letter, identify three specific ways that teens in your community can demonstrate responsibility.

____

(your address)

____

(date)

Dear Editor:

____

____

____

____

____

____

____

____

____

____

____

____

____

____

____

____

____

Sincerely,

____

Name ______________________ Class ______________________ Date __________

Section 20-2 **Quiz**

Write the letter of the correct answer in the space provided.

______ **1.** listening to a peer's problems	**a.** responsibility to yourself
______ **2.** following traffic laws	**b.** responsibility to your friends
______ **3.** performing household chores	**c.** responsibility to your family
______ **4.** choosing healthy school lunches	**d.** responsibility to your community
______ **5.** volunteering at the community center	
______ **6.** planning for your future career	

Decide whether each statement is true or false. Write true *or* false *in the space provided.*

______ **7.** Responsibilities to family increase during adolescence.

______ **8.** During adolescence, teens move toward autonomy, or independence.

______ **9.** Encouraging a friend to take part in risky behaviors shows responsibility.

______ **10.** Littering shows a lack of responsibility to the community.

Name______________________ Class__________ Date__________ M T W T F

Section 20-3

Adulthood and Marriage Lesson Plan

Section Objectives

- **Summarize** the changes that people undergo during adulthood.
- **List** three keys to a successful marriage.
- **Analyze** how decisions made in youth can affect the aging process.

Vocabulary physical maturity • emotional maturity • dementia • Alzheimer's disease

Time
2 periods
1 block

Local Standards

1. FOCUS

Warm-Up: Health Stats Challenge students to interpret a graph indicating that the number of older Americans will increase in the coming years. Then have students predict how this trend will impact the need for health care.

Targeted Resources
- ❑ Transparency W71

2. TEACH

Building Health Skills Have students develop an action plan for staying in good physical condition during adulthood. L3

Active Learning Have students create a picture or cartoon strip that illustrates an adult's journey to emotional maturity. L1

Differentiated Instruction Instruct students to use a dictionary to find the meanings of unfamiliar terms related to qualities of a successful marriage, such as *compromise*. EL

Differentiated Instruction Ask students to use index cards to summarize and organize the information about marriage. L2

Cultural Connection Have students research the perception of older adults in various other cultures. L4

Targeted Resources
- ❑ RN Note Taking Guide 20-3 L3 EL
- ❑ ARN Note Taking Guide 20-3 L2
- ❑ TR Practice 20-3
- ❑ TR Enrich 20-3 L4
- ❑ Audio Summary 20-3 L1 L2 EL
- ❑ PHSchool.com: More on perceptions of aging

3. ASSESS

Evaluate Understanding The assignments listed in the Teacher's Edition can help you assess students' mastery of the section content.

Reteach Ask students to generate a concept web, showing the changes that individuals undergo as they age. L2

Targeted Resources
- ❑ TR Section 20-3 Quiz
- ❑ CTB Chapter 20

KEY

L1 Special Needs	L4 Gifted and Talented
L2 Less Proficient Readers	EL English Language Learners
L3 All Students	

Name ______________________ Class ________________ Date ______

Section 20-3 **Practice**

Skill-Building Activity: Planning Ahead

Have you thought about the next stage of your life? Setting goals can help adolescents plan for young adulthood.

For each aspect of life listed below, make a long-term goal based on what you want your life to be like as a young adult. Then, record several steps that you can take now to help you achieve your goals.

Emotional development

Long-term goal: ____

Steps I can take now: ____

____

____

____

Career

Long-term goal: ____

Steps I can take now: ____

____

____

____

Relationships

Long-term goal: ____

Steps I can take now: ____

____

____

____

Achievements

Long-term goal: ____

Steps I can take now: ____

____

____

____

Name ______________________ Class ________________ Date ______

Section 20-3

Enrich

Family Involvement: Sharing Generational Stories

Most people enjoy hearing and telling good stories. Older adults usually have many stories to tell about the way things used to be when they were younger.

Ask a grandparent or another older adult to tell you a story about his or her adolescence. Summarize the story below, and with the older adult's permission, share his or her story with the class. Then answer the follow-up questions.

Story:

1. Based on the story above, describe any similarities you noted between the storyteller's life and your own.

2. Describe any differences you noted between the storyteller's life and your own.

Name ______________ Class ______________ Date ______

Section 20-3 **Quiz**

Decide whether each statement is true or false. Write true *or* false *in the space provided.*

______ **1.** Most people reach physical maturity in their early teens.

______ **2.** Emotional maturity develops over a lifetime.

______ **3.** Successful marriages require only love.

______ **4.** It is usually more difficult for teens to be successful in marriage than it is for adults.

______ **5.** Practicing healthy behaviors now will have no impact on how you age.

Write the letter of the correct answer in the space provided.

______ **6.** At what stage of life do physical abilities reach their peak?

a. childhood **b.** adolescence
c. young adulthood **d.** older adulthood

______ **7.** What term describes the determination to make a marriage work, despite the challenges?

a. commitment **b.** communication
c. compatibility **d.** companionship

______ **8.** The effects of aging on the body include all of the following *except*

a. secondary sex characteristics appear.
b. reflexes slow down.
c. bones shrink and become more brittle.
d. skin becomes drier and less elastic.

______ **9.** Which of these diseases could cause an older adult to struggle with stiff muscles, shaky movements, and progressive loss of muscle function?

a. heart disease **b.** Alzheimer's disease
c. lung disease **d.** Parkinson's disease

______ **10.** Which of these diseases associated with older adulthood is caused by loss of bone calcium?

a. Alzheimer's disease **b.** dementia
c. Parkinson's disease **d.** osteoporosis

Name____________________ Class__________ Date__________ M T W T F

Section 20-4

Death and Dying

Lesson Plan

Section Objectives

- **List** the five stages of dying that some people experience.
- **Summarize** healthy strategies for coping with a dying loved one and coping after a death.

Vocabulary hospice • terminal illness

Time
1 period
1/2 block

Local Standards

1. FOCUS

Warm-Up: Myth/Fact Encourage students to write about and share their knowledge of cultural beliefs about death and dying.

Targeted Resources
- ❑ Transparency W72

2. TEACH

Differentiated Instruction Have students create flowcharts to show the five stages of dying experienced by terminally ill patients and their families. L2

Building Vocabulary Help students relate the word *hospice* to its Latin root, *hospes*. EL

Visual Learning: Figure 17 Have students review the five stages of dying that are explained in the figure. Ask students to compare the ways that dying individuals and their loved ones experience grief. L2

Cultural Connection Discuss how different cultures honor the memories of dead loved ones in different ways. L3

Class Discussion Have students analyze how artists have portrayed grief in paintings, musical compositions, or other artwork. L4

Targeted Resources
- ❑ RN Note Taking Guide 20-4 L3 EL
- ❑ ARN Note Taking Guide 20-4 L2
- ❑ Transparency and Worksheet 59
- ❑ TR Practice 20-4
- ❑ TR Enrich 20-4 L4
- ❑ Audio Summary 20-4 L1 L2 EL
- ❑ Health Links: Updates on the grieving process

3. ASSESS

Evaluate Understanding The assignments listed in the Teacher's Edition can help you assess students' mastery of the section content.

Reteach Ask small groups of students to generate a list of specific ways to help a grieving friend. L2

Targeted Resources
- ❑ TR Section 20-4 Quiz
- ❑ CTB Chapter 20

KEY

L1 Special Needs	L4 Gifted and Talented
L2 Less Proficient Readers	EL English Language Learners
L3 All Students	

Name ______________________ Class ______________________ Date __________

Section 20-4

Practice

Skill-Building Activity: Support for a Grieving Friend

Good communication skills, such as asking caring questions and being a good listener, can be used to help friends and neighbors who have experienced the loss of a loved one.

For each scenario below, list two questions you could ask to show caring and respect to the grieving person.

1. A friend's grandmother recently passed away. Your friend seems to want to talk about his grandmother's life.

   Question 1: ______________________________

   ____

   Question 2: ______________________________

   ____

2. Your neighbor, a busy mom with a full-time job, just experienced the death of her aunt. Your neighbor is serving a meal at her home for everyone who attends the funeral.

   Question 1: ______________________________

   ____

   Question 2: ______________________________

   ____

3. Your lab partner's father just died unexpectedly. You have heard that your lab partner will miss the next week of school.

   Question 1: ______________________________

   ____

   Question 2: ______________________________

   ____

4. Your friend has seemed very sad and depressed since his grandfather died three months ago. Your friend has quit basketball and his grades have dropped.

   Question 1: ______________________________

   ____

   Question 2: ______________________________

   ____

Name ______________________ Class ______________ Date ________

Cultural Connection: Grief

Grief is an emotion that is experienced by people of all cultures. Although different cultures have unique ways of grieving, there are similarities in the ways that people of all cultures view the process.

Read the following quotes about grief. Then answer the questions that follow.

"One often calms one's grief by recounting it."
Pierre Cornielle, French poet, 1606–1684

"There is no grief like the grief that does not speak."
Henry Wadsworth Longfellow, American poet, 1807–1882

"He that conceals his grief finds no remedy for it."
Turkish proverb

"Give sorrow words. The grief that does not speak whispers the o'er-fraught heart, and bids it break."
William Shakespeare, English playwright, 1564–1616

"Suppressed grief suffocates, it rages within the breast, and is forced to multiply its strength."
Ovid, poet, Ancient Rome

1. Although these quotes are from different cultures and different time periods, they express similar ideas. Write a short paragraph that summarizes the ideas presented in these quotes and explains how you could apply these ideas to your own life.

____

____

____

____

____

____

____

____

2. Write your own quote that expresses the same idea as those above.

____

____

____

Name ______________________ Class ______________________ Date ________

Section 20-4

Quiz

Write the letter of the correct answer in the space provided.

______ **1.** There must be a mistake; I'm not going to die.	**a.** acceptance	
______ **2.** If I eat healthy foods, I'll get better.	**b.** bargaining	
______ **3.** I'm ready for death.	**c.** anger	
______ **4.** This isn't fair!	**d.** denial	
______ **5.** I just don't care anymore.	**e.** depression	

Decide whether each statement is true or false. Write true *or* false *in the space provided.*

______ **6.** A hospice provides only physical care for the dying and their families.

______ **7.** A terminal illness is one with no hope of recovery.

______ **8.** It is important to stay involved in the life of a dying loved one.

______ **9.** Keeping your feelings inside is a healthy way to grieve.

______ **10.** A sympathy note is one way to support a grieving friend.

Name ______________________ Class ____________________ Date ______

Chapter 20 Test

Write the letter of the correct answer in the space provided.

______ **1.** Which of the following is a physical change that occurs during adolescence?
a. the process of aging begins
b. a sense of self is established
c. the reproductive system matures
d. responsibility to the community increases

______ **2.** Which secondary sex characteristics occur in girls?
a. body fat increases
b. perspiration increases
c. production of skin oil increases
d. all of the above

______ **3.** The emotional center of the brain, responsible for impulses, is the
a. amygdala. **b.** cerebellum.
c. frontal cortex. **d.** corpus callosum.

______ **4.** Using positive peer pressure can help you demonstrate
a. responsibility to yourself.
b. responsibility to friends.
c. responsibility to family.
d. responsibility to community.

______ **5.** Establishing a career and reaching physical maturity are milestones associated with which stage of life?
a. childhood **b.** adolescence
c. young adulthood **d.** older adulthood

Write the letter of the correct answer in the space provided.

______ **6.** a disease that causes brittleness of the bones

______ **7.** a disease that attacks the body's joints

______ **8.** a disease that causes brain cells to die

______ **9.** a disease that causes muscles to become stiff

______ **10.** a disorder that causes abnormal behaviors and personality changes

a. heart disease
b. arthritis
c. Alzheimer's disease
d. dementia
e. osteoporosis
f. Parkinson's disease

Name ______________________ Class ____________________ Date ________

Chapter 20: Test *(continued)*

Decide whether each statement is true or false. Write true *or* false *in the space provided.*

______ **11.** Following negative influences is a way to demonstrate responsibility.

______ **12.** Physical activity is a good way to adjust to rapidly changing body proportions.

______ **13.** One emotional change that occurs during adolescence is the search for self.

______ **14.** Most terminally ill people and their families pass through seven stages of dying.

______ **15.** Continuing your normal routine is a healthy way to deal with grief.

Write the word that best completes each sentence in the space provided.

16. A teenager's ______________________, or independence, can cause friction in the family.

17. The three key factors in a successful marriage are love, commitment, and ______________________.

18. A(an) ________________ provides physical, mental, and emotional support to terminally ill patients and their families.

Use complete sentences to answer the following questions.

19. Identify and briefly describe three mental changes that occur during adolescence.

____

____

____

____

____

____

20. Explain how healthy habits established early in life can impact the aging process.

____

____

____

____

____

____

Name ____________________ Class ____________ Date ________

Chapter 21

Personal Inventory

Immunization Record

Use this chart to make and keep an accurate record of the immunizations you have received. This information can come from your parents, your doctors, or written records you may have from school or camp.

My Record of Immunization			
Vaccine	**Original (month/year)**	**Booster (month/year)**	**Doctor/Clinic**
Diphtheria, Tetanus, Pertussis		**1.** **2.**	**1.** **2.**
Haemophilus influenzae type b			
Pneumococcal conjugate			
Hepatitis B			
Polio		**1.** **2.**	
Varicella (chickenpox)			
Influenza		**1.** **2.**	
Measles, Mumps, Rubella		**1.**	
Tetanus, Diphtheria			

Name______________________ Class__________ Date__________ M T W T F

Section 21-1

Understanding Infectious Diseases Lesson Plan

Section Objectives

- **Identify** the causes of infectious diseases.
- **Describe** four ways in which infectious diseases are spread.

Vocabulary infectious disease • microorganism • pathogen • bacteria • toxin • virus • fungi • protozoan

Time
1 period
1/2 block

Local Standards

1. FOCUS

Warm-Up: Myth/Fact Ask students whether they think teens wash their hands as much as they should. Then discuss ways to encourage more hand washing.

Targeted Resources

- ❑ Transparency W73

2. TEACH

Class Discussion Ask students to brainstorm a list of diseases they think humans can catch. Then ask students what it means to "catch" a disease. L2

Differentiated Instruction Help students create a detailed concept map to organize and record the most important information in Section 1. L2

Active Learning To demonstrate how pathogens are spread by direct contact, have students observe the spread of talcum powder as they shake one another's hands. L1

Building Health Skills Ask students to consider how eating undercooked meat could affect their health. L3

Targeted Resources

- ❑ RN Note Taking Guide 21-1 L3 EL
- ❑ ARN Note Taking Guide 21-1 L2
- ❑ TR Practice 21-1
- ❑ TR Enrich 21-1 L4
- ❑ Audio Summary 21-1 L1 L2 EL
- ❑ PHSchool.com: More on infectious diseases

3. ASSESS

Evaluate Understanding The assignments listed in the Teacher's Edition can help you assess students' mastery of the section content.

Reteach Call on students to identify the different ways pathogens are spread. Call on other students to describe and give an example of each way. L2

Targeted Resources

- ❑ TR Section 21-1 Quiz
- ❑ CTB Chapter 21

KEY

L1 Special Needs	L4 Gifted and Talented
L2 Less Proficient Readers	EL English Language Learners
L3 All Students	

Name ________________ Class ________________ Date ________

Section 21-1

Practice

Concept Check: Passing It On

Most infectious diseases are spread through direct or indirect contact with a person who has the disease. The common cold is spread in this way. The diagram below can give you an idea of how an infectious disease can spread from one person to the next. Each box represents a person, and the lines connecting the boxes represent handshakes. For example, the person in Level A shook hands with both people in Level B.

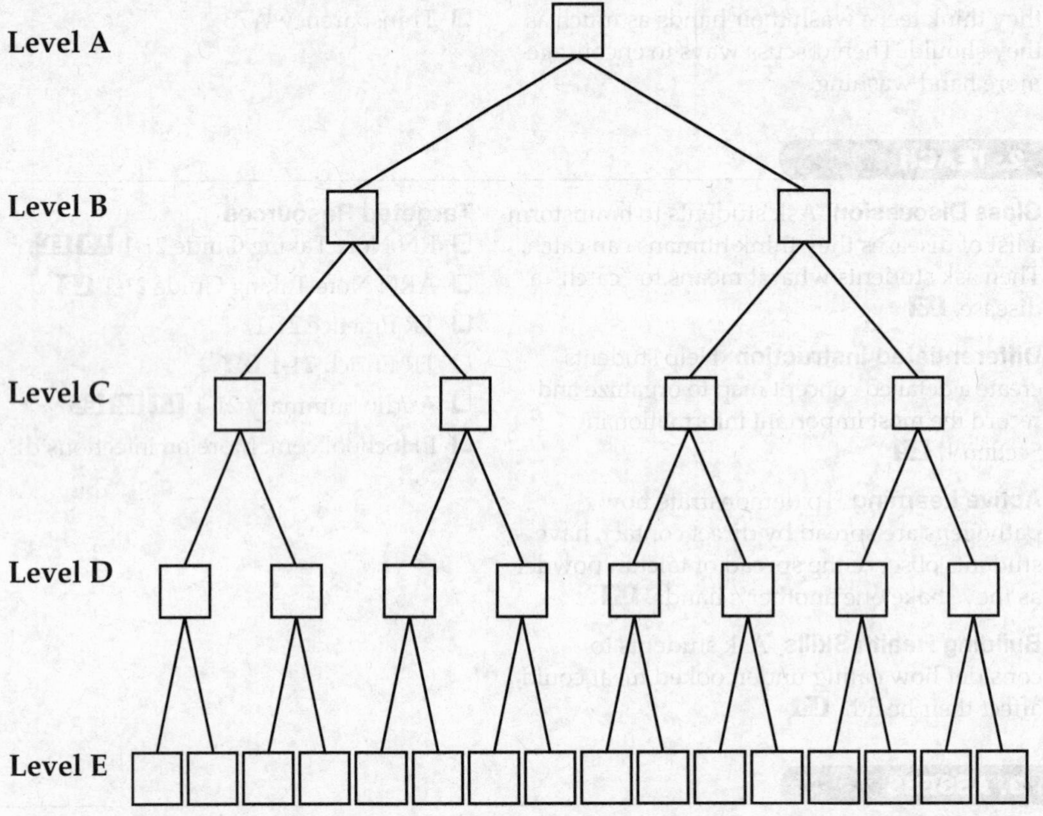

1. If the person in Level A has an infectious disease that can be spread by direct contact, how many people in Level E can trace their exposure back to that person? ________________________________

2. How can people with colds avoid exposing others to the disease?

____

____

____

Name ______________________ Class ____________________ Date ______

Section 21-1 **Enrich**

Family Involvement: The Kitchen Safety Test

How safe is your kitchen? The way food is handled and stored in kitchens, as well as how kitchens are cleaned, can affect people's health. Contaminated food and contaminated objects are two ways that pathogens are spread.

Take this worksheet home, and together with a parent or guardian use it to assess how safe your kitchen is.

1. What is the temperature of the refrigerator in your home? ____________

Best temperature: The temperature should be 40°F (5°C) or less.

2. How are meat, poultry, and fish usually defrosted?

____

____

Best practice: Defrosting should either be done gradually overnight in the refrigerator or in a microwave following package instructions.

3. When someone handles raw meat, poultry, or fish in your kitchen, how does that person clean his or her hands?

____

____

Best practice: Hands should be washed with soap and warm water.

4. When your family finishes a meal, what is done with the leftovers?

____

____

Best practice: The leftovers should be put in the refrigerator immediately after a meal is served.

5. When a cutting board is used to cut meat, poultry, or fish, how is it cleaned?

____

____

Best practice: The cutting board should be washed with soap and hot water and then sanitized with a solution of water and chlorine bleach.

6. When was the last time the kitchen sink drain and disposal were sanitized and how? ____

____

Best practice: They should be sanitized periodically with a solution of 1 teaspoon of chlorine bleach per 1 quart of water.

Name ______________________ Class ____________________ Date ________

Section 21-1

Quiz

Write the letter of the correct answer in the space provided.

______	**1.** organisms such as yeasts, molds, and mushrooms	**a.** pathogens
______	**2.** single-celled organisms that are much larger and more complex than bacteria	**b.** bacteria
______	**3.** simple, single-celled microorganisms	**c.** toxins
______	**4.** microorganisms and viruses that cause disease	**d.** fungi
______	**5.** the smallest pathogens	**e.** protozoan
		f. viruses

Decide whether each statement is true or false. Write true *or* false *in the space provided.*

______ **6.** Some infectious diseases are transmitted to humans through the bites of animals.

______ **7.** An infected person cannot spread a disease to another person.

______ **8.** Pathogens can cause an infectious disease when they enter your body and multiply.

______ **9.** It is important to refrigerate food promptly to prevent the growth of harmful bacteria.

______ **10.** All pathogens die immediately when they leave a person's body.

Name________________________ Class__________ Date__________ M T W T F

Section 21-2

Defenses Against Disease — Lesson Plan

Section Objectives

- **Identify** the body's physical and chemical defenses against infectious disease.
- **Describe** the inflammatory response.
- **Summarize** how the immune system works.
- **Compare** passive and active immunity.

Vocabulary mucous membrane • inflammation • phagocyte • immune system • lymphocyte • immunity • T cell • B cell • antibody • lymphatic system • immunization • vaccine

Time
1 period
1/2 block

Local Standards

1. FOCUS

Warm-Up: Quick Quiz Discuss how behavior affects the chances of getting or spreading an infectious disease.

Targeted Resources
- ❑ Transparency W74

2. TEACH

Teacher Demo Show students how the skin of an apple functions like a person's skin as a physical defense. L2

Differentiated Instruction Provide students with an analogy of how the body's physical and chemical defenses fight pathogens. L1

Addressing Misconceptions Point out that the heat, swelling, pain, and redness of inflammation are not signs of disease but instead signs that the body is fighting pathogens. L3

Visual Learning: Figure 5 Use the illustration to clarify students' understanding of the immune response. L3

Building Vocabulary Explain that the word *vaccinate* is derived from the Latin word *vacca* (cow) because of Edward Jenner's successful immunization of people against smallpox using the cowpox virus. EL

Targeted Resources
- ❑ RN Note Taking Guide 21-2 L3 EL
- ❑ ARN Note Taking Guide 21-2 L2
- ❑ Transparencies and Worksheets 60, 61, 62
- ❑ TR Practice 21-2
- ❑ TR Enrich 21-2 L4
- ❑ Audio Summary 21-2 L1 L2 EL
- ❑ PHSchool.com: More on the immune response

3. ASSESS

Evaluate Understanding The assignments listed in the Teacher's Edition can help you assess students' mastery of the section content.

Reteach Have pairs of students make an outline of the section and use it to quiz each other on section content. L2

Targeted Resources
- ❑ TR Section 21-2 Quiz
- ❑ CTB Chapter 21

KEY
- L1 Special Needs
- L2 Less Proficient Readers
- L3 All Students
- L4 Gifted and Talented
- EL English Language Learners

Name ______________________ Class ______________________ Date ________

Section 21-2 **Practice**

Group Activity: Defending Against Infection

The body uses three lines of defense to guard against infection: physical and chemical defense systems, inflammation, and the immune system. The three lines of defense can be abbreviated as follows: P & C = physical and chemical defense systems; INF = inflammation; IMM = immune system.

With a partner, identify and discuss the line of defense used in the infectious situations listed in the left column of the chart below. Then fill in the right column of the chart using your own words. A sample is provided.

Infectious Situation	Body's Line of Defense
Bacteria and pathogens on skin surface	P & C—hard skin cells with no gaps keep out pathogens; sweat acids kill bacteria; pathogens shed with old skin
Pathogens in nose, mouth, or eyes	
Pathogens in digestive tract	
Pathogens in burn or cut	
Influenza virus enters body for first time	
Chickenpox virus enters body for second time	
Measles virus enters body soon after measles vaccination	
Rabies pathogens enter body from bite by rabid dog	

Name ______________________ Class __________________ Date ______

Section 21-2 **Enrich**

Consumer Skills: Immunizations

Almost all schools require that students have the recommended immunizations before they can attend classes. The reasons for this requirement include both protection of the individual student from getting a disease and protection of all students from being exposed to an infected person. Not all people agree with such a requirement, though. For example, some people are concerned that some immunizations are risky to the health of children. However, the vast majority of public health experts maintain that the benefits of immunizations far outweigh the risks.

Research the benefits and risks of immunizations on the Internet. Find at least two Web sites that give information about both benefits and risks. Be sure to make a note of how reliable you think the information is on each site and why. List two benefits and two risks of required immunizations. Then weigh the benefits and risks against each other, taking into account the research that supports both. Write a brief analysis, explaining whether you think the benefits of required immunizations outweigh the risks.

Benefits of required immunizations:

1. ______________________________

____

2. ______________________________

____

Risks of required immunizations:

1. ______________________________

____

2. ______________________________

____

Source(s): ______________________________

____

Risk-benefit analysis:

____

____

____

____

____

Name ____________________ Class ____________________ Date ________

Section 21-2 Quiz

Write the letter of the correct answer in the space provided.

______ **1.** white blood cells that carry out most of the immune system's functions		**a.** phagocytes
______ **2.** injections that cause a person to become immune to a disease		**b.** B cells
______ **3.** white blood cells that engulf and destroy pathogens		**c.** lymphocytes
______ **4.** proteins that attach to the surface of pathogens or to the toxins produced by pathogens		**d.** antibodies
______ **5.** lymphocytes that produce antibodies		**e.** T cells
		f. immunizations

Write the letter of the correct answer in the space provided.

______ **6.** What is a physical defense that prevents pathogens from entering the body?

a. inflammation **b.** active immunity
c. skin **d.** stomach acid

______ **7.** What is the body's most sophisticated line of defense against pathogens?

a. mucous membranes
b. vaccines
c. inflammation
d. the immune system

______ **8.** What results from either having a disease or from receiving a vaccine?

a. active immunity
b. the first line of defense
c. inflammation
d. passive immunity

______ **9.** What does a person acquire by receiving antibodies from a source other than one's own immune system?

a. passive immunity **b.** T cells
c. inflammation **d.** active immunity

______ **10.** What is the body's general response to all kinds of injury, from cuts and scrapes to internal damage?

a. the lymphatic system
b. inflammation
c. antibodies
d. the immune system

Name____________________ Class__________ Date__________ M T W T F

Section 21-3

Common Infectious Diseases Lesson Plan

Section Objectives

- **Identify** some diseases caused by bacteria and by viruses.
- **Describe** behaviors that can help you get healthy and stay healthy.

Vocabulary antibiotic

Time
2 periods
1 block

Local Standards

1. FOCUS

Warm-Up: Health Stats Ask students to explain why none of the leading causes of death in 2000 were infectious diseases.

Targeted Resources
- ❑ Transparency W75

2. TEACH

Building Health Skills Ask students to read through the descriptions of common infectious diseases and think of a way they could avoid getting each disease. L2

Differentiated Instruction Pair up English language learners with proficient speakers and have each pair prepare a short presentation about an infectious disease. EL

Cooperative Learning Have groups create a comic strip that shows a person in each stage of the flu. L1

Building Health Skills Ask each student to set a goal related to one of the healthful behaviors that can be practiced to avoid disease. L3

Targeted Resources
- ❑ RN Note Taking Guide 21-3 L3 EL
- ❑ ARN Note Taking Guide 21-3 L2
- ❑ Transparencies and Worksheets 63, 64
- ❑ TR Practice 21-3
- ❑ TR Enrich 21-3 L4
- ❑ Audio Summary 21-3 L1 L2 EL
- ❑ Health Links: Updates on infectious diseases

3. ASSESS

Evaluate Understanding The assignments listed in the Teacher's Edition can help you assess students' mastery of the section content.

Reteach Have students make a compare/contrast table that includes the type of pathogen, symptoms, and treatment of the bacterial and viral diseases discussed in the section. L2

Targeted Resources
- ❑ TR Section 21-3 Quiz
- ❑ CTB Chapter 21

KEY

L1	Special Needs	L4	Gifted and Talented
L2	Less Proficient Readers	EL	English Language Learners
L3	All Students		

Name ________________ Class ________________ Date ________

Section 21-3

Practice

Decision Making: Avoiding Infectious Disease

Sometimes people need to make decisions and choices about protecting themselves and others from infectious diseases. If you do contract an infectious disease, there may be things you can do to treat yourself and to help stop the spread of the disease.

Read the following descriptions of situations and answer the questions.

1. Marsha has a cold. She is supposed to sing in the school choir tonight. What should she do? Why? ________________

2. George knows that influenza can be very serious for the elderly. What action can he suggest to his grandmother to help her stay healthy?

3. John will be traveling to another country where some people he knows have contracted hepatitis A. What can he do to avoid getting hepatitis A?

4. Miguelito has a sore throat. His physician says he has strep throat. How should he prevent spreading it? How should he treat the problem?

5. A friend has a family member who has tuberculosis. She doesn't really understand what it is and how it is transmitted. What information could you give her? ________________

6. You will play in an important basketball game soon. Many students in your school have a cold or the flu. You want to do your best to protect yourself from a cold or the flu. What are some things you could do?

Name ______________________ Class ______________ Date ______

Enrich

Research Project: Infectious Diseases

Despite the body's three lines of defense, some pathogens still get into the body, multiply, and cause disease. As you have learned, pathogens include bacteria, viruses, fungi, and protozoans. The table below lists some additional infectious diseases to those discussed in your text.

Choose one of the diseases listed in the table to investigate.

Infectious Diseases	
Pathogen	**Diseases**
Bacteria	botulism, cholera, diphtheria, Hansen's disease (leprosy), whooping cough (pertussis), pinkeye (contagious conjunctivitis), plague, scarlet fever, tetanus, typhoid fever
Viruses	chickenpox, infectious mononucleosis, measles (rubeola), mumps, polio (poliomyelitis), rabies, rubella (German measles)
Fungi	athlete's foot, ringworm, thrush (oropharyngeal candidiasis)
Protozoans	amebic dysentery (amebiasis), giardiasis, malaria, sleeping sickness (African trypanosomiasis)

Record the results of your research in the spaces provided.

Disease: ____

Pathogen: ____

How Pathogen Spreads: ____

____

Symptoms: ____

____

Treatment: ____

____

____

Sources: 1. ____

2. ____

Name ________________________ Class ____________________ Date ________

Section 21-3

Quiz

Write the letter of the correct answer in the space provided.

_______ **1.** Which disease is a highly contagious bacterial disease of the lungs?
a. tuberculosis
b. hepatitis
c. Lyme disease
d. pneumonia

_______ **2.** What should you *not* do to avoid disease?
a. skip meals
b. exercise regularly
c. wash your hands several times a day
d. manage stress effectively

_______ **3.** A common viral infection of the upper respiratory system is
a. Lyme disease.
b. strep throat.
c. tuberculosis.
d. influenza.

_______ **4.** You need to seek medical care if you have
a. a body temperature of 98.6°F that lasts more than two days.
b. any illness that lasts for more than a day.
c. a runny nose, a cough, and chest congestion.
d. difficulty breathing, or severe pain anywhere.

_______ **5.** A viral disease that is transmitted in human wastes and contaminated water and food is
a. tuberculosis.
b. hepatitis A.
c. influenza.
d. hepatitis C.

Decide whether each statement is true or false. Write true *or* false *in the space provided.*

_______ **6.** You can protect yourself from infectious diseases by avoiding contact with pathogens.

_______ **7.** There is no cure for the common cold.

_______ **8.** An antibiotic is a drug that inhibits or kills viruses.

_______ **9.** A fever indicates that the body is fighting an infection.

_______ **10.** An infection of the fluid in the spinal cord and the fluid that surrounds the brain is called pneumonia.

Name________________________ Class____________ Date____________ M T W T F

Section 21-4

Emerging Infectious Diseases Lesson Plan

Section Objectives

- **Define** the term *emerging disease.*
- **Identify** five reasons why diseases emerge.

Vocabulary epidemic • emerging disease

Time
1 period
1/2 block

Local Standards

1. FOCUS

Warm-Up: Health Stats Ask students to interpret a map that shows how dengue fever has spread since 1960 and explain whether the United States should be concerned about dengue fever.

Targeted Resources

- ❑ Transparency W76

2. TEACH

Building Vocabulary Analyze the word *emerge* so that students will have a better understanding of the concept of emerging diseases. EL

Visual Learning: Figure 11 Help students learn about emerging diseases by discussing the viral diseases listed in the table. L2

Building Media Literacy Ask students to evaluate recent news reports about infectious diseases. L3

Differentiated Instruction Have pairs of students quiz each other on the details of emerging diseases. L2

Targeted Resources

- ❑ RN Note Taking Guide 21-4 L3 EL
- ❑ ARN Note Taking Guide 21-4 L2
- ❑ TR Practice 21-4
- ❑ TR Enrich 21-4 L4
- ❑ Audio Summary 21-4 L1 L2 EL
- ❑ Health Links: Updates on modern epidemics

3. ASSESS

Evaluate Understanding The assignments listed in the Teacher's Edition can help you assess students' mastery of the section content.

Reteach Ask students to write a newspaper article that would inform the public about emerging diseases. L2

Targeted Resources

- ❑ TR Section 21-4 Quiz
- ❑ CTB Chapter 21

KEY

L1 Special Needs	L4 Gifted and Talented
L2 Less Proficient Readers	EL English Language Learners
L3 All Students	

Name ______________________ Class ______________________ Date ____________

Section 21-4 **Practice**

Concept Check: Factors Responsible for SARS Spread

SARS (Severe Acute Respiratory Syndrome) is a frightening infectious disease that emerged in the early twenty-first century. At first, scientists had little idea about where the pathogen came from. An investigation followed, and by 2005, researchers felt confident that they understood how SARS emerged.

The description below contains examples of two factors that contributed to the spread of the emerging disease SARS. Show your understanding of these contributing factors by circling each sentence that first mentions a factor. Then answer the questions that follow.

Cases of SARS first appeared in southern China in 2002. The illness usually begins with a high fever—over 100°F. Other symptoms include headache, body aches, and a dry cough. A type of pneumonia can follow. The disease can be deadly.

Researchers discovered that the SARS virus is spread by close person-to-person contact. When an infected person coughs or sneezes, infected droplets spread through the air and can be breathed in by others. An infected person can also contaminate objects such as a doorknob.

Scientists found that SARS emerged mainly because of close contact between humans and infected animals. Investigators in China discovered that the virus is widespread both in a type of bat and another wild mammal called a civet. These animals were sold for food at markets in China and likely spread the virus to humans.

People became sick from SARS in China and in other countries. For example, there were over 100 cases reported in Canada in 2003. There were also cases reported in the United States, though no deaths. The movement of the disease from country to country was the result of international travel by people on business or vacation.

1. What are the symptoms of SARS? ______________________

____

2. How does SARS spread from person to person? ______________________

____

____

3. Explain how the first contributing factor you identified contributed to the spread of SARS. ______________________

____

____

4. Explain how the second contributing factor you identified contributed to the spread of SARS. ______________________

____

Name ____________________ Class ____________________ Date __________

Section 21-4 **Enrich**

Community Involvement: Planning for Disease

An emerging disease can pose a serious threat to communities. Every community needs a detailed plan for how to react to an epidemic in an organized way. For instance, if a vaccine is developed for the disease, who should be first to receive that vaccine? There probably won't be enough for everyone. These and other issues need to be considered before such a crisis occurs.

Suppose that you have been given responsibility for developing a plan for your community. Record the details of your plan in the spaces provided.

1. What groups of people should be first to get a vaccine against the disease?

____

____

2. Where can people who become ill with the disease go to be treated?

____

____

3. What government official will be in charge of keeping as many people as possible safe from the disease?

____

4. Should people who become ill with the disease be quarantined—kept apart from all other people? Why or why not?

____

____

5. Should an effort be made to keep people with the disease from traveling into your community? Why or why not?

____

____

6. What other details should your plan include?

____

____

____

____

After you have worked out the details of your plan, find out whether public officials in your community have a detailed plan for how to react to an epidemic in your area. If they have a plan, compare their plan to yours.

Name ______________________ Class ______________________ Date __________

Section 21-4 Quiz

Decide whether each statement is true or false. Write true *or* false *in the space provided.*

______ **1.** Immunizations can contribute to the spread of emerging diseases.

______ **2.** Sometimes mutations result in a strain of pathogen that no longer responds to medicine.

______ **3.** Diseases can emerge when humans come into contact with infected animals.

______ **4.** When an epidemic affects many areas of the world, it is sometimes called a pandemic.

______ **5.** The 1918 flu outbreak was stopped before it became an epidemic.

Write the letter of the correct answer in the space provided.

______ **6.** Which term refers to an unusually high occurrence of a disease in a certain place during a certain time period?
a. emerging disease
b. epidemic
c. avian flu
d. infectious disease

______ **7.** What is a viral disease that is spread by droplet inhalation from an infected person's cough or sneeze?
a. SARS
b. dengue fever
c. West Nile virus
d. yellow fever

______ **8.** What is one factor that is responsible for emerging diseases around the world?
a. widespread immunization
b. prevention of international travel
c. drug resistance
d. food grown in China

______ **9.** Which term refers to a disease that threatens to become more common in the near future?
a. pandemic
b. emerging disease
c. globalization
d. viral disease

______ **10.** What is one method of preventing avian flu?
a. drug resistance
b. avoiding mosquito bites
c. not eating contaminated beef
d. avoiding contact with birds and poultry farms

Name ______________________ Class ______________________ Date ______

Chapter 21 Test

Write the letter of the correct answer in the space provided.

_____ 1. What can cause an infectious disease when they enter your body and multiply?
- a. phagocytes
- b. antibodies
- c. pathogens
- d. T cells

_____ 2. The part of the body that provides a physical defense against infectious disease is the
- a. immune system.
- b. skin.
- c. liver.
- d. lymphatic system.

_____ 3. When a baby receives antibodies from its mother's breast milk, it is called
- a. passive immunity.
- b. epidemic.
- c. active immunity.
- d. inflammation.

_____ 4. Which behavior can help you get healthy and stay healthy?
- a. skipping breakfast most mornings
- b. going to school when you are ill
- c. getting at least eight hours of sleep at night
- d. washing your hands only once a day

_____ 5. Which of the following animals is a common carrier of emerging diseases?
- a. dogs
- b. mosquitoes
- c. deer
- d. ticks

Decide whether each statement is true or false. Write true *or* false *in the space provided.*

_____ 6. Inflammation is the body's general response to all kinds of injuries.

_____ 7. Pathogens cannot be spread from person to person on objects such as doorknobs.

_____ 8. The immune system produces a separate set of weapons for each kind of pathogen it encounters.

_____ 9. An antibiotic is a drug that kills or inhibits bacteria.

_____ 10. Strep throat is a viral infection of the upper respiratory system.

Name ______________ Class ______________ Date ______

Chapter 21: Test *(continued)*

Write the letter of the correct answer in the space provided.

____	**11.** white blood cells that engulf and destroy pathogens	**a.** antibodies
____	**12.** lymphocytes that destroy any body cell that has been infected by a pathogen	**b.** bacteria
____	**13.** proteins that attach to the surface of pathogens	**c.** phagocytes
____	**14.** injections that cause a person to become immune to a disease	**d.** immunizations
____	**15.** simple, single-celled microorganisms	**e.** viruses
		f. T cells

Write the word that best completes each sentence in the space provided.

16. Diseases caused by organisms or viruses that enter and multiply within the body are called ______________ diseases.

17. Some bacteria injure cells by giving off poisons called ______.

18. Infectious diseases that threaten to become more common in the near future are called ______________ diseases.

Use complete sentences to answer the following questions.

19. How does a vaccine cause a person to have active immunity?

____

____

____

____

____

20. What are three ways you can protect yourself from infectious diseases?

____

____

____

____

____

Name ______________________ Class ________________ Date ______

Chapter 22

Personal Inventory

Sexually Transmitted Infections and AIDS

How much do know about STIs (sexually transmitted infections), AIDS, and HIV (the virus that causes AIDS)? To protect yourself from STIs and HIV/AIDS, you need to know the facts about them. How are they spread? How can you tell if you have them? How can they be treated?

Read the statements below, and decide whether you think they are true or false. For each statement that you think is false, write a statement that you think is true on the line below it.

______ **1.** STIs include trichomoniasis and hepatitis.

____

______ **2.** Syphilis and gonorrhea are the most common STIs.

____

______ **3.** STIs and HIV spread only through sexual contact.

____

______ **4.** Teenagers rarely are infected with STIs or HIV.

____

______ **5.** A mother with AIDS can infect her baby with HIV.

____

______ **6.** You can get HIV by hugging a person with AIDS.

____

______ **7.** STIs always cause symptoms.

____

______ **8.** STIs rarely cause lasting problems.

____

______ **9.** All STIs can be cured with antibiotics.

____

______ **10.** There is no cure for AIDS.

____

Are there any statements you are uncertain of? Be sure to find the correct information about these statements when you read the chapter.

Name_________________________ Class___________ Date__________ M T W T F

Section 22-1

The Risks of Sexual Activity Lesson Plan

Section Objectives

- **Identify** risky behaviors associated with the current epidemic of sexually transmitted infections.
- **Decribe** behaviors that can help prevent the spread of sexually transmitted infections.

Vocabulary sexually transmitted infection (STI)

Time
1 period
1/2 block

Local Standards

1. FOCUS

Warm-Up: Quick Quiz Ask students to explain why each statement in the quiz is true. Discuss how thinking the statements are false might lead people to engage in risky behaviors.

Targeted Resources

- ❑ Transparency W77

2. TEACH

Building Health Skills Ask students to identify factors that might influence young people to adopt risky behaviors and how they could resist the influences. L3

Visual Learning: Figure 1 Ask a volunteer to describe the trend in chlamydia cases in young Americans. Discuss what young people should do if they think they have chlamydia. L2

Differentiated Instruction Show students how to use the headings in the text to create a concept map that can help them identify main ideas. L2

Cooperative Learning Have pairs of students write dialogues in which a teen resists peer pressure to try intravenous drugs, which could put them at risk for STIs. L1

Targeted Resources

- ❑ RN Note Taking Guide 22-1 L3 EL
- ❑ ARN Note Taking Guide 22-1 L2
- ❑ Transparency and Worksheet 65
- ❑ TR Practice 22-1
- ❑ TR Enrich 22-1 L4
- ❑ Audio Summary 22-1 L1 L2 EL
- ❑ Health Links: Updates on sexually transmitted infections

3. ASSESS

Evaluate Understanding The assignments listed in the Teacher's Edition can help you assess students' mastery of the section content.

Reteach Begin a general outline of section content, and have students work with partners to complete the outline. L2

Targeted Resources

- ❑ TR Section 22-1 Quiz
- ❑ CTB Chapter 22

KEY

L1 Special Needs
L2 Less Proficient Readers
L3 All Students
L4 Gifted and Talented
EL English Language Learners

Name ______________________ Class ____________________ Date ______

Section 22-1 **Practice**

Skill-Building Activity: Accessing STI Information

Do you know how to find reliable, up-to-date information in the library? This worksheet will help you access library sources to answer a question you have about STIs.

Follow the steps below. Record any information requested in the spaces provided.

Step 1: Identify Your Topic

What question do you have about STIs? (*Example:* How can I avoid STIs?)

____

Reword your question as a topic. (*Example:* Avoiding STIs)

____

Step 2: Search for Books on Your Topic

Do a subject search of the library catalog, using your topic as the subject. Record the authors, titles, dates, and call numbers of three recent books on your topic.

____

____

Step 3: Search for Magazine Articles on Your Topic

What source can you search for magazine articles on your topic? (Ask a reference librarian if you do not know. *Example:* InfoTrac)

____

Do a subject search of this source, using your topic as the subject. Record the authors, titles, dates, and citations of three recent magazine articles on your topic.

____

____

Step 4: Choose the Best Source

Try to find the books and magazine articles you listed in Steps 2 and 3. Skim all the sources you find, and put aside any that are less relevant to your topic. Of the remaining sources, which one is most reliable and up-to-date? This is likely to be your best source.

____

Reread the question you had about STIs. Can you answer it using the source you listed in Step 4? If not, how might you change your search for a more successful outcome?

____

____

Name ______________ Class ______________ Date ______

Section 22-1 **Enrich**

Cultural Connection: Culture and STIs

Some cultural beliefs and behaviors may indirectly promote the spread of STIs. They may prevent people from learning about STIs, protecting themselves from STIs, or being tested for STIs.

Choose one of the examples below or one of your own, and learn more about that belief or behavior. You can record the main points about what you learn in the spaces provided. Use an extra sheet of paper if necessary.

1. In some cultures, it is considered improper for adults to talk with children about matters relating to sex.
2. In some cultures, drawing blood is believed to weaken the body, so people are reluctant to donate blood or have blood drawn for tests.
3. In some cultures, it is extremely important to avoid bringing shame upon one's family. People may try to keep evidence of improper behavior hidden within the family for this reason.
4. In many cultures, gender roles put women in submissive positions that make it difficult for them to control their own abstinence or protect themselves from infection.
5. Write your own example here.

____

____

Record what you learn on the lines below.

____

____

____

____

____

____

Explain how the beliefs and behaviors you learned about might indirectly promote the spread of STIs.

____

____

____

____

____

Name ______________________ Class ______________________ Date ________

Section 22-1

Quiz

Write the letter of the correct answer in the space provided.

_____ **1.** Which choice is a reason that the STI epidemic is so serious?
a. STIs increase the risk of pregnancy.
b. All STIs are incurable.
c. STIs cannot be treated.
d. Some STIs are fatal if left untreated.

_____ **2.** What increases the risk of contracting an STI?
a. adopting the attitude, "It can't happen to me"
b. learning about the risks of sexual activity
c. having only one sexual partner
d. practicing sexual abstinence

_____ **3.** What is the main way that STIs are spread?
a. tattoos
b. body piercings
c. sexual activity
d. hugging

_____ **4.** What role does alcohol play in the STI epidemic?
a. It impairs judgment.
b. It causes some STIs.
c. It decreases risky behaviors.
d. It stops the spread of most STIs.

_____ **5.** Which is the best way to ensure that you practice healthy behaviors and avoid STIs?
a. Choose friends who have STIs, so they can tell you how to avoid them.
b. Choose friends who practice abstinence and avoid drugs, so they will support your healthy decisions.
c. Choose friends who pressure you to use drugs, so you can practice refusal skills.
d. Choose friends who pressure you to be sexually active, so you can test your resolve.

Decide whether each statement is true or false. Write true *or* false *in the space provided.*

_____ **6.** Any pathogen that spreads from one person to another during sexual contact is called an STI.

_____ **7.** Some STIs increase the risk of developing cancer later in life.

_____ **8.** People usually develop immunity to an STI after being infected.

_____ **9.** People who engage in sexual activity with multiple partners have the same risk of STIs as other people.

_____ **10.** If someone has never engaged in sexual activity, you can safely assume they do not have an STI.

Name______________________ Class__________ Date__________ M T W T F

Section 22-2

Kinds of STIs

Lesson Plan

Section Objectives

- **Identify** three of the most common STIs, including their symptoms and treatments.
- **List** four other STIs and describe their symptoms.
- **Know** when a person should seek treatment for an STI.

Vocabulary trichomoniasis • urethritis • vaginitis • human papilloma virus • chlamydia • pelvic inflammatory disease • gonorrhea • genital herpes • syphilis • chancre

Time
2 periods
1 block

Local Standards

1. FOCUS

Warm-Up: Myth/Fact Call on several students to get a diversity of views about the myth. Make sure students realize that some STIs infect people for life.

Targeted Resources

- ❑ Transparency W78

2. TEACH

Building Media Literacy Ask students to come up with criteria to assess media sources of STI information. L3

Building Vocabulary Give the meaning of *-itis* as "inflammation of," and have students identify which structures are inflamed in urethritis and vaginitis. L2

Visual Learning: Figure 6 Challenge students to brainstorm how each of the STIs in the table could be prevented. L2

Differentiated Instruction Have pairs of students make a compare/contrast table for hepatitis, gonorrhea, and genital herpes. L1

Active Learning Ask small groups of students to learn about clinics in their community that test for STIs. L3

Targeted Resources

- ❑ RN Note Taking Guide 22-2 L3 EL
- ❑ ARN Note Taking Guide 22-2 L2
- ❑ TR Practice 22-2
- ❑ TR Enrich 22-2 L4
- ❑ Audio Summary 22-2 L1 L2 EL
- ❑ PHSchool.com: More on sexually transmitted infections

3. ASSESS

Evaluate Understanding The assignments listed in the Teacher's Edition can help you assess students' mastery of the section content.

Reteach Have pairs of students play a quiz game in which one student chooses an STI and the partner asks a series of questions to try to identify which STI it is. L2

Targeted Resources

- ❑ TR Section 22-2 Quiz
- ❑ CTB Chapter 22

KEY

- L1 Special Needs
- L2 Less Proficient Readers
- L3 All Students
- L4 Gifted and Talented
- EL English Language Learners

Name ______________________ Class ________________ Date ________

Section 22-2 **Practice**

Vocabulary Activity: Common STIs

Solve the crossword puzzle below.

Clues Down

1. bacterial STI that infects the urinary tract
2. viral disease that may cause outbreaks of blisters
3. common STI that causes PID
6. bacterial STI that goes through multiple stages

Clues Across

4. type of virus that causes genital warts
5. most common protozoan STI in the United States
7. viral STI that attacks the liver

Name ______________________ Class ______________________ Date ____________

Section 22-2 **Enrich**

Consumer Skills: OTC Products for STIs

Many products that claim to be effective treatments for STIs are available without a prescription. For example, some herbal products claim to prevent genital herpes outbreaks and others claim to cure chlamydia.

Find two advertisements for products of this nature. You can look for advertisements in magazines or on the Internet. Answer the following questions about the products.

1. What is the advertised product supposed to do?

Product A: ______________________ Product B: ______________________

2. What side effects may the product cause?

Product A: ______________________ Product B: ______________________

3. In what way has the product been tested and shown to be effective?

Product A: ______________________ Product B: ______________________

4. What is the cost of the product, and where is it available?

Product A: ______________________ Product B: ______________________

Review your answers and decide whether you would recommend either of the two products. Check off your decisions and explain your reasoning.

5. Product A: [ ] Recommend [ ] Not Recommend

____

6. Product B: [ ] Recommend [ ] Not Recommend

____

7. Why might these products do more harm than good for people infected with STIs?

____

Name ______________ Class ______________ Date ______

Section 22-2

Quiz

Write the letter of the correct answer in the space provided.

______ **1.** common STI caused by a protozoan

______ **2.** pathogen that causes genital warts

______ **3.** STI that may lead to cirrhosis

______ **4.** STI that may cause painful blisters

______ **5.** STI that starts with a chancre

a. hepatitis

b. chlamydia

c. trichomoniasis

d. syphilis

e. genital herpes

f. human papilloma virus

Decide whether each statement is true or false. Write true *or* false *in the space provided.*

______ **6.** The three most common STIs are gonorrhea, syphilis, and genital herpes.

______ **7.** Chlamydia can cause pelvic inflammatory disease in females.

______ **8.** Gonorrhea is a viral STI that infects the urinary tract in males and females.

______ **9.** People who practice high-risk behaviors do *not* need medical checkups every six months.

______ **10.** People who think they have an STI should wait six months to see if the symptoms go away.

Name________________________ Class__________ Date__________ M T W T F

Section 22-3

HIV and AIDS

Lesson Plan

Section Objectives

- **Explain** how HIV infection leads to AIDS.
- **Describe** how HIV is transmitted from person to person.
- **Summarize** the state of HIV infection and AIDS throughout the world.

Vocabulary HIV • AIDS • asymptomatic stage • opportunistic infection

Time
2 periods
1 block

Local Standards

1. FOCUS

Warm-Up: Health Stats Ask volunteers to read the factors they identified that might explain the increase in young people living with HIV and AIDS.

Targeted Resources

- ❑ Transparency W79

2. TEACH

Addressing Misconceptions Explain the difference between HIV and AIDS, and point out that people may have HIV infections for years before developing AIDS. L2

Visual Learning: Figure 9 Guide students in interpreting the graph of T cell count and HIV infection. L3

Building Health Skills Have the class brainstorm healthful behaviors that would decrease the risk of HIV infection. L3

Differentiated Instruction Ask interested students to interview a local public health official about HIV and AIDS and share what they learn in an oral report. L4

Active Learning Have students find out how the American Red Cross protects the blood supply and display what they learn. L3

Targeted Resources

- ❑ RN Note Taking Guide 22-3 L3 EL
- ❑ ARN Note Taking Guide 22-3 L2
- ❑ Transparencies and Worksheets 66, 67
- ❑ TR Practice 22-3
- ❑ TR Enrich 22-3 L4
- ❑ Audio Summary 22-3 L1 L2 EL
- ❑ Health Links: Updates on AIDS

3. ASSESS

Evaluate Understanding The assignments listed in the Teacher's Edition can help you assess students' mastery of the section content.

Reteach Ask students to write a paragraph in which they correctly use each of the section vocabulary terms. Have students work in pairs to check and correct their work. L2

Targeted Resources

- ❑ TR Section 22-3 Quiz
- ❑ CTB Chapter 22

KEY

L1 Special Needs	L4 Gifted and Talented
L2 Less Proficient Readers	EL English Language Learners
L3 All Students	

Name ______________ Class ______________ Date ______

Section 22-3 **Practice**

Group Activity: HIV/AIDS Pamphlet

Educating people about the ways HIV is transmitted and how they can protect themselves from HIV infection is an important step in controlling the spread of HIV. Teens are one of the groups at highest risk of HIV infection. Think about how you could design a pamphlet that would help other teens understand HIV and AIDS and protect themselves from HIV infection. What kind of pamphlet would be interesting and easy to understand? How could you illustrate it?

With a group of other students, answer the questions below in complete sentences. Then use the questions and answers to develop a pamphlet on HIV and AIDS with other members of your group.

1. What is AIDS?

____

____

2. What causes AIDS?

____

____

____

____

3. How is HIV transmitted?

____

____

____

____

4. Who is at greatest risk of HIV infection?

____

____

____

5. How can you protect yourself from HIV?

____

____

____

Name ______________________ Class ____________________ Date ______

Section 22-3 **Enrich**

Community Involvement: AIDS Survey

Many people are confused about HIV and AIDS. They are uncertain about how it is spread, who is at risk, and how to protect themselves from infection. What misunderstandings about AIDS do people in your community have?

Make copies of the questionnaire below. Ask several adults and teens in your community to complete the questionnaire anonymously. Respondents should check if they agree with, disagree with, or are undecided about each statement. Keep their answers confidential.

AIDS Questionnaire

Statement	Agree	Disagree	Undecided
1. AIDS is a virus that weakens the immune system.			
2. AIDS affects only homosexual men and drug addicts.			
3. You can get AIDS by hugging someone who is infected.			
4. You can get AIDS from public drinking fountains and toilets.			
5. A person with AIDS can spread the virus only if he or she has symptoms.			
6. People with AIDS should not be allowed to work with the public.			
7. Students with AIDS should not be allowed to attend school.			
8. Condoms are completely effective in preventing the spread of AIDS.			
9. AIDS can be cured if it is treated early.			

For each statement, count how many people gave each response. Based on the counts, identify areas where people seem to have misunderstandings or lack information. Describe a way the misunderstandings could be cleared up and the information could be delivered to people who need it.

____

____

____

____

Name ______________________ Class ______________________ Date ______

Section 22-3 Quiz

Write the letter of the correct answer in the space provided.

______	**1.** cause of AIDS	**a.**	asymptomatic stage
______	**2.** what HIV attacks	**b.**	HIV
______	**3.** first stage of HIV infection	**c.**	immune system
______	**4.** second stage of HIV infection	**d.**	AIDS
______	**5.** third stage of HIV infection	**e.**	bacteria
		f.	symptomatic stage

Write the letter of the correct answer in the space provided.

______ **6.** What happens to helper T cells after a person is infected with HIV?
- **a.** Helper T cells increase in number.
- **b.** Helper T cells decrease in number.
- **c.** Helper T cells reproduce inside the virus.
- **d.** Helper T cells multiply and kill all the virus.

______ **7.** The first symptoms of an HIV infection are
- **a.** flulike symptoms.
- **b.** persistent fever and diarrhea.
- **c.** weight loss and diarrhea.
- **d.** fungal infections.

______ **8.** What determines the onset of AIDS in an HIV-infected person?
- **a.** The initial symptoms go away.
- **b.** Symptoms such as weight loss begin.
- **c.** The helper T cell count becomes very low.
- **d.** Symptoms such as blindness develop.

______ **9.** Which behavior is an example of a way in which you *cannot* become infected with HIV?
- **a.** sharing a needle when getting a tattoo
- **b.** having sexual contact with a person who has used needles to inject drugs
- **c.** having lunch with someone who is HIV-positive
- **d.** touching another person's open sore

______ **10.** In what part of the world are the majority of HIV infections concentrated?
- **a.** North America
- **b.** South and Southeast Asia
- **c.** Sub-Saharan Africa
- **d.** North Africa and the Middle East

Name______________________ Class__________ Date__________ M T W T F

Section 22-4

Protecting Yourself From HIV and AIDS Lesson Plan

Section Objectives

- **Identify** three behaviors that can prevent the spread of HIV.
- **Describe** how a person gets tested for HIV.
- **Describe** the goal of HIV treatment.

Vocabulary universal precautions • HIV-positive • viral load

Time
1 period
1/2 block

Local Standards

1. FOCUS

Warm-Up: Advice Line Ask students to explain why abstinence is the only sure way to avoid becoming infected with HIV in a relationship.

Targeted Resources
- ❑ Transparency W80

2. TEACH

Journal Writing Have students write a private journal entry describing ways they could respond to someone who pressures them to engage in sexual activity. L3

Class Discussion Discuss with students why it is important for people who test positive for HIV to receive counseling. L3

Cooperative Learning Challenge small groups of students to brainstorm ways to help people with HIV and AIDS comply with treatment. EL

Building Health Skills Have students find out how they can volunteer to help people in their community who are living with HIV, and urge them to follow through. L2

Differentiated Instruction Ask volunteers to help you demonstrate ways that HIV is *not* spread, and explain why it is safe to go to school with people with HIV. L1

Targeted Resources
- ❑ RN Note Taking Guide 22-4 L3 EL
- ❑ ARN Note Taking Guide 22-4 L2
- ❑ TR Practice 22-4
- ❑ TR Enrich 22-4 L4
- ❑ Audio Summary 22-4 L1 L2 EL
- ❑ PHSchool.com: More on HIV/AIDS prevention

3. ASSESS

Evaluate Understanding The assignments listed in the Teacher's Edition can help you assess students' mastery of the section content.

Reteach Ask students to rewrite the section objectives as questions and then write answers to each question. Have them check their answers by looking in the text. L2

Targeted Resources
- ❑ TR Section 22-4 Quiz
- ❑ CTB Chapter 22

KEY

L1 Special Needs	L4 Gifted and Talented
L2 Less Proficient Readers	EL English Language Learners
L3 All Students	

Name ______________________ Class __________________ Date ______

Section 22-4 **Practice**

Skill-Building Activity: Reducing the Risk of HIV

How would you respond in a risky situation involving HIV? Would you know what healthful behaviors to choose to avoid the risk of HIV?

Read about each of the situations below. Decide what you would do in each situation and explain why you would respond that way.

Situation 1: Wen-Lee has been dating Tanya for a year. Lately, Tanya has been pressuring Wen-Lee to have a sexual relationship. Wen-Lee is afraid that Tanya may have been exposed to HIV in a previous relationship. He doesn't want to risk becoming infected, but he also doesn't want to lose his girlfriend.

If you were Wen-Lee, what would you do and why?

____

____

____

____

____

Situation 2: Tara and Manuel have been involved in a sexual relationship for a few months. Tara recently noticed a vaginal discharge. Now she wonders if Manuel told her the truth when he said he never had a sexual relationship before. She's worried that Manuel may have given her an STI.

If you were Tara, what would you do and why?

____

____

____

____

____

Situation 3: Gilberto is at a party, and his friend Keisha is trying to convince him to try injecting heroin. Keisha tells Gilberto that it's safe and that everyone else is doing it. She says that Gilberto will miss all the fun if he doesn't join in.

If you were Gilberto, what would you do and why?

____

____

____

____

Name ______________________ Class __________________ Date ______

Section 22-4 **Enrich**

Class Debate: Should HIV Testing Be Mandatory?

One reason HIV has spread so quickly in the last few decades is that people may be infected and pass the virus to others months or even years before they know they have HIV. Some people argue in favor of mandatory HIV testing for this reason. They say that if certain groups of people had to be tested, then most infected people would be identified, and the infected people could take steps to avoid transmitting the infection to others. Another argument for mandatory testing is that it would help public health authorities track the disease and better understand it.

There are just as many arguments against mandatory HIV testing. Many people argue that mandatory testing would be an infringement of civil rights. Another argument is that mandatory testing would be too expensive and less effective than other, cheaper measures, such as educational programs about how to prevent HIV infections.

Several other arguments have been made for and against mandatory HIV testing. Find out what some of the other arguments are, and summarize them in the spaces provided below.

Arguments in Favor of Mandatory HIV Testing:

____

____

____

____

____

____

Arguments Against Mandatory HIV Testing:

____

____

____

____

____

____

Organize a debate with at least one other student. Choose a student to argue each side of the issue, and present the debate to the rest of the class. After the debate, ask other students to express their opinions on the issue.

Name ______________________ Class ____________________ Date ______

Section 22-4

Quiz

Decide whether each statement is true or false. Write true *or* false *in the space provided.*

______ **1.** There is no cure for HIV infection or AIDS.

______ **2.** The best way to avoid HIV and AIDS is sexual abstinence.

______ **3.** You cannot get HIV by sharing personal items such as razors.

______ **4.** Condoms are 100% effective in preventing the transmission of HIV.

______ **5.** A goal of HIV treatment is to keep the T cell count as low as possible.

Write the letter of the correct answer in the space provided.

______ **6.** What does an HIV test detect?
a. HIV virus
b. AIDS virus
c. antibodies to HIV
d. helper T cells

______ **7.** What does it mean if you are HIV-positive?
a. You are free of HIV.
b. You definitely have AIDS.
c. You are infected with HIV.
d. You might develop HIV in a few years.

______ **8.** How long after a risky sexual contact should one wait to be tested for HIV?
a. three months
b. three years
c. six months
d. six days

______ **9.** What is a drawback of the drugs that are used to treat HIV infections?
a. The drugs can cause liver and kidney damage.
b. The drugs rarely cause drug resistance to develop.
c. The drugs keep the viral load in the blood very low.
d. The drugs encourage the virus to reproduce inside T cells.

______ **10.** One way that HIV can be transmitted is
a. by hugging.
b. by shaking hands.
c. through breast milk.
d. through casual contact.

Name ______________________ Class ____________________ Date ______

Section 22-4 Test

Write the letter of the correct answer in the space provided.

______ **1.** Which behavior helps account for the current STI epidemic?
a. practicing sexual abstinence
b. having multiple sexual partners
c. getting proper treatment
d. knowing the symptoms of STIs

______ **2.** The most common bacterial STI in the United States is
a. gonorrhea. **b.** trichomoniasis.
c. syphilis. **d.** chlamydia.

______ **3.** Which is *not* a way that HIV can pass from one person to another?
a. blood **b.** semen
c. vaginal secretions **d.** hair

______ **4.** How many people are infected with HIV and AIDS worldwide?
a. 4 million **b.** 13 million
c. 40 million **d.** 40 billion

______ **5.** Why is a second HIV test done if antibodies are detected in the first test?
a. to detect the virus **b.** to verify the result
c. to count T cells **d.** to detect AIDS

Write the letter of the correct answer in the space provided.

______ **6.** condition of being unable to have children

______ **7.** vaginal infection or irritation

______ **8.** infection that attacks a person who has a weakened immune system

______ **9.** disposing of syringes and needles properly

______ **10.** number of virus particles circulating in the body

a. opportunistic infection
b. infertility
c. vaginitis
d. T cell count
e. viral load
f. universal precaution

Decide whether each statement is true or false. Write true *or* false *in the space provided.*

______ **11.** Choosing responsible friends is an important way to avoid STIs.

______ **12.** Trichomoniasis is rare in the United States.

______ **13.** A mother can pass HIV to her child only during birth.

______ **14.** HIV infections may cause no symptoms for months or years.

______ **15.** The main goal of HIV treatment is to kill all the HIV viruses in the body.

Name ______________________ Class ____________________ Date ______

Chapter 22: Test *(continued)*

Write the word or phrase that best completes each sentence in the space provided.

16. Any pathogen that is transmitted through sexual contact is a(an) ______________ ______________________.

17. Inflammation of the lining of the urethra is called ______________.

18. The best way to avoid STIs and HIV is to practice ______________ ______________________.

Use complete sentences to answer the following questions.

19. Describe risky behaviors that contribute to the spread of STIs.

____

____

____

____

____

____

20. Explain how to protect yourself from HIV infection.

____

____

____

____

____

____

____

Name ______________________ Class ____________________ Date ______

Chapter 23

Personal Inventory

Family Health History

Use this chart to begin a family health history of chronic diseases and disabilities. In the columns headed Family Member, write the name of any close relative who has or had the disease or disability. (Close relatives include your parents, grandparents, brothers, sisters, uncles, aunts, and the brothers and sisters of your grandparents.) Good sources for this kind of information include family records or a knowledgeable older relative.

Fill in the chart below. Continue the chart on another sheet of paper, if necessary.

Condition	Family Member	Condition	Family Member
Alcoholism		Hypertension	
Allergies		Impaired mobility	
Arrhythmia		Inherited disorder	
Asthma		Mental disability	
Cancer Type:			
Congestive heart failure		Obesity	
Diabetes, type 1		Osteoarthritis	
Diabetes, type 2		Osteoporosis	
Emphysema		Rheumatoid arthritis	
Epilepsy		Sickle-cell disease	
Hearing impairment		Stroke	
Heart attack		Visual impairment	

What did you learn about your family history that you did not know before?

____

____

____

What can you do to decrease the risk for each condition that appears in your family health history?

____

____

____

Name_________________________ Class__________ Date__________ M T W T F

Section 23-1

Cardiovascular Diseases Lesson Plan

Section Objectives

- **List** six types of cardiovascular disease.
- **Describe** the ways in which cardiovascular disease is detected and treated.
- **Identify** risk factors for cardiovascular disease and ways to lower your risk.

Vocabulary chronic disease • cardiovascular disease • angina pectoris • heart attack • fibrillation • stroke • cerebral hemorrhage • aneurysm

Time
2 periods
1 block

Local Standards

1. FOCUS

Warm-Up: Quick Quiz Ask students to complete the Quick Quiz and predict how their behaviors could affect their chances of developing cardiovascular disease.

Targeted Resources

- ❑ Transparency W81

2. TEACH

Class Discussion Discuss what a chronic disease is and what the three types of risk factors are that cause chronic diseases. **L2**

Differentiated Instruction Help students understand the difference between the terms *atherosclerosis* and *arteriosclerosis*. **L2**

Active Learning Have students make wallet cards that contain the warning signs of a heart attack. **L1**

Visual Learning: Figure 4 Lead a discussion on the testing tools and treatment methods described in the chart. **L3**

Building Health Skills Have students determine the meanings of some commonly used terms on food labels in order to help them choose healthful foods. **L2**

Targeted Resources

- ❑ RN Note Taking Guide 23-1 **L3** **EL**
- ❑ ARN Note Taking Guide 23-1 **L2**
- ❑ Transparency and Worksheet 68
- ❑ TR Practice 23-1
- ❑ TR Enrich 23-1 **L4**
- ❑ Audio Summary 23-1 **L1** **L2** **EL**
- ❑ PHSchool.com: More on cardiovascular disease

3. ASSESS

Evaluate Understanding The assignments listed in the Teacher's Edition can help you assess students' mastery of the section content.

Reteach Work with students to create a bulletin board illustrating information about cardiovascular disease. **L2**

Targeted Resources

- ❑ TR Section 23-1 Quiz
- ❑ CTB Chapter 23

KEY

L1	Special Needs	**L4**	Gifted and Talented
L2	Less Proficient Readers	**EL**	English Language Learners
L3	All Students		

Name ______________________ Class ______________ Date ________

Section 23-1 **Practice**

Concept Check: Cardiovascular Disease Risk Factors

The risk factors for developing cardiovascular disease vary from person to person. An individual's lifestyle can provide clues about his or her risk factors.

Read each case study, and list the risk factors each person has for developing cardiovascular disease. List your own risk factors at the bottom of the page.

Case Studies	Risk Factors
1. Bill is 45 years old. He has high blood pressure but is very careful about taking his medication. He takes brisk walks five days a week. This routine has helped to keep his weight down. Lately, Bill has reduced his fat intake. His work is stressful, and he often comes home in a grouchy mood. Bill is a former smoker who has not had a cigarette in two years.	______________________
2. Liz is 20 years old and plays tennis, jogs, and swims regularly. These activities help her maintain her ideal body weight. Liz has diabetes, so she is careful to keep her intake of sugar and fats at a minimum. She uses jogging or swimming to relieve job-related stress.	______________________
3. Rob is in his 30s. He finds the stresses of family life upsetting and has little patience with his wife and his children. Rob is always under a great deal of pressure at work. He smokes two packs of cigarettes a day and has high blood pressure but does not take his medication. Since college, Rob has gained a lot of weight, and he cannot seem to find the time to exercise.	______________________
4. What factors in your lifestyle may contribute to cardiovascular disease? What factors in your lifestyle may help to reduce the risk of cardiovascular disease?	______________________

Name ____________________ Class ____________________ Date __________

Section 23-1 **Enrich**

Consumer Skills: Evaluating Products Low in Saturated Fats

One way to reduce your risk of cardiovascular disease is by eating a healthy diet, including foods that are low in saturated fats. Often, you have a choice between a food that is high in saturated fats and an alternative that is lower in saturated fats. The alternatives are often labeled as "lite," "low-fat," or "healthy." In the case of milk, the low-fat alternative is skim milk. You can check the saturated fat content of a food by reading the Nutrition Facts label on the package. The Nutrition Facts label states the amount of saturated fat in one serving of the food, as well as what percent of the recommended daily value one serving provides.

At a local grocery store, compare the products you might normally buy with alternative products that are lower in saturated fat. For each product, record the amount of saturated fat in one serving and the percent of the recommended daily value one serving provides.

Milk

Vitamin D milk: ____________________

Skim milk: ____________________

Butter

Butter: ____________________

Low-fat spread: ____________________

Lunch meat

Regular package: ____________________

Low-fat package: ____________________

Cottage cheese

Regular carton: ____________________

Low-fat carton: ____________________

Soup

Regular soup: ____________________

Low-fat soup: ____________________

Snack crackers

Regular box: ____________________

Low-fat box: ____________________

Ice Cream

Regular carton: ____________________

Low-fat carton: ____________________

Cookies

Regular package: ____________________

Low-fat package: ____________________

Other

Regular: ____________________

Low-fat: ____________________

Other

Regular: ____________________

Low-fat: ____________________

Answer the questions in the spaces provided.

1. In general, how did the low-fat foods compare in saturated fats with the regular foods?

____

____

2. You have probably tasted some low-fat foods. Do you think there is any difference in taste between regular foods and low-fat foods? Explain your answer.

____

____

Name ______________ Class ______________ Date ________

Section 23-1 **Quiz**

Write the letter of the correct answer in the space provided.

_____ **1.** occurs when some of the tissue in the heart doesn't receive its normal blood supply and dies

_____ **2.** a sudden disruption of blood flow to part of the brain

_____ **3.** the chest pain that occurs when an area of the heart does not get enough oxygen-rich blood

_____ **4.** a blood-filled weak spot that balloons out from an artery wall

_____ **5.** a life-threatening arrhythmia in which the heart twitches rapidly in an uncoordinated fashion

a. angina pectoris

b. heart attack

c. aneurysm

d. stroke

e. fibrillation

f. cerebral hemorrhage

Decide whether each statement is true or false. Write true *or* false *in the space provided.*

_____ **6.** A person's heart is replaced by a heart from an organ donor during coronary bypass surgery.

_____ **7.** Hardening of the arteries is called arteriosclerosis.

_____ **8.** In an electrocardiogram, electrodes are attached to the skin to detect the heart's electrical activity.

_____ **9.** Feelings of stress and anxiety can raise blood pressure and contribute to cardiovascular disease.

_____ **10.** Having a family history of cardiovascular disease does not increase a person's risk of developing cardiovascular disease.

Name__________________ Class__________ Date__________ M T W T F

Section 23-2

Cancer

Lesson Plan

Section Objectives

- **Describe** how cancer affects the body.
- **Identify** the tests and treatments for cancer.
- **List** seven ways you can prevent cancer.

Vocabulary cancer • tumor • malignant • metastasis • oncogene • carcinogen • biopsy

Time
2 periods
1 block

Local Standards

1. FOCUS

Warm-Up: Health Stats Ask students to interpret a graph of common cancers in the United States and propose explanations for the difference in the number of lung cancer cases between males and females.

Targeted Resources

- ❑ Transparency W82

2. TEACH

Differentiated Instruction Have students make flashcards of difficult terms in the section, including pronunciations and definitions written in their own words. EL

Teacher Demo Use a large illustration of the human body to clarify how cancers metastasize. L1

Building Health Skills Have students consider the consequences of taking advantage of a free membership to a tanning salon. L2

Cooperative Learning Assign one of the ten cancers listed in Figure 8 each to ten groups of students, and have each group research and prepare a report about its type of cancer. L3

Class Discussion Lead a discussion on the treatments available for cancer. L3

Building Health Skills Have student groups make a poster conveying to other teens behaviors that can reduce their risk of cancer. L2

Targeted Resources

- ❑ RN Note Taking Guide 23-2 L3 EL
- ❑ ARN Note Taking Guide 23-2 L2
- ❑ TR Practice 23-2
- ❑ TR Enrich 23-2 L4
- ❑ Audio Summary 23-2 L1 L2 EL
- ❑ Health Links: Updates on skin cancer

3. ASSESS

Evaluate Understanding The assignments listed in the Teacher's Edition can help you assess students' mastery of the section content.

Reteach Have students write a paragraph that could be used to inform the public about cancer. L2

Targeted Resources

- ❑ TR Section 23-2 Quiz
- ❑ CTB Chapter 23

KEY

L1 Special Needs
L2 Less Proficient Readers
L3 All Students
L4 Gifted and Talented
EL English Language Learners

Name ______________________ Class ______________________ Date __________

Section 23-2 **Practice**

Vocabulary Activity: Cancer

The development and diagnosis of cancer proceed through a series of steps. *For each step of the process, fill in the blank with one of the section's vocabulary terms.*

1. A normal gene of a man mutates to become a(an) ______________________, a cancer-causing gene.

2. The man is exposed to a(an) ______________________, a cancer-causing agent in the environment.

3. A mass of tissue, called a(an) ______________________, grows in the man's lungs.

4. The ______________________ tumor, a cancerous tumor, grows into surrounding tissues and destroys them.

5. The tumor cells spread from the lungs to other parts of the body, a process called ______________________.

6. The man feels ill and goes to a physician, who has a surgeon perform a(an) ______________________, the removal of a small piece of tissue for examination.

7. Examination of the biopsy confirms a diagnosis that the man has ______________________, a disease that involves the rapid, uncontrolled growth and spread of abnormal cells.

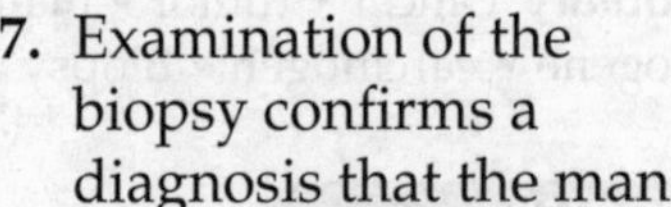

Name ____________________ Class ____________________ Date ________

Section 23-2 **Enrich**

Research Project: Who Treats Cancer Patients?

A person who is diagnosed with cancer usually comes into contact with a number of different doctors as he or she moves through various stages of treatment. Use print or online resources to research the following list of physicians who may play a role in the treatment of a cancer patient.

dermatologist	pathologist
proctologist	surgical oncologist
medical oncologist	personal physician
radiation oncologist	urologist

Write the name of each type of physician in the spaces provided.

1. Physician of internal medicine who specializes in treating specific cancers by administering a variety of drugs: ____________________

2. Physician who specializes in the treatment of the urinary system and treats men who have prostate cancer: ____________________

3. Physician who performs biopsies and also surgically removes cancerous tumors: ____________________

4. Physician who studies and interprets biopsy samples to identify cancerous tissue: ____________________

5. Physician who refers a patient to other doctors and coordinates the patient's treatment: ____________________

6. Physician who treats skin cancer and other skin conditions:

____

7. Physician who supervises radiation therapy:

____

8. Physician who treats colon and rectal conditions, including cancers:

____

Name ______________________ Class ____________________ Date ________

Section 23-2

Quiz

Decide whether each statement is true or false. Write true *or* false *in the space provided.*

______ **1.** The key to curing cancer is early detection and treatment.

______ **2.** Maintaining a healthy weight is a behavior that has been shown to decrease the risk of cancer.

______ **3.** Regularly examining yourself for abnormal lumps or growths is a poor habit to develop.

______ **4.** Cancer harms the body by destroying healthy body tissues.

______ **5.** To prevent colorectal cancer, you should eat a diet high in saturated fat.

Write the letter of the correct answer in the space provided.

______ **6.** The environment contains cancer-causing agents known as
a. oncogenes.
b. carcinogens.
c. tumors.
d. biopsies.

______ **7.** What word is used to describe a cancerous tumor?
a. malignant
b. radiation
c. remission
d. carcinogen

______ **8.** Cancer cells typically form a mass called a(an)
a. metastasis.
b. tumor.
c. oncogene.
d. remission.

______ **9.** Metastasis is the
a. use of drugs to slow the reproduction of cancer cells.
b. procedure in which a small piece of tissue is removed and examined.
c. body's system that controls cell reproduction.
d. spread of cancer from where it first develops to other parts of the body.

______ **10.** What kind of cancer treatment uses drugs to slow the reproduction of cancer cells?
a. radiation
b. metastasis
c. chemotherapy
d. biopsy

Name_______________________ Class__________ Date__________ M T W T F

Section 23-3 Other Chronic Diseases Lesson Plan

Section Objectives

- **Distinguish** between the two types of diabetes.
- **Describe** how allergies and asthma affect the body.
- **Identify** the symptoms of arthritis.

Vocabulary diabetes • insulin • allergy • allergen • histamine • arthritis • osteoarthritis • rheumatoid arthritis

Time
2 periods
1 block

Local Standards

1. FOCUS

Warm-Up: Advice Line Ask students to write a draft response to a question about diabetes and revise the response after reading the section.

Targeted Resources

- ❑ Transparency W83

2. TEACH

Visual Learning: Figure 10 Have students infer trends about diabetes from the graph titled Americans With Diabetes. L2

Differentiated Instruction Pair special needs students with more proficient students, and ask pairs to make a table comparing and contrasting type 1 and type 2 diabetes. L1

Teacher Demo Show students an over-the-counter allergy medicine label and ask them to explain what an antihistamine does for someone with an allergy. L2

Cooperative Learning Have pairs of students create a cause and effect chart for asthma. EL

Building Health Skills Ask students to identify behaviors that might prevent the development of osteoarthritis. L3

Targeted Resources

- ❑ RN Note Taking Guide 23-3 L3 EL
- ❑ ARN Note Taking Guide 23-3 L2
- ❑ Transparency and Worksheet 69
- ❑ TR Practice 23-3
- ❑ TR Enrich 23-3 L4
- ❑ Audio Summary 23-3 L1 L2 EL
- ❑ Health Links: Updates on allergies

3. ASSESS

Evaluate Understanding The assignments listed in the Teacher's Edition can help you assess students' mastery of the section content.

Reteach Have members of small groups review section content using the section objectives. L2

Targeted Resources

- ❑ TR Section 23-3 Quiz
- ❑ CTB Chapter 23

KEY

L1 Special Needs	L4 Gifted and Talented
L2 Less Proficient Readers	EL English Language Learners
L3 All Students	

Name ______________________ Class ______________ Date ________

Skill-Building Activity: Advocating for the Prevention of Type 2 Diabetes

It is possible to prevent type 2 diabetes by practicing healthful behaviors. Risk factors for diabetes include a family history, being overweight, and a lack of physical activity. The prevention of type 2 diabetes involves maintaining a desirable weight and exercising regularly.

Write a letter to persuade a relative to adopt healthy habits that could prevent the development of type 2 diabetes. In your letter, include what you know about type 2 diabetes as well as a diet and exercise plan that could prevent development of the disease.

____

____
(your address)

____
(date)

Dear ______________________,

Sincerely,

____

Name ______________________ Class ______________________ Date __________

Section 23-3 **Enrich**

Family Involvement: Living With Osteoarthritis

Osteoarthritis is caused by wear and tear on joints after years of use or by repeated injuries to joints. Most people who live past 60 years develop some form of osteoarthritis. The effects of the disease vary from person to person. A person with osteoarthritis might have occasional pain in the fingers or severe pain in the hips, knees, and spine. Osteoarthritis can make performing even simple tasks painful and difficult.

Interview an older relative who has osteoarthritis. Prepare a list of questions, including when symptoms of the disease first appeared, what problems the disease causes, and what behaviors, habits, and medicines help relieve the symptoms.

After you conduct your interview, answer the following questions in the spaces provided.

1. What symptoms of osteoarthritis did your relative describe?

2. What problems does your relative face during a typical day because of the symptoms of osteoarthritis?

3. What medicines does your relative take for osteoarthritis?

4. What exercises, foods, or habits does your relative say help in coping with the symptoms of osteoarthritis?

Name ______________________ Class ____________________ Date ______

Section 23-3 Quiz

Decide whether each statement is true or false. Write true *or* false *in the space provided.*

______ **1.** In osteoarthritis, the membrane surrounding a joint becomes inflamed.

______ **2.** Type 1 diabetes usually first appears in children.

______ **3.** A person with type 2 diabetes produces little or no insulin.

______ **4.** Both types of diabetes result in a high level of glucose in the blood.

______ **5.** Managing asthma involves avoiding the triggers that bring on asthma attacks.

Write the letter of the correct answer in the space provided.

______ **6.** a hormone produced by the pancreas that stimulates body cells to take up and use blood sugar

______ **7.** a disorder in which a person's respiratory passages become inflamed and narrow significantly in reaction to certain "triggers"

______ **8.** a disorder in which the immune system is overly sensitive to a particular substance not normally found in the body

______ **9.** a disease in which the body's ability to use glucose is impaired

______ **10.** inflammation or irritation of a joint

a. diabetes
b. allergy
c. histamine
d. insulin
e. arthritis
f. asthma

Name______________________ Class__________ Date__________ M T W T F

Section 23-4

Disabilities — Lesson Plan

Section Objectives

- **Identify** the three most common physical disabilities.
- **Explain** how the rights of people with disabilities are protected.

Vocabulary disability • macular degeneration • tinnitus • Americans with Disabilities Act

Time
1 period
1/2 block

Local Standards

1. FOCUS

Warm-Up: Myth/Fact Ask students to read the myth/fact about people with disabilities and identify other misconceptions people hold about disabilities.

Targeted Resources
- ❑ Transparency W84

2. TEACH

Cooperative Learning Divide the class into pairs, and have a member of each pair perform a task while blindfolded, with the partner helping the blindfolded student. L1

Visual Learning: Figure 15 Have students explain the importance of each of the guidelines in the figure. L3

Writing and Health Ask students to write a description of how a physical disability would change their daily lives. Students with physical disabilities should describe their typical day. L1

Addressing Misconceptions Emphasize to students that people with disabilities affecting muscular coordination are not necessarily mentally disabled also. L2

Class Discussion Lead a discussion on the purpose and necessity of the Americans with Disabilities Act. L2

Targeted Resources
- ❑ RN Note Taking Guide 23-4 L3 EL
- ❑ ARN Note Taking Guide 23-4 L2
- ❑ Transparency and Worksheet 70
- ❑ TR Practice 23-4
- ❑ TR Enrich 23-4 L4
- ❑ Audio Summary 23-4 L1 L2 EL
- ❑ PHSchool.com: More on disabilities

3. ASSESS

Evaluate Understanding The assignments listed in the Teacher's Edition can help you assess students' mastery of the section content.

Reteach Call on students to identify causes for each of the three most common physical disabilities and describe technologies, devices, or techniques used to help people with each type of disability. L2

Targeted Resources
- ❑ TR Section 23-4 Quiz
- ❑ CTB Chapter 23

KEY

L1 Special Needs	L4 Gifted and Talented
L2 Less Proficient Readers	EL English Language Learners
L3 All Students	

Name ______________________ Class ______________ Date ________

Section 23-4

Practice

Role-Playing: Interacting With a Disabled Person

When you interact with a person who has a physical disability, you should be helpful if asked, but always be respectful of the person's privacy and independence. People with physical disabilities sometimes have to put up with strangers who do not understand how to be respectful.

Work with a partner to create a role-play between a person with a disability and a person who "helps" in a disrespectful way. In your role-play, have the person with a disability teach the "helpful" person how to interact in a way that respects the disabled person's independence.

Physical disability of person in role-play: ______________________________

____

Description of situation: ______________________________

____

____

Role-Play:

Person with disability: ______________________________

____

Helper: ______________________________

____

Person with disability: ______________________________

____

Helper: ______________________________

____

Person with disability: ______________________________

____

Helper: ______________________________

____

Person with disability: ______________________________

____

Helper: ______________________________

____

Name ______________________ Class ________________ Date ______

Section 23-4

Enrich

Community Involvement: The ADA's Impact on Business

The Americans with Disabilities Act (ADA) guarantees that the civil rights of people with physical and mental disabilities are protected. Businesses are required by the ADA to make accommodations for people with disabilities. Businesses in older buildings are required to make changes to accommodate people with disabilities. New buildings are required to have accommodations for people with disabilities as part of the design.

Contact a local business and set up an interview with the owner, manager, or person in charge of human resources. Write the answers to the following questions in the spaces provided. Add at least one question of your own.

1. Name of business: ______________________

2. What accommodations, if any, were required to make your business entrances accessible to people with disabilities?

3. What accommodations, if any, were required within the building to comply with the ADA?

4. Approximately what did it cost for your company to implement the required changes?

5. Do you foresee any future improvements to comply with the ADA?

6. Question/Answer:

7. Question/Answer:

Name ______________________ Class __________________ Date ________

Section 23-4 Quiz

Write the letter of the correct answer in the space provided.

______ **1.** Any physical or mental impairment that limits or reduces normal activities is called a(an)

a. injury. **b.** disability.
c. retardation. **d.** disease.

______ **2.** What condition is the leading cause of vision loss in older Americans?

a. tinnitus
b. cerebral palsy
c. macular degeneration
d. epilepsy

______ **3.** Diabetes, cataracts, and glaucoma are all leading causes of

a. impaired vision.
b. impaired mobility.
c. mental retardation.
d. impaired hearing.

______ **4.** What does the Americans with Disabilities Act guarantee for Americans who have physical or mental disabilities?

a. a college education
b. civil rights
c. special telephones and doorbells
d. membership in an organization

______ **5.** A condition in which ringing is heard in the ears is called

a. macular degeneration.
b. muscular dystrophy.
c. tinnitus.
d. deafness.

Decide whether each statement is true or false. Write true *or* false *in the space provided.*

______ **6.** Hearing loss is more common in younger people than older people.

______ **7.** When you interact with a mobility-impaired person, you should sit down if the person is seated.

______ **8.** The signing into law of the Americans with Disabilities Act was an important move toward integrating people with disabilities into the workplace.

______ **9.** Both diseases and injuries can cause impaired mobility.

______ **10.** Cochlear implants can help people who are visually impaired to sense light.

Name ______________________ Class ______________________ Date ________

Chapter 23 Test

Write the letter of the correct answer in the space provided.

_____ **1.** Which is a behavior that can lower your risk for cardiovascular disease?
a. eating foods high in saturated fats
b. drinking alcohol every day
c. exercising regularly
d. never taking time to relax

_____ **2.** A cancerous tumor is known as
a. chronic. **b.** disabled.
c. malignant. **d.** metastasis.

_____ **3.** What chemical is responsible for the symptoms of an allergy?
a. histamine **b.** insulin
c. aspirin **d.** PSA

_____ **4.** In which disease does the membrane surrounding a joint become inflamed?
a. type 2 diabetes
b. osteoarthritis
c. leukemia
d. rheumatoid arthritis

_____ **5.** When interacting with a hearing-impaired person, you should
a. describe where things are and who is present.
b. touch the person gently to gain attention.
c. shout to make sure the person hears you.
d. grab the person by the arm.

Write the letter of the correct answer in the space provided.

_____ **6.** a disorder in which the immune system is overly sensitive to a particular substance not normally found in the body

_____ **7.** inflammation or irritation of a joint

_____ **8.** a group of diseases that involves rapid, uncontrolled growth and spread of abnormal cells

_____ **9.** a disorder in which a person's respiratory passages become inflamed and narrow significantly in reaction to certain "triggers"

_____ **10.** a disease in which the body's ability to use glucose is impaired

a. cancer
b. diabetes
c. asthma
d. allergy
e. arthritis
f. tinnitis

Name ______________ Class ______________ Date ______

Chapter 23: **Test** *(continued)*

Decide whether each statement is true or false. Write true *or* false *in the space provided.*

______ **11.** The key to curing cancer is early detection and treatment.

______ **12.** Oncogenes are cancer-causing agents in the environment.

______ **13.** You can prevent type 2 diabetes by maintaining a desirable body weight and exercising regularly.

______ **14.** Managing asthma involves exposing oneself to triggers to prevent asthma attacks.

______ **15.** The Americans with Disabilities Act guarantees the civil rights of Americans who have physical or mental disabilities.

Write the word that best completes each sentence in the space provided.

16. Diseases that persist for a long period or recur throughout life are called ______________ diseases.

17. The spread of cancer from where it first develops to other parts of the body is called ______________.

18. A hormone produced by the pancreas that stimulates body cells to take up and use blood sugar is ______________.

Use complete sentences to answer the following questions.

19. Explain why managing stress is important for your cardiovascular health.

____

____

____

____

____

20. How are type 1 diabetes and type 2 diabetes similar, and how are they different?

____

____

____

____

____

____

____

Name ____________ Class ____________ Date ____________

Chapter 24

Personal Inventory

Healthcare Choices

Just as consumers make choices among sweaters, cars, cereal, and other things they buy, consumers also make choices about healthcare. Consider what you would do in each of these situations.

Put a check beside any healthcare choice you choose. (In some cases, you may make more than one choice.) Then give the reasons for your decision.

1. If I were told I had a serious illness, I would want to

_______ do whatever my doctor advised.

_______ ask to have a second opinion from another doctor.

_______ look for a clinic or hospital offering a new "miracle" treatment.

Reasons: ____________

____

2. If I moved to a new town and needed to find a doctor, I would

_______ look in the phone book for someone with an office nearby.

_______ consider only female (or only male) doctors.

_______ ask my former doctor for recommendations.

Reasons: ____________

____

3. If my doctor does not give me time to ask questions about my health, I would

_______ be more assertive at my next visit and insist on getting answers.

_______ look for a different doctor.

_______ continue seeing this doctor anyway.

Reasons: ____________

____

4. If I were buying insurance, I would choose

_______ a traditional plan in which I could see any doctor at any facility.

_______ a simple, inexpensive plan covering hospitalization only.

_______ a managed care plan with a network of doctors to choose from.

Reasons: ____________

____

Name________________________ Class__________ Date__________ M T W T F

Section 24-1

The Healthcare System — Lesson Plan

Time
1 period
1/2 block

Local Standards

Section Objectives

- **Identify** the healthcare providers who work together to care for patients.
- **Describe** different types of healthcare facilities.
- **Analyze** how technology has affected healthcare.

Vocabulary healthcare system • primary care physician • diagnosis • medical specialist • primary healthcare • outpatient • secondary healthcare • inpatient • tertiary healthcare

1. FOCUS

Warm-Up: Quick Quiz Use the Quick Quiz to asses students' understanding of healthcare.

Targeted Resources
- ❑ Transparency W85

2. TEACH

Journal Writing Have students write a private journal entry about their experience seeing a primary care physician or medical specialist. L3

Differentiated Instruction Have students interview a healthcare provider in their community. EL

Visual Learning: Figure 2 Have students compare and contrast the responsibilities of the healthcare providers shown in Figure 2. L2

Differentiated Instruction Help students map the locations of various doctors' offices, medical clinics, and hospitals in their community. L1

Building Health Skills Have students evaluate a Web site that gives health information for teens. L3

Targeted Resources
- ❑ RN Note Taking Guide 24-1 L3 EL
- ❑ ARN Note Taking Guide 24-1 L2
- ❑ TR Practice 24-1
- ❑ TR Enrich 24-1 L4
- ❑ Audio Summary 24-1 L1 L2 EL
- ❑ Health Links: Updates on healthcare professionals

3. ASSESS

Evaluate Understanding The assignments listed in the Teacher's Edition can help you assess students' mastery of the section content.

Reteach Have students list the kinds of healthcare providers who work in each type of healthcare facility. L2

Targeted Resources
- ❑ TR Section 24-1 Quiz
- ❑ CTB Chapter 24

KEY

L1 Special Needs	L4 Gifted and Talented
L2 Less Proficient Readers	EL English Language Learners
L3 All Students	

Name ____________________ Class ____________________ Date __________

Section 24-1

Practice

Vocabulary Activity: The Healthcare System

Match each definition in the left column with the correct term in the right column. Then write the number of each term in the appropriate box below. When you have filled all the boxes, add up the numbers in each column, row, and two diagonals. All the sums should be the same.

Definitions

A. healthcare given to a patient in a hospital

B. a doctor's opinion of the nature or cause of a medical condition

C. a person admitted to a clinic for tests that do not require an overnight stay

D. healthcare provided in specialty hospitals and teaching hospitals

E. includes all available medical services, the ways individuals pay for medical care, and programs aimed at preventing disease and disability

F. a doctor with additional training in a particular branch of medicine

G. a doctor who takes care of most people's routine medical needs

H. a person who is required to stay in a hospital overnight or longer

I. routine healthcare provided in a doctor's office

Terms

1. diagnosis

2. primary care physician

3. medical specialist

4. primary healthcare

5. healthcare system

6. secondary healthcare

7. tertiary healthcare

8. outpatient

9. inpatient

				↗ = ______
A ______	B ______	C ______	= ______	
D ______	E ______	F ______	= ______	
G ______	H ______	I ______	= ______	
= ______	= ______	= ______		↘ = ______

Name ______________________ Class ______________________ Date ______

Section 24-1 **Enrich**

Community Involvement: Community Health Nurses

Community health nurses provide nursing care outside of doctors' offices. For example, school nurses provide on-site care for students. Home-health nurses provide care to patients in their homes. Others work for local health departments to staff immunization clinics and conduct basic health exams.

Interview a community health nurse. You may use the questions below, as well as questions of your own.

1. Name of nurse: ______________________

Place of employment: ______________________

2. What kind of training did you have for your job?

____

____

3. What health problems do you encounter most often?

____

____

4. What was the worst crisis you have faced? What did you do?

____

____

5. What kinds of medications are you licensed to dispense?

____

____

6. How has technology, such as the Internet and e-mail, affected your job?

____

____

7. In your opinion, what kind of healthcare information should everyone know?

____

____

____

8. Question/Answer: ______________________

____

____

Name ______________________ Class ________________ Date ________

Section 24-1 Quiz

Write the letter of the correct answer in the space provided.

______	**1.** healthcare provided in a teaching hospital	**a.** inpatient
______	**2.** routine healthcare provided in a doctor's office	**b.** outpatient
		c. healthcare system
______	**3.** includes all available medical services	**d.** primary healthcare
______	**4.** person receiving tests or treatment without staying overnight	**e.** secondary healthcare
		f. tertiary healthcare
______	**5.** healthcare provided in a general hospital	

Write the letter of the correct answer in the space provided.

______ **6.** Which healthcare provider takes care of most people's routine medical needs?
- **a.** registered dietician
- **b.** physical therapist
- **c.** dermatologist
- **d.** primary care physician

______ **7.** Which is a medical specialist?
- **a.** nurse
- **b.** dietician
- **c.** orthopedic surgeon
- **d.** physician's assistant

______ **8.** A doctor's opinion of the cause of a medical condition is a
- **a.** diagnosis.
- **b.** medical checkup.
- **c.** prescription.
- **d.** medical test.

______ **9.** Which healthcare facility will often have an emergency department to treat sudden conditions or injuries?
- **a.** doctor's office
- **b.** clinic
- **c.** hospital
- **d.** long-term care facility

______ **10.** The Internet has made it easier for
- **a.** doctors to see more patients.
- **b.** people to gather health information.
- **c.** hospitals to use imaging technology.
- **d.** doctors to write prescriptions.

Name________________________ Class__________ Date__________ M T W T F

Section 24-2

Participating in Your Healthcare Lesson Plan

Section Objectives

- **Describe** how to choose and participate fully in your healthcare.
- **Compare** different options for paying for healthcare.

Vocabulary medical history • physical examination • premium • copayment • deductible

Time
2 periods
1 block

Local Standards

1. FOCUS

Warm-Up: Advice Line Use the activity to stimulate students to think about how to choose a doctor.

Targeted Resources
- ❑ Transparency W86

2. TEACH

Building Health Skills Have students work in small groups to develop an action plan for a friend who is looking for a doctor. L2

Visual Learning: Figure 6 Have students use the checklist in the figure to privately evaluate their own doctor. L2

Cooperative Learning Instruct student groups to list questions to ask a doctor during a teen's routine medical examination. L2

Differentiated Instruction Review with students the steps in a routine physical examination. L1

Building Health Skills Have students write a plan for improving communication with their doctor, using the Patients' Bill of Rights as encouragement. L3

Active Learning Have students interview an older relative about his or her experience with Medicare. L1

Targeted Resources
- ❑ RN Note Taking Guide 24-2 L3 EL
- ❑ ARN Note Taking Guide 24-2 L2
- ❑ Transparencies and Worksheets 71, 72
- ❑ TR Practice 24-2
- ❑ TR Enrich 24-2 L4
- ❑ Audio Summary 24-2 L1 L2 EL
- ❑ Health Links: Updates on the Patients' Bill of Rights

3. ASSESS

Evaluate Understanding The assignments listed in the Teacher's Edition can help you assess students' mastery of the section content.

Reteach Have student groups make a public service announcement that describes the different types of health insurance. L2

Targeted Resources
- ❑ TR Section 24-2 Quiz
- ❑ CTB Chapter 24

KEY

L1 Special Needs	L4 Gifted and Talented
L2 Less Proficient Readers	EL English Language Learners
L3 All Students	

Name ______________________ Class __________________ Date ______

Section 24-2

Practice

Role-Playing: Interviewing a New Doctor

Suppose you have just moved to a new town and are looking for a new doctor. You have made an appointment to interview a doctor who was recommended by your former doctor. You would like to know more about the doctor's education, experience, personality, hospital affiliations, and philosophy of healthcare.

With a partner, complete the script for an interview with a new doctor. You may use the evaluation questions in Figure 6 of the Student Edition to help you write interview questions. Use a separate sheet of paper if you need more space.

Title of Role-Play: *Interviewing a New Doctor*

Characters: patient and doctor

Setting: doctor's office

Doctor: It is very nice to meet you. Please sit down. What questions would you like to ask me?

Patient: Thank you for taking the time to meet with me. First of all, tell me how you know my former doctor, Dr. Smith?

Doctor: ____

Patient: ____

Doctor: ____

Patient: ____

Doctor: ____

Patient: ____

Doctor: ____

Patient: ____

Name ______________________ Class ____________________ Date ________

Consumer Skills: Choosing an Insurance Plan

Many companies offer employees a choice of healthcare options. Evaluating and comparing the information to make the best decision can be confusing. Often, no single health plan satisfies every need. People may have to make compromises on cost, choice, or services.

Obtain copies of a traditional insurance plan and a managed care insurance plan. Use the insurance plans to answer the questions below based on coverage for a single adult.

1. Write a brief description of each plan.

Traditional: ____

____

Managed Care: ____

____

2. What is the out-of-pocket expense for each plan?

Traditional:

premium __________ copayment __________ deductible __________

Managed Care:

premium __________ copayment __________ deductible __________

3. What is the coverage for prescription drugs under each plan?

Traditional: ____

Managed Care: ____

4. What is the coverage for hospitalization under each plan?

Traditional: ____

Managed Care: ____

5. Can you stay with your current doctor under each plan? How much extra would it cost to see your current doctor?

Traditional: ____

Managed Care: ____

6. Which insurance plan covers more medical services and procedures?

____

7. Which insurance plan would you choose? Explain.

____

____

Name ________________________ Class ____________________ Date ________

Section 24-2

Quiz

Write the letter of the correct answer in the space provided.

______ **1.** Which is a record of your present and past health and the health of your family members?
a. physical examination
b. medical history
c. medical checkup
d. medical insurance

______ **2.** During a physical examination, the doctor will
a. review the health of your family members.
b. review your past health.
c. explain your insurance coverage.
d. check your body to identify any medical problems.

______ **3.** A monthly or yearly fee paid to belong to a health insurance plan is called a
a. copayment.
b. deductible.
c. premium.
d. percentage.

______ **4.** Which is a small fee paid whenever you visit the doctor?
a. copayment
b. premium
c. deductible
d. prescription

______ **5.** Which is *not* a factor that contributes to rising healthcare costs?
a. prescription drug costs
b. chronic diseases
c. healthy behaviors
d. an aging population

Decide whether each statement is true or false. Write true *or* false *in the space provided.*

______ **6.** A doctor who is right for you will listen to you and respond thoughtfully.

______ **7.** You should not ask a doctor questions during a physical exam.

______ **8.** It is your responsibility to answer your doctor's questions honestly.

______ **9.** A traditional insurance plan has a network of doctors who agree to provide healthcare at lower costs.

______ **10.** Healthcare costs are decreasing because of the growing population of elderly Americans.

Name________________________ Class__________ Date__________ M T W T F

Section 24-3 Public Health — Lesson Plan

Section Objectives

- **Summarize** the main goal of public health programs today.
- **Describe** how the United States' public health system is organized.

Vocabulary public health • quarantine • epidemiology • health code • vital statistics

Time
2 periods
1 block

Local Standards

1. FOCUS

Warm-Up: Myth/Fact List student responses on the board and refer to them as you teach the lesson.

Targeted Resources
- ❑ Transparency W87

2. TEACH

Class Discussion Lead the class in a discussion on the current goals of public health programs aimed at changing people's unhealthful behaviors. L3

Building Health Skills Have students write a letter to their legislator in support of public health programs. L4

Building Health Skills Instruct students to choose one federal public health agency and explore its Web site. Have students write a summary describing the kinds of information it provides. L3

Differentiated Instruction Help students prepare information cards for public health agencies that may provide services for them when they are adults. L1

Cooperative Learning Have student groups identify a local public health agency and describe the services that agency provides to the community. L2

Targeted Resources
- ❑ RN Note Taking Guide 24-3 L3 EL
- ❑ ARN Note Taking Guide 24-3 L2
- ❑ TR Practice 24-3
- ❑ TR Enrich 24-3 L4
- ❑ Audio Summary 24-3 L1 L2 EL
- ❑ PHSchool.com: More on public health

3. ASSESS

Evaluate Understanding The assignments listed in the Teacher's Edition can help you assess students' mastery of the section content.

Reteach Have students summarize the role of public health programs in the United States. L2

Targeted Resources
- ❑ TR Section 24-3 Quiz
- ❑ CTB Chapter 24

KEY

L1	Special Needs	L4	Gifted and Talented
L2	Less Proficient Readers	EL	English Language Learners
L3	All Students		

Name ______________ Class ______________ Date ______

Section 24-3 **Practice**

Group Activity: Public Health Agencies

As a group, complete the chart by writing the name of the public health agency that would provide service for each situation. Use the agencies listed in Figure 14 in the Student Edition.

ublic Health Problem	Responsible Public Health Agency
1. A certain type of diet pill has caused five deaths from cardiac arrest.	
2. A manufacturing plant does not install safety rails along a flight of stairs.	
3. Children from low-income families do not get adequate healthcare.	
4. Smog produced from industrial emissions causes asthma attacks and other respiratory problems in a nearby town.	
5. Hamburger from a meat processing plant has been packaged incorrectly, causing several people to become ill.	
6. Homeless people have a higher incidence of infectious diseases and injuries due to violence than people with homes.	
7. A person needs help overcoming his addiction to crack cocaine.	
8. Researchers need money to help them find out how to prevent chronic health problems.	
9. Rising healthcare costs are making it more difficult for the average person to afford quality medical care.	
0. An older person cannot get to the store to purchase groceries.	

Name ______________________ Class ______________ Date ________

Family Involvement: Benefits of Immunization

The results of public health programs can be seen in just three generations of Americans. Infectious diseases that were common during your parents' and grandparents' childhoods are no longer common today. These diseases are now controlled because of immunization programs.

Interview two family members or other adults, one who is 30 to 45 years of age and one who is 60 years or older. Find out what diseases were common during their childhoods.

1. What are the ages of the people you interviewed?

Person A: ____________ Person B: ____________

2. What diseases were common during their childhoods?

Person A: ______________________________

Person B: ______________________________

3. What diseases were they immunized against?

Person A: ______________________________

Person B: ______________________________

Answer the following questions about yourself.

4. What diseases were common during your own childhood?

____

____

5. What diseases have you been immunized against?

____

____

6. How has the immunization program benefited your generation?

____

____

____

7. Some diseases that had been eradicated, such as whooping cough, have had recent outbreaks and spread quickly through the community. Find out why.

____

____

____

Name ______________________ Class __________________ Date ________

Section 24-3 **Quiz**

Write the letter of the correct answer in the space provided.

______	**1.** the numbers of births and deaths and the numbers and kinds of diseases that occur within a population	**a.** public health
______	**2.** the study and practice of protecting and improving the health of people in a group or community	**b.** quarantine
______	**3.** standard established by the state for certain factors that affect health	**c.** chronic disease
______	**4.** period of isolation imposed on people who may have been exposed to an infectious disease	**d.** epidemiology
______	**5.** the study of disease among populations	**e.** health code
		f. vital statistics

Write the letter of the correct answer in the space provided.

______ **6.** Today, public health programs emphasize
a. quarantine. **b.** abstinence.
c. epidemiology. **d.** prevention.

______ **7.** Which is *not* one of the three main categories of public health programs?
a. safety and environmental health
b. helping populations at risk
c. monitoring quarantines
d. fighting chronic diseases

______ **8.** Who is primarily responsible for public health in the United States?
a. federal, state, and local governments
b. churches
c. private organizations
d. hospitals

______ **9.** Which federal agency has the widest range of responsibilities for public health?
a. National Institutes of Health
b. Environmental Protection Agency
c. Department of Health and Human Services
d. Centers for Disease Control and Prevention

______ **10.** Local government is often responsible for
a. inspecting healthcare facilities.
b. enforcing health codes.
c. monitoring pollution levels.
d. sponsoring health research.

Name____________________ Class__________ Date__________ M T W T F

Section 24-4

Global Public Health — Lesson Plan

Section Objectives

Time
1 period
1/2 block

- **Explain** the importance of global public health efforts.
- **Describe** the types of public health problems that international health organizations work to overcome.

Local Standards

Vocabulary developing nation • World Health Organization (WHO) • United Nations Children's Fund (UNICEF)

1. FOCUS

Warm-Up: Health Stats Provide students with statistics about the United States to compare with the statistics about Africa. Challenge students to come up with ideas for improving the lives of Africans.

Targeted Resources
- ❑ Transparency W88

2. TEACH

Class Discussion Begin a discussion on the need for global relief efforts, and challenge students to speculate what would happen to developing countries without this relief. L2

Building Media Literacy Ask students to compare the coverage of a current world health problem in different newspapers or magazines. EL

Cooperative Learning Have student groups invent a fictional country with a public health crisis, then act as representatives of the country seeking help from an international health organization. Have other class members play the role of health organization officials. L3

Differentiated Instruction Have students evaluate the management and funding of an international health organization they are interested in. L4

Targeted Resources
- ❑ RN Note Taking Guide 24-4 L3 EL
- ❑ ARN Note Taking Guide 24-4 L2
- ❑ TR Practice 24-4
- ❑ TR Enrich 24-4 L4
- ❑ Audio Summary 24-4 L1 L2 EL
- ❑ PHSchool.com: More on global public health

3. ASSESS

Evaluate Understanding The assignments listed in the Teacher's Edition can help you assess students' mastery of the section content.

Reteach Have student groups make a list of global public health problems and then write a statement explaining why global efforts are important for overcoming these problems. L2

Targeted Resources
- ❑ TR Section 24-4 Quiz
- ❑ CTB Chapter 24

KEY
L1 Special Needs
L2 Less Proficient Readers
L3 All Students
L4 Gifted and Talented
EL English Language Learners

Name ______________ Class ______________ Date ______

Section 24-4 **Practice**

Concept Check: Global Public Health

International health organizations work in developing nations to overcome public health problems such as malnutrition, lack of basic medical care, poor sanitation, and lack of clean water. These international health organizations have different sponsors.

In the chart below, list organizations that are sponsored by the United Nations, the United States, and private sponsors. Include in your list the main services of these organizations.

United Nations	United States	Private Sponsors

Name ______________________ Class __________________ Date ______

Section 24-4 **Enrich**

Research Project: Helping on a Global Scale

All over the world, international organizations respond to global health crises. Many of these organizations are not associated with any single country or the United Nations. One organization that has a long history of emergency work is the International Committee of the Red Cross (ICRC).

The ICRC was organized in the 1860s by Henri Dunant, a Swiss humanitarian. The original purpose of the organization was to care for the injured on battlefields, regardless of whom they were fighting for. Today, the organization's goals have broadened to include the prevention and relief of human suffering wherever it is found and regardless of whether it is caused by wars or natural disasters.

Organizations like the ICRC are called nongovernmental organizations, or NGOs, and they operate all over the world. Many specialize in a particular area. For example, Amnesty International investigates human rights violations. Doctors Without Borders work wherever medical services are needed, whether on battlefields, in refugee camps, or areas caught in a civil war or a famine. The International Eye Foundation is run by volunteer ophthalmologists—doctors who specialize in eye care.

Choose a nongovernmental organization that provides some sort of global public health assistance. Use the questions below to help you learn more about the organization.

1. The organization you are investigating: ______________________

2. Its Web address: ______________________

3. Describe the work that the organization is doing.

____

____

____

4. Describe the global needs the organization is meeting.

____

____

____

5. Research a recent event, either a war or natural disaster. How is one NGO, either the Red Cross or another organization, helping with this crisis?

____

____

____

____

Name ____________________ Class ____________________ Date ________

Section 24-4

Quiz

Decide whether each statement is true or false. Write true *or* false *in the space provided.*

______ **1.** Developing nations rely on global efforts to make their public health programs successful.

______ **2.** International health organizations avoid countries devastated by wars.

______ **3.** The World Health Organization focuses only on programs that aid children.

______ **4.** The Red Cross provides medical care, food, water, and temporary shelter for disaster victims.

______ **5.** Churches and missionary groups are banned from providing international public health assistance.

Write the letter of the correct answer in the space provided.

______ **6.** Developing nations are countries with
a. weak economies.
b. high standards of living.
c. advanced medical care.
d. few public health problems.

______ **7.** Which is *not* a public health problem in developing nations?
a. malnutrition
b. lack of clean water
c. aging population
d. poor sanitation

______ **8.** Which are two agencies of the United Nations?
a. the World Health Organization and the Red Cross
b. UNICEF and the Peace Corps
c. the Red Cross and the Peace Corps
d. UNICEF and the World Health Organization

______ **9.** Which is a responsibility of UNICEF?
a. organizes programs that help children
b. sends professionals to help boost food production
c. collects worldwide health statistics
d. organizes disaster assistance

______ **10.** The Peace Corps
a. funds medical programs.
b. distributes food to countries stricken by famine.
c. sends volunteers to provide healthcare or improve food production.
d. provides emergency assistance to refugees and disaster victims.

Name ______________________ Class ____________________ Date __________

Chapter 24

Test

Write the letter of the correct answer in the space provided.

_______ **1.** Which healthcare provider would you visit for your annual medical examination?
a. nurse
b. orthopedic surgeon
c. physical therapist
d. primary care physician

_______ **2.** Which healthcare facility provides secondary healthcare?
a. teaching hospital
b. hospital
c. doctor's office
d. assisted living facility

_______ **3.** E-mail can make patients feel more involved in their care because it enables patients to
a. get an instant diagnosis.
b. see their doctor even though they are in separate locations.
c. communicate with their doctor.
d. share their files with other doctors.

_______ **4.** Which is *not* your responsibility as a patient?
a. choosing a doctor who is suited to your needs
b. asking your doctor questions about your health
c. diagnosing your medical condition
d. answering your doctor's questions honestly

_______ **5.** A deductible is
a. a monthly or yearly fee paid to join an insurance plan.
b. the percentage of the medical expenses covered by the insurance plan.
c. a small fee paid whenever a plan member visits the doctor.
d. money paid by the member before the insurance company begins paying for medical bills.

_______ **6.** Public health programs today emphasize the need for
a. prevention.
b. research.
c. abstinence.
d. quarantine.

_______ **7.** In the United States, public health is primarily the responsibility of
a. healthcare facilities.
b. the government.
c. private organizations.
d. global efforts.

Name ______________ Class ______________ Date ______

Chapter 24: Test *(continued)*

Write the letter of the correct answer in the space provided.

_____ 8. federal agency that protects the public from environmental hazards

_____ 9. United Nations agency that works to improve food production and medical care in developing nations

_____ 10. federal agency with widest range of responsibilities for public health

_____ 11. U.S. organization that sends trained volunteers to developing nations

_____ 12. United Nations agency that focuses on programs that help children

_____ 13. federal agency that collects data and conducts research on all types of diseases, disorders, and disabilities

a. World Health Organization
b. United Nations Children's Fund
c. Centers for Disease Control and Prevention
d. Peace Corps
e. Department of Health and Human Services
f. Environmental Protection Agency

Write the word or phrase that best completes each sentence in the space provided.

14. A period of isolation imposed on people who may have been exposed to an infectious disease is called ______________.

15. A doctor's opinion of the nature or cause of a medical condition is a(an) ______________.

16. Standards established by the state for certain factors that affect health are ______________ ______________.

17. A patient who is required to stay in a hospital overnight or longer is called a(an) ______________.

18. A record of your present and past health as well as the health of your family members is your ______________ ______________.

Use complete sentences to answer the following questions.

19. What should you consider when choosing a primary care physician?

____

____

____

20. Explain why international health organizations are necessary.

____

____

Name ______________________ Class ______________ Date ________

Chapter 25

Personal Inventory

My Community, My Environment

The health of your community and your environment depends in part on the actions you take in your personal life.

Complete the statements below to identify ways you can improve your civic engagement in your community and your participation in the health of your environment.

My Community:

I stay informed about health-related issues facing the community by

____

____

I volunteer my time for the health of the community by

____

____

I take a stand on health issues in my community by

____

____

My Environment:

When I need to run an errand, I help reduce air pollution by

____

____

I dispose of any hazardous wastes I use by

____

____

Whenever I use recyclable products, I protect the environment by

____

____

Review your answers. Identify any areas in which you think you could make more of an effort. Explain how on a separate sheet.

Name______________ Class________ Date________ M T W T F

Section 25-1 Your Community, Your Health Lesson Plan

Section Objectives

- **Identify** the different kinds of communities to which you belong.
- **Describe** how communities affect personal health.

Vocabulary social network • community service organization • mixed-use development • urban sprawl

Time
2 periods
1 block

Local Standards

1. FOCUS

Warm-Up: Quick Quiz Call on students to explain how being connected to your community is important to overall health and well-being.

Targeted Resources
- ❑ Transparency W89

2. TEACH

Cultural Connection Ask volunteers to share with the class how cultural community contributes to their overall sense of community. L3

Building Health Skills Have students find out about emergency medical services in their community. L4

Visual Learning: Figure 3 Ask students to examine the data in the graphs and discuss what accounts for the differences observed. L2

Differentiated Instruction Display aerial photos to help students understand the difference between urban sprawl and mixed-use development. L1

Cultural Connection Have students put together a booklet of recipes for traditional foods from cultural communities represented in the class. L3

Targeted Resources
- ❑ RN Note Taking Guide 25-1 L3 EL
- ❑ ARN Note Taking Guide 25-1 L2
- ❑ TR Practice 25-1
- ❑ TR Enrich 25-1 L4
- ❑ Audio Summary 25-1 L1 L2 EL
- ❑ Health Links: Updates on community actions

3. ASSESS

Evaluate Understanding The assignments listed in the Teacher's Edition can help you assess students' mastery of the section content.

Reteach Assign groups to make a concept map that ties together the main ideas of the section. L2

Targeted Resources
- ❑ TR Section 25-1 Quiz
- ❑ CTB Chapter 25

KEY

L1	Special Needs	L4	Gifted and Talented
L2	Less Proficient Readers	EL	English Language Learners
L3	All Students		

Name ______________________ Class ______________________ Date ________

Section 25-1

Practice

Group Activity: The Communities to Which We Belong

You belong to a number of different kinds of communities. Each of these communities affects your health.

As a group, describe the communities to which you belong in the spaces provided below.

1. What village, town, or city do you live in?

   Name: ______________________

   Population: ______________________

   Form of Government: ______________________

2. What neighborhood or neighborhoods are the students in your class from? What are these neighborhoods like? Describe at least two.

   ____

3. Describe three aspects of your school community that you and fellow students find important.

   ____

4. What cultural communities are represented by students in your class?

   ____

5. What community service organizations are important to your class? Name three organizations to which you or fellow students belong.

   ____

Name ______________________ Class ______________________ Date __________

Section 25-1 **Enrich**

Cultural Connection: Your Cultural Community

The cultural community to which you belong can have an important effect on your health. To explore the characteristics of this community, interview two older adult friends or family members about the cultural community to which you belong. These adults might be grandparents, neighbors, or leaders in your cultural community. Include questions about basic values, cultural traditions, organizations of the cultural community, and traditional foods.

After you conduct the interviews, respond to the following questions in the spaces provided.

1. Whom did you interview? ______________________________

____

2. How would you describe the cultural community to which you belong?

____

____

____

____

3. What are some basic values of your cultural community?

____

____

____

4. What are some traditions of your cultural community?

____

____

____

5. Which organizations are important to your cultural community?

____

____

____

6. What are some traditional foods of your cultural community?

____

____

____

Name ______________________ Class ______________________ Date ________

Section 25-1

Quiz

Write the letter of the correct answer in the space provided.

______ **1.** You can see urban sprawl in
- **a.** cultural communities.
- **b.** mixed-use communities.
- **c.** a school system.
- **d.** spread-out suburbs.

______ **2.** Family gatherings at which cultural traditions are celebrated strengthen
- **a.** your school community.
- **b.** social health.
- **c.** mixed-use development.
- **d.** community design.

______ **3.** The people with whom you interact and look for friendship, information, and social support make up your
- **a.** community service organization.
- **b.** basic health services.
- **c.** social network.
- **d.** local government.

______ **4.** Boys and Girls Clubs of America is an example of a
- **a.** community service organization.
- **b.** cultural community.
- **c.** piece of health legislation.
- **d.** social network.

______ **5.** In mixed-use development, homes are close to
- **a.** highways.
- **b.** cultural communities.
- **c.** businesses and schools.
- **d.** urban sprawl.

Decide whether each statement is true or false. Write true *or* false *in the space provided.*

______ **6.** There are many communities to which you belong.

______ **7.** Your local government is not involved with water sewage treatment.

______ **8.** Many neighborhood activities promote social health.

______ **9.** Your school community has no effect on your health.

______**10.** Religious organizations are often involved in efforts to improve the health of their communities.

Name______________________ Class__________ Date__________ M T W T F

Section 25-2

Air Quality and Health — Lesson Plan

Section Objectives

- **Summarize** the potential health effects of air pollution.
- **Evaluate** factors that affect indoor air pollution.
- **Analyze** how government and personal actions can help improve air quality.

Vocabulary pollution • fossil fuels • smog • ozone layer • asbestos • radon

Time
1 period
1/2 block

Local Standards

1. FOCUS

Warm-Up: Advice Line Call on students to share items on their list of indoor conditions that might affect indoor air quality.

Targeted Resources

- ❑ Transparency W90

2. TEACH

Visual Learning: Figure 6 Assign the pollutants listed in the table to groups for research about how the pollutants are measured and regulated. L3

Differentiated Instruction Pair English language learners with proficient speakers to review difficult terms in Figure 6. EL

Building Media Literacy Have students assess an ad for a product that claims to be able to remove all forms of indoor air pollution. L3

Building Health Skills Have small groups devise strategies for making the general public more aware of how to reduce air pollution. L3

Differentiated Instruction Call on students to read aloud the bulleted sentences about government regulations on air quality and have volunteers describe an example for each. L2

Targeted Resources

- ❑ RN Note Taking Guide 25-2 L3 EL
- ❑ ARN Note Taking Guide 25-2 L2
- ❑ Transparency and Worksheet 73
- ❑ TR Practice 25-2
- ❑ TR Enrich 25-2 L4
- ❑ Audio Summary 25-2 L1 L2 EL
- ❑ Health Links: Updates on health effects of air pollution

3. ASSESS

Evaluate Understanding The assignments listed in the Teacher's Edition can help you assess students' mastery of the section content.

Reteach Ask students to bring in pictures from magazines to create an air pollution collage on a bulletin board. L2

Targeted Resources

- ❑ TR Section 25-2 Quiz
- ❑ CTB Chapter 25

KEY

L1	Special Needs	L4	Gifted and Talented
L2	Less Proficient Readers	EL	English Language Learners
L3	All Students		

Name ______________ Class ______________ Date ________

Section 25-2 **Practice**

Concept Check: Air Pollutants

Air pollutants—both indoors and outside—can affect your health. Knowing the sources of various air pollutants can help you reduce both your risk of exposure and your contribution to the overall levels of air pollutants.

Fill in the table below to review the sources and health effects of several air pollutants.

Pollutant	Source	Health Effects
Carbon monoxide		
Sulfur dioxide		
Nitrogen oxides		
Ozone		
Particulate matter		
Asbestos		
Radon		

Answer the following questions in the spaces provided.

1. How does the burning of fossil fuels contribute to air pollution?

2. Describe two ways you can conserve energy in order to reduce the burning of fossil fuels.

3. List five sources of indoor pollution.

4. Describe two ways you can reduce your exposure to indoor pollutants.

Name ____________ Class ____________ Date ______

Section 25-2

Enrich

Research Project: Air Quality Index

An Air Quality Index (AQI) is determined each day for over 300 cities in the United States. Scientists determine the AQI for a city by measuring the level of five different pollutants in the air above the city.

You can find details of the AQI by going to the Web site of the U.S. Environmental Protection Agency (EPA) or a Web site dedicated to the AQI called AIRNow. Online, you can also find the AQI each day for major U.S. cities. The U.S. EPA—in coordination with state EPAs and other local agencies—determines the AQI, identifies the primary pollutant involved, and gives a health message for that AQI.

Respond to the following questions in the spaces provided.

1. What five pollutants are measured to determine the AQI of a city?

____

____

2. What are the six rankings for AQI and their color codes?

______________ ______________

______________ ______________

______________ ______________

Record the AQI, the primary pollutant, and the health message for a major U.S. city for each of three days.

AQI for ____________ **Source of data:** ____________

Date	AQI	Primary Pollutant	Health Message
______			
______			
______			

3. How would you characterize the air quality of the city for the days you checked?

____

____

Name ______________________ Class ____________________ Date ______

Section 25-2 **Quiz**

Write the letter of the correct answer in the space provided.

______	**1.** the presence or release of substances into the environment in quantities that are harmful to living organisms	**a.** radon
______	**2.** coal, oil, and natural gas	**b.** smog
______	**3.** a fibrous mineral that was once used in building materials	**c.** pollution
______	**4.** a naturally occurring radioactive gas	**d.** asbestos
______	**5.** a brown haze that can form when there is little or no wind	**e.** fossil fuels
		f. ozone layer

Write the letter of the correct answer in the space provided.

______ **6.** What layer of Earth's atmosphere absorbs most of the ultraviolet light radiated by the sun?
- **a.** carbon layer
- **b.** ozone layer
- **c.** ultraviolet layer
- **d.** smog layer

______ **7.** Which is *not* a health effect of air pollution?
- **a.** reducing your protection from the sun's radiation
- **b.** harming parts of your body through the bloodstream
- **c.** destroying your body's chlorofluorocarbons
- **d.** damaging your respiratory system

______ **8.** Indoor air pollution is most severe in buildings that have been sealed against
- **a.** radon leaks.
- **b.** nitrogen.
- **c.** mold.
- **d.** air leaks.

______ **9.** To comply with the Clean Air Act, what did some factories install on smokestacks to remove pollutants?
- **a.** scrubbers
- **b.** fossil fuels
- **c.** asbestos
- **d.** an ozone layer

______ **10.** Which actions can you take to reduce air pollution?
- **a.** use an automobile instead of public transportation
- **b.** set the thermostat higher during winter months
- **c.** turn off lights and appliances not being used
- **d.** set the home air conditioner at its lowest possible temperature

Name______________________ Class__________ Date__________ M T W T F

Section 25-3 Protecting Land and Water Lesson Plan

Section Objectives

Time
2 periods
1 block

Local Standards

- **Summarize** the threats that hazardous wastes pose to human health.
- **Identify** three sources of water pollution.
- **Describe** three solutions for protecting land and water.

Vocabulary biodegradable waste • hazardous waste • landfill • recycling • sewage • runoff • conservation

1. FOCUS

Warm-Up: Myth/Fact Have students share their ideas about why people think it is healthier to drink bottled water than tap water.

Targeted Resources
- ❑ Transparency W91

2. TEACH

Differentiated Instruction Help English language learners grasp the concept of "hazardous waste" by restating the categories of hazardous materials in everyday terms. EL

Cooperative Learning Have students work in small groups to write a questionnaire to survey attitudes about hazardous waste disposal. L3

Visual Learning: Figure 10 Help students understand that the graphs in the figure show percentages and not actual amounts. L2

Active Learning Make a display of recyclable items and discuss how the items could be properly recycled. L1

Building Health Skills Have students make a poster advocating for environmental health by following the "three Rs." L3

Targeted Resources
- ❑ RN Note Taking Guide 25-3 L3 EL
- ❑ ARN Note Taking Guide 25-3 L2
- ❑ TR Practice 25-3
- ❑ TR Enrich 25-3 L4
- ❑ Audio Summary 25-3 L1 L2 EL
- ❑ PHSchool.com: More on health effects of mercury

3. ASSESS

Evaluate Understanding The assignments listed in the Teacher's Edition can help you assess students' mastery of the section content.

Reteach Read descriptions of pollution problems to students and have them identify the source of each problem. L2

Targeted Resources
- ❑ TR Section 25-3 Quiz
- ❑ CTB Chapter 25

KEY	
L1 Special Needs	L4 Gifted and Talented
L2 Less Proficient Readers	EL English Language Learners
L3 All Students	

Name ______________________ Class ________________ Date ________

Vocabulary Activity: Protecting Land and Water

Use vocabulary terms from the section to complete this concept map about protecting land and water.

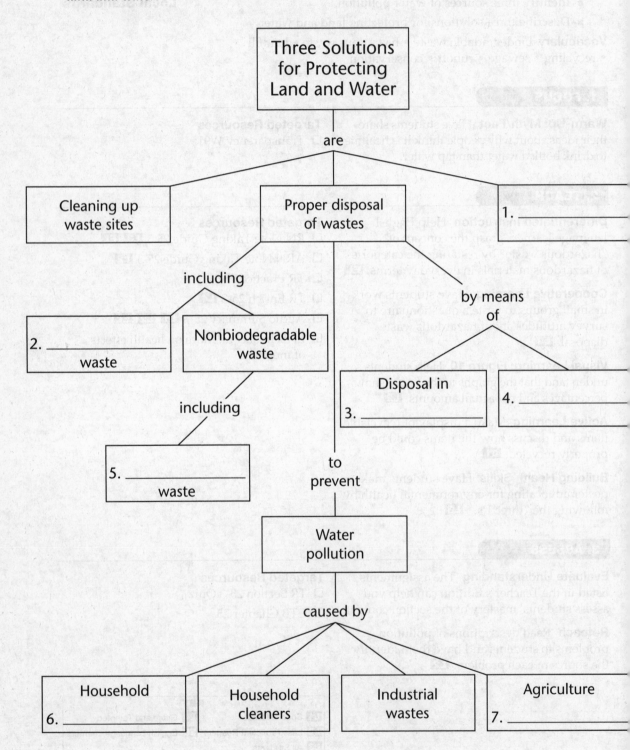

Three Solutions for Protecting Land and Water

are

Cleaning up waste sites

Proper disposal of wastes

1. ______________

including

2. ______________ waste

Nonbiodegradable waste

including

5. ______________ waste

by means of

Disposal in 3. ______________

4. ______________

to prevent

Water pollution

caused by

Household 6. ______________

Household cleaners

Industrial wastes

Agriculture 7. ______________

Name ____________ Class ____________ Date ______

Section 25-3 **Enrich**

Consumer Skills: Products Made From Recycled Material

What happens to the materials you recycle? Most are used to make other products. Products made from recycled materials include printer paper made from recycled paper, and tote bags made from recycled plastic. Recycling helps the environment in at least two ways. First, raw materials do not have to be mined or harvested to make the new products. Second, it often takes less energy to make recycled products than to make products from raw materials.

Use print or online sources to learn about products made from recycled materials.

1. What are five products made from recycled materials, in addition to those listed above?

____

____

____

Choose a type of product from your list, and go to a store that sells a variety of brands of that product. Complete the compare/contrast table below, and then answer the question.

pe of Product: ____________ **Store:** ____________

eature	Brand A	Brand B	Brand C
ontains ecycled material?			
ost			
ppearance			
ther feature			

2. Which product would you buy? Explain your decision.

____

____

____

Name ______________________ Class ____________________ Date ______

Section 25-3 Quiz

Write the letter of the correct answer in the space provided.

______ **1.** What is waste called that can be broken down with microorganisms?
- **a.** household waste
- **b.** recycled waste
- **c.** biodegradable waste
- **d.** runoff waste

______ **2.** What is the process of reclaiming raw materials from discarded products?
- **a.** recycling
- **b.** conservation
- **c.** waste reduction
- **d.** incineration

______ **3.** What do some household cleaners contain that pollutes water supplies?
- **a.** sewage
- **b.** mercury
- **c.** phosphates
- **d.** lead

______ **4.** What does runoff from agricultural land often contain that pollutes water supplies?
- **a.** sewage
- **b.** toxic chemicals
- **c.** hepatitis A
- **d.** rainwater

______ **5.** Which is *not* one of the "three Rs"?
- **a.** reuse
- **b.** recycle
- **c.** reduce
- **d.** return

Write the letter of the correct answer in the space provided.

______ **6.** any waste that is flammable, explosive, corrosive, or toxic to humans or other living things

______ **7.** a permanent storage area where garbage and other wastes are deposited

______ **8.** the waste material carried from toilets and drains

______ **9.** the protection and preservation of the natural environment by managing natural resources wisely

______ **10.** the water that drains from land into streams

- **a.** landfill
- **b.** conservation
- **c.** hazardous waste
- **d.** runoff
- **e.** sewage
- **f.** biodegradable waste

Name________________________ Class__________ Date__________ M T W T F

Section 25-4

Working for Community Health Lesson Plan

Section Objectives

- **Examine** two keys to building a sense of community.
- **Identify** three steps to getting more involved in your community.

Vocabulary civic engagement • consensus-building

Time
1 period
1/2 block

Local Standards

1. FOCUS

Warm-Up: Health Stats Call on students to explain why they think teens volunteer and what benefits teens get from doing so.

Targeted Resources
- ❑ Transparency W92

2. TEACH

Active Learning Have students find out the locations of local government meetings and attend a meeting. L3

Visual Learning: Figure 16 Lead a discussion on the ways that different age groups tend to stay informed. L2

Cooperative Learning Have students conduct a survey of other students in their school to see how common volunteering is. L3

Building Health Skills Have the class role-play a public meeting in which students speak out about an issue. L3

Differentiated Instruction Read aloud examples of volunteering from the text, and call on students to describe what each experience would be like. L1

Targeted Resources
- ❑ RN Note Taking Guide 25-4 L3 EL
- ❑ ARN Note Taking Guide 25-4 L2
- ❑ TR Practice 25-4
- ❑ TR Enrich 25-4 L4
- ❑ Audio Summary 25-4 L1 L2 EL
- ❑ PHSchool.com: More on getting involved

3. ASSESS

Evaluate Understanding The assignments listed in the Teacher's Edition can help you assess students' mastery of the section content.

Reteach Ask students to rewrite the section objectives as questions and then answer the questions. L2

Targeted Resources
- ❑ TR Section 25-4 Quiz
- ❑ CTB Chapter 25

KEY

L1 Special Needs	L4 Gifted and Talented
L2 Less Proficient Readers	EL English Language Learners
L3 All Students	

Name ______________________ Class ______________________ Date __________

Section 25-4 **Practice**

Skill-Building Activity: Advocating for Community Health

One way to get involved in your community is to be an advocate for an issue that is important to you. You might feel strongly about protecting air quality, proper disposal of hazardous wastes, recycling, or community volunteering. There may be another health-related issue you care deeply about. One way to advocate for an issue is to write a letter to the editor of the local newspaper.

Write a letter to the editor of your local paper in which you take a stand on a health-related issue important to your community.

____

____

(your address)

____

(date)

Dear Editor,

____

____

____

____

____

____

____

____

____

____

____

____

____

____

Sincerely,

____

Name ______________________ Class ______________________ Date ______

Section 25-4 **Enrich**

Community Involvement: Recycling in the Community

One step in getting involved in your community is becoming informed about important health-related issues. The recycling of materials in your community is one of those issues. Find out how and where materials are recycled in your community by talking to a local official who has responsibility in this area.

Record the details of recycling in your community in the spaces provided.

1. What materials can be recycled in your community?

____

____

____

____

2. How are items recycled in your community?

____

____

____

____

3. What happens to recycled items after they are collected or deposited?

____

____

____

____

____

4. Does recycling save the community money? If so, how much on an annual basis?

____

____

____

5. On a separate sheet, draw a flowchart that shows what happens to items that are recycled in your community.

Name ______________________ Class __________________ Date ______

Section 25-4 Quiz

Decide whether each statement is true or false. Write true *or* false *in the space provided.*

______ **1.** Attending a school board meeting is an example of civic engagement.

______ **2.** One key to building a sense of community is a shared vision of the future.

______ **3.** Very few teenagers volunteer to do community service work.

______ **4.** Consensus-building requires give-and-take among citizens.

______ **5.** One way to be an advocate is by speaking out about an issue at a public meeting.

Write the letter of the correct answer in the space provided.

______ **6.** The level of involvement that average citizens have in the planning and decision-making that affects their community is called
- **a.** community government.
- **b.** civic engagement.
- **c.** advocating change.
- **d.** consensus-building.

______ **7.** Achieving goals for the future often means that a community has to make
- **a.** money from its school system.
- **b.** negative changes.
- **c.** volunteering required.
- **d.** sacrifices in the short term.

______ **8.** What is the process by which a community arrives at an agreed-upon vision for the future?
- **a.** consensus-building
- **b.** political campaigning
- **c.** voting
- **d.** volunteering

______ **9.** How can you become informed about health-related issues facing your community?
- **a.** read the local newspaper
- **b.** interview community leaders
- **c.** attend board of health meetings
- **d.** all of the above

______ **10.** How many American teens volunteer?
- **a.** over half
- **b.** hardly any
- **c.** almost all
- **d.** about 25 percent

Name ______________________ Class ________________ Date ______

Chapter 25 Test

Write the letter of the correct answer in the space provided.

______ **1.** Your local government is responsible for providing
  a. mixed-use development.
  b. road maintenance.
  c. urban sprawl.
  d. the cultural community.

______ **2.** One of the biggest sources of air pollution is the burning of
  a. fossil fuels.
  b. sewage.
  c. household waste.
  d. asbestos.

______ **3.** What is waste that is flammable, explosive, corrosive, or toxic to humans or other living things?
  a. biodegradable waste
  b. landfilled waste
  c. hazardous waste
  d. illegal waste

______ **4.** By keeping any materials that can be reprocessed into new products separate from trash, you can
  a. recycle.
  b. reuse.
  c. reduce.
  d. reprocess.

______ **5.** Which is *not* an example of civic engagement?
  a. registering to vote when you turn 18
  b. attending a public hearing
  c. avoiding contact with the community government
  d. volunteering during a political campaign

Decide whether each statement is true or false. Write true *or* false *in the space provided.*

______ **6.** You belong to many different kinds of communities.

______ **7.** Air pollutants can harm the respiratory system.

______ **8.** Indoor air pollution is most severe in buildings that have many air leaks.

______ **9.** Many industrial wastes are hazardous or nonbiodegradable.

______ **10.** Paving an area usually decreases runoff of pollutants into streams and lakes.

Name ______________ Class ______________ Date ________

Chapter 25: Test *(continued)*

Write the letter of the correct answer in the space provided.

______ **11.** a brown haze that forms when air pollutants react in the presence of sunlight		**a.** sewage
______ **12.** the process by which a community arrives at an agreed-upon vision for the future		**b.** urban sprawl
______ **13.** the waste material carried from toilets and drains		**c.** landfill
______ **14.** a naturally occurring radioactive gas that can cause indoor pollution		**d.** consensus-building
______ **15.** a permanent storage area where garbage and other wastes are deposited and covered with soil		**e.** smog
		f. radon

Write the word that best completes each sentence in the space provided.

16. The presence or release of substances into the environment in quantities that are harmful to living organisms is ______________.

17. The process of reclaiming raw materials from discarded products and using them to create new products is ______________.

18. The protection and preservation of the natural environment by managing resources wisely and developing land for new construction responsibly is ______________.

Use complete sentences to answer the following questions.

19. What are three solutions for protecting land and water?

____

____

____

____

____

20. What are three steps in getting more involved in your community?

____

____

____

____

Name ______________________ Class ______________________ Date ________

Chapter 26

Personal Inventory

Safety Risks

Five factors that can help prevent unintentional injuries or lessen their damage are awareness, knowledge, ability, state of mind, and environmental conditions. Do you put these factors in action in your daily life?

Read each item below. Put a check in the column that best describes your behavior.

Reducing Risk	Always	Usually	Sometimes	Seldom/Never
I avoid piling objects on steps or stairways.				
I make sure medications, cleaners, and cosmetics are stored out of the reach of children.				
I store flammable materials properly.				
I avoid touching electrical appliances with wet hands or when standing near water.				
I make sure all firearms are unloaded and locked in a place where children cannot reach them.				
I do not meet face-to-face with anyone I meet on the Internet.				
I do not leave home without telling someone where I'm going and when I'll be back.				
I speak up when I'm working at a job and I see a hazard that may cause an injury or illness.				
I do not swim alone or in an unsupervised area.				
I wear a personal flotation device when I'm in a boat.				
I warm up before playing a sport.				
I wear a helmet when I bicycle, skate, or skateboard.				
I wear a seat belt when I'm in a car.				
I do not ride in a car with a driver who has been drinking.				

Name______________________ Class__________ Date__________ M T W T F

Section 26-1

Safety at Home and in Your Community

Lesson Plan

Section Objectives

- **Describe** five factors that can help you prevent unintentional injuries.
- **Identify** unintentional injuries that commonly occur in the home.
- **Summarize** ways to stay safe in natural disasters.
- **Explain** how to protect yourself from crime.

Time
3 periods
1 1/2 blocks

Local Standards

Vocabulary unintentional injury • flammable material • electrocution • assault • rape • stalker

1. FOCUS

Warm-Up: Myth/Fact Call on students to explain why they think people do or do not behave in ways to prevent injuries.

Targeted Resources
- ❑ Transparency W93

2. TEACH

Class Discussion Have students brainstorm a list of common home hazards and explain how one or more of the five factors to prevent unintentional injuries could help. L3

Building Health Skills Post the poison control phone number on a bulletin board for students to copy and take home. L1

Building Vocabulary Explain that *flammable* and *inflammable* have the same meaning. EL

Visual Learning: Figure 3 Using the questions in the figure, lead a discussion on being prepared for a natural disaster. L2

Cooperative Learning Have small groups create a handbook about the type of natural disaster that is most common in their area. L2

Journal Writing Have students write a private journal entry about ways they can protect themselves from assault. L2

Targeted Resources
- ❑ RN Note Taking Guide 26-1 L3 EL
- ❑ ARN Note Taking Guide 26-1 L2
- ❑ Transparency and Worksheet 74
- ❑ TR Practice 26-1
- ❑ TR Enrich 26-1 L4
- ❑ Audio Summary 26-1 L1 L2 EL
- ❑ PHSchool.com: More on hurricanes

3. ASSESS

Evaluate Understanding The assignments listed in the Teacher's Edition can help you assess students' mastery of the section content.

Reteach Work with students to make an outline of section content. L2

Targeted Resources
- ❑ TR Section 26-1 Quiz
- ❑ CTB Chapter 26

KEY

L1 Special Needs	L4 Gifted and Talented
L2 Less Proficient Readers	EL English Language Learners
L3 All Students	

Name ______________________ Class ____________________ Date ______

Section 26-1 **Practice**

Concept Check: Avoiding Risky Situations

You can prevent assault or reduce the likelihood of injury by avoiding risky situations. Yet, sometimes situations occur through no fault of your own that can place you in danger if you do not take actions to reduce your risks.

Read the description of each situation, and think about the best way to avoid assault and injury. For each situation, describe how you can best stay safe.

1. You are home alone. A stranger knocks on your door and asks for help.

____

____

____

2. After shopping one night, you return alone to your car in the parking lot.

____

____

____

3. Your car breaks down while you are driving to a party one evening. You are alone, and a stranger stops to help.

____

____

____

4. You are being followed by a stranger as you walk down a deserted street.

____

____

____

5. As you pass by a shopping center in your car, you see a robbery in progress.

____

____

____

6. It is night, and you remember you left your coat on a park bench.

____

____

____

Name ____________ Class ____________ Date ____________

Section 26-1 **Enrich**

Community Involvement: Natural Disasters

Natural disasters such as hurricanes, tornadoes, and floods often come with little warning. The fury of a storm or natural disaster can be devastating and costly. *Contact your local American Red Cross chapter and find out the answers to the following questions.*

1. Location of nearest American Red Cross office: ____________
2. Telephone number of nearest office: ____________
3. What services are provided for people who are victims of natural disasters?
4. How does the local chapter cooperate with local officials?
5. How does the local chapter cooperate with state and federal officials when there is a local emergency? ____________
6. When did the local chapter last provide relief services for people in your community? ____________
7. What were the circumstances? ____________
8. How is the American Red Cross funded? ____________
9. How many volunteers does the local chapter have? ____________
10. What training does a person receive as an American Red Cross volunteer?

Name ______________________ Class ____________________ Date ________

Section 26-1

Quiz

Write the letter of the correct answer in the space provided.

______ **1.** Which factor is *not* one of the factors that can help prevent unintentional injuries or lessen their damage?

a. state of mind **b.** suffocation

c. awareness **d.** ability

______ **2.** Why should you never use water on a grease fire?

a. Water causes the fire to spread.

b. Grease mixes well with water.

c. The water will catch on fire.

d. Water can put out any fire.

______ **3.** If you are indoors when an earthquake occurs, you should

a. run immediately outdoors.

b. turn off your home's electricity.

c. place tape across windows and board them up.

d. stand under the frame of an interior door.

______ **4.** If you are stalked, you should

a. call the stalker's parents.

b. notify the police.

c. seek medical help.

d. identify the stalker on the Internet.

______ **5.** What is the most basic guideline to prevent assault?

a. Always keep a house key under the doormat.

b. Park your car in dark places.

c. Avoid risky situations.

d. Always keep the doors unlocked at home.

Write the letter of the correct answer in the space provided.

______ **6.** an unplanned injury

______ **7.** death from direct contact with electricity

______ **8.** an unlawful attempt or threat to harm someone

______ **9.** when one person forces another to have sexual relations

______ **10.** someone who makes repeated, unwanted contact with a person

a. rape

b. assault

c. unintentional injury

d. stalker

e. flammable material

f. electrocution

Name_________________________ Class__________ Date__________ M T W T F

Section 26-2

Safety at Work and Play Lesson Plan

Section Objectives

- **Describe** how occupational injuries and illnesses can be prevented.
- **Summarize** the four basic guidelines for recreational safety.

Vocabulary occupational injury • occupational illness • survival floating • active supervision • capsizing

Time
2 periods
1 block

Local Standards

1. FOCUS

Warm-Up: Quick Quiz Ask students to predict how their behaviors affect their risk of injury.

Targeted Resources
- ❑ Transparency W94

2. TEACH

Active Learning Have students interview an adult about the hazards of his or her job. L3

Differentiated Instruction Ask students to consider the occupational safety of non-English speakers in the American workforce. EL

Class Discussion Call on students to generate a list of favorite recreational activities, and then ask volunteers how they can apply the four basic safety guidelines to each activity. L2

Building Health Skills Ask students to analyze the influence their friends have on them when it comes to recreational safety. L2

Teacher Demo Bring a personal flotation device to class and allow students to examine it. L1

Visual Learning: Figure 11 Lead a discussion on the reasoning behind the safety guidelines listed in the figure. L2

Targeted Resources
- ❑ RN Note Taking Guide 26-2 L3 EL
- ❑ ARN Note Taking Guide 26-2 L2
- ❑ Transparencies and Worksheets 75, 76
- ❑ TR Practice 26-2
- ❑ TR Enrich 26-2 L4
- ❑ Audio Summary 26-2 L1 L2 EL
- ❑ Health Links: Updates on water safety

3. ASSESS

Evaluate Understanding The assignments listed in the Teacher's Edition can help you assess students' mastery of the section content.

Reteach Have students write a paragraph that applies the four basic safety guidelines to one of the recreational activities discussed in the section. L2

Targeted Resources
- ❑ TR Section 26-2 Quiz
- ❑ CTB Chapter 26

KEY

L1 Special Needs
L2 Less Proficient Readers
L3 All Students
L4 Gifted and Talented
EL English Language Learners

Name ______________________ Class ____________________ Date ______

Section 26-2 **Practice**

Skill-Building Activity: Advocating Sports Safety

Every year, millions of high school and college students who participate in organized sports experience injuries that cause them to lose playing time. Some injuries cannot be avoided, but many injuries can be prevented or reduced in severity by following the four basic guidelines of recreational safety.

Write a letter to a friend who has been chosen to play on a high school team. Persuade your friend to stay as safe as possible while playing the sport. Address each of the four basic guidelines of recreational safety in your letter.

____

____

(your address)

____

(date)

Dear ______________________,

Sincerely,

____

Name ______________________ Class ____________________ Date ________

Section 26-2 **Enrich**

Consumer Skills: Which Helmet to Buy?

Not all bicycle helmets are alike. Different brands have different features, and different brands vary in price. How does one decide which helmet to buy?

What to Look For

- Choose a helmet with a CPSC sticker inside. CPSC is the U.S. Consumer Product Safety Commission, which sets standards for helmets.
- Choose a helmet that is smoothly rounded.
- Look for a strong strap and a strong strap fastener.
- The helmet should fit snugly, so when you shake your head the helmet doesn't move.
- Choose a helmet that feels comfortable.
- The helmet should have vents to provide air flow.
- Choose a light-colored helmet that can be easily seen by motorists.

What to Avoid

- Avoid a helmet with sharp ribs or snags on the surface.
- Avoid a helmet with too many vents, which weaken a helmet.
- Avoid skinny straps—they may be weaker and less comfortable.

Go to a store that sells a variety of bicycle helmets. Compare helmets and decide which would be the best buy.

1. Compare and contrast at least three different brands.

Feature	Brand A	Brand B	Brand C
Cost			
CPSC sticker			
Shape of Helmet			
Strap and Fastener			
Fit			
Comfort/Look			
Vents			

2. Which helmet is the best buy, based on the data? Explain your choice.

____

____

Name ______________________ Class ______________________ Date ______

Section 26-2 Quiz

Write the letter of the correct answer in the space provided.

______ **1.** Many occupational injuries and illnesses can be either prevented or made less serious by
a. survival floating.
b. checking the weather forecast.
c. removing potential hazards from the workplace.
d. adding a rearview mirror to a recreational vehicle.

______ **2.** Which is *not* one of the basic safety guidelines that you should follow for recreational activities?
a. Learn and apply the proper skills.
b. Have appropriate, well-maintained equipment.
c. Always wear a PFD.
d. Know the safety rules specific to the activity.

______ **3.** A lifesaving technique in the water that does not take much energy is
a. survival floating.
b. capsizing.
c. active supervision.
d. sunscreen application.

______ **4.** Capsizing is the
a. hunting of small animals.
b. overturning of a boat.
c. flipping of an ATV.
d. wearing of a PFD.

______ **5.** When you skateboard or ride a bicycle, you should always
a. use roads with heavy traffic.
b. wear goggles.
c. wear long pants.
d. wear a helmet.

Decide whether each statement is true or false. Write true *or* false *in the space provided.*

______ **6.** An occupational illness is any abnormal condition or disorder caused by exposure to the work environment.

______ **7.** In the United States, very few teens work.

______ **8.** One basic safety guideline is to prepare adequately for the activity.

______ **9.** If you are watching children around water, you must actively supervise them.

______ **10.** When riding a recreational vehicle, you should wear headphones.

Name________________________ Class__________ Date__________ M T W T F

Section 26-3

Motor Vehicle Safety Lesson Plan

Section Objectives

- **Identify** the skills you need to be a safe driver.
- **List** safety rules you should follow when riding in a school bus.

Vocabulary defensive driving • road rage

Time
1 period
1/2 block

Local Standards

1. FOCUS

Warm-Up: Health Stats Call on students to describe the trend in the graph and explain why driver deaths are more common at some ages than at other ages.

Targeted Resources
- ❑ Transparency W95

2. TEACH

Class Discussion Ask students to explain the reasoning behind each of the factors you can control when driving a motor vehicle. L2

Cooperative Learning Have students put together a role-play in which friends try to convince an intoxicated friend not to drive. L1

Building Health Skills Ask student groups to evaluate a car for the safety of the brakes, lights, tires, and windshield wipers. L3

Building Vocabulary Make sure students understand what is meant by the term *defensive driving* and ask them to give an example of defensive driving. EL

Building Health Skills Have groups of students make a poster that conveys to younger students the rules school bus riders should follow. L3

Targeted Resources
- ❑ RN Note Taking Guide 26-3 L3 EL
- ❑ ARN Note Taking Guide 26-3 L2
- ❑ TR Practice 26-3
- ❑ TR Enrich 26-3 L4
- ❑ Audio Summary 26-3 L1 L2 EL
- ❑ Health Links: Updates on motor vehicle safety

3. ASSESS

Evaluate Understanding The assignments listed in the Teacher's Edition can help you assess students' mastery of the section content.

Reteach Have students rewrite the section objectives as questions and then answer the questions using material in the section. L2

Targeted Resources
- ❑ TR Section 26-3 Quiz
- ❑ CTB Chapter 26

KEY

L1 Special Needs	L4 Gifted and Talented
L2 Less Proficient Readers	EL English Language Learners
L3 All Students	

Name ______________________ Class ________________ Date ________

Section 26-3 **Practice**

Role-Playing: Safety on a School Bus

A school bus can be a dangerous place—it is a large vehicle, often moving at fast speeds. If passengers do not follow basic rules, unintentional injuries can result.

With a group of at least six other students, create a role-play that could be used to teach younger students proper school bus behavior. Use the spaces below, plus extra paper if needed, to organize your role-play. Practice with your group so you are prepared to present your role-play if your teacher asks you.

Cast

Bus driver: ______________________________

Bully: ______________________________

Unruly student: ______________________________

Student walking in aisle: ______________________________

Student who obeys rules: ______________________________

Student who obeys rules: ______________________________

Student who obeys rules: ______________________________

Props

You can use chairs, signs, and other objects to show the inside of the bus and which roles students are playing.

____

____

____

Overview

Describe any actions and dialogue you will use to show what happens on the bus.

____

____

____

____

____

____

____

Name ______________________ Class ____________________ Date ________

Section 26-3 **Enrich**

Class Debate: Should Seat Belts Be Required by Law?

Most states have laws requiring drivers and front seat passengers to use seat belts. Despite these laws, many people do not buckle up when they drive or ride in a car. Do you think people should be ticketed if police see them not wearing a seat belt? Should your state add a law or keep its law requiring the use of seat belts? Your teacher will schedule a class debate on whether or not your state should have a seat belt law. You may be asked to argue for or against seat belt laws.

Read the arguments below and use print and online resources to find more information that supports each side. You should prepare to argue either side of the issue.

Arguments for Seat Belt Laws:

- According to the National Highway Traffic Safety Administration, seat belts reduce the risk of a fatal injury by 45 percent.
- Air bags in vehicles are designed to work with seat belts. If the seat belt is not buckled and there is a crash, the air bag is much less effective.
- People are more likely to use seat belts when there is a law requiring them to.
- The nonuse of seat belts results in about $26 billion in costs to society, including higher healthcare costs and higher insurance costs.
- Other arguments for: ____

____

____

____

____

Arguments Against Seat Belt Laws:

- Many seat belts are poorly designed or installed improperly. Such seat belts may cause injuries in crashes.
- It is unconstitutional to deny individuals the freedom to choose between wearing or not wearing a seat belt.
- A person should have the freedom to risk injury if he or she wants to.
- Other arguments against: ____

____

____

____

____

Name ____________________ Class ____________________ Date ______

Section 26-3

Quiz

Decide whether each statement is true or false. Write true *or* false *in the space provided.*

______ **1.** You can be a safe driver, regardless of your age.

______ **2.** Excessive speed is a factor in many crashes.

______ **3.** You should always drive carefully when you have been drinking alcohol.

______ **4.** When visibility is low due to rain or fog, you should drive as fast as the law allows.

______ **5.** When a school bus stops, you must stop your car whether you are behind the bus or driving in the opposite direction.

Write the letter of the correct answer in the space provided.

______ **6.** To be a safe driver, you need to
- **a.** be older than 25.
- **b.** avoid the lines painted on the side of the road.
- **c.** know how to respond to risky situations.
- **d.** avoid having regular tune-ups.

______ **7.** Which will reduce your chances of being involved in a motor vehicle crash?
- **a.** Drive when you are tired and angry.
- **b.** Minimize your distractions.
- **c.** Carry a flammable substance in your vehicle.
- **d.** Never wear a seatbelt.

______ **8.** Defensive driving means that you
- **a.** keep very little distance between your car and the car ahead of you.
- **b.** do not assume that other drivers will do what you think they should do.
- **c.** speed up when driving through a construction zone.
- **d.** pay as little attention as possible to the drivers around you.

______ **9.** A driver who becomes violent or dangerous is a driver with
- **a.** road rage.
- **b.** poor visibility.
- **c.** good driving skills.
- **d.** alcohol in the vehicle.

______ **10.** Which is a rule that ensures everyone's safety on a school bus?
- **a.** Start a fight when someone starts bullying.
- **b.** Put your head out a window to see what is ahead.
- **c.** Know where the emergency exits are located.
- **d.** Stand in the school bus's aisle when the bus slows down.

Name ______________________ Class ____________________ Date __________

Chapter 26 **Test**

Write the letter of the correct answer in the space provided.

______ **1.** The main factor in avoiding falls is to
a. stay away from dark doorways and hedges.
b. vent garages and appliances properly.
c. keep medicines out of reach of children.
d. consider environmental conditions.

______ **2.** The most basic guideline for preventing assault is to
a. avoid risky situations.
b. make sure outdoor steps are in good repair.
c. put together a first-aid kit.
d. drink lots of water to stay hydrated.

______ **3.** Whose responsibility is it to keep your workplace as safe as possible and to inform you of any on-the-job hazards?
a. your parents
b. the police
c. the federal government
d. your employer

______ **4.** Which is a safety precaution that can prevent drownings?
a. Avoid survival floating when in the water.
b. Never swim alone or in unsupervised areas.
c. Dive immediately into the water when there is a thunderstorm.
d. Always wear a personal flotation device when you go swimming.

______ **5.** A driver with road rage is one that
a. drives faster than the speed limit.
b. avoids driving when angry or feeling stressed.
c. becomes violent or dangerous while driving.
d. always stops when a school bus's red lights are flashing.

Decide whether each statement is true or false. Write true *or* false *in the space provided.*

______ **6.** Being realistic when you judge your abilities and those of others can help prevent unintentional injuries.

______ **7.** Earthquakes, tornadoes, and oil spills are all examples of natural disasters.

______ **8.** Many occupational injuries can either be prevented or made less serious by removing potential hazards from the workplace.

______ **9.** You do not need to wear a helmet to be safe on a skateboard.

______ **10.** When riding on a school bus, you should stay seated at all times.

Name ____________________ Class ________________ Date ________

Chapter 26: **Test** *(continued)*

Write the letter of the correct answer in the space provided.

_____ **11.** any abnormal condition or disorder caused by exposure to the work environment

_____ **12.** someone who makes repeated, unwanted contact with a person

_____ **13.** an unplanned injury

_____ **14.** an unlawful attempt or threat to harm someone

_____ **15.** a lifesaving technique that allows you to survive in the water without using much energy

a. unintentional injury
b. assault
c. survival floating
d. flammable material
e. occupational illness
f. stalker

Write the word that best completes each sentence in the space provided.

16. When one person forces another to have sexual relations, it is called ________________.

17. Any wound or damage to the body that results from an event in the work environment is a(an) ________________ injury.

18. When you do not assume that drivers around you will do what you think they should do, you are practicing ________________ driving.

Use complete sentences to answer the following questions.

19. What are five factors that can help you prevent unintentional injuries?

____

____

____

____

20. What are the four basic guidelines for recreational safety?

____

____

____

____

____

____

Answer Key

Chapter 1

Personal Inventory

Assure students that you will not be collecting the completed Personal Inventory.

Section 1-1 Practice

(Note: answers 1–3 may be in any order)

1. Physical
a–b. *Sample answers:* healthy diet, regular exercise

2. Mental and Emotional
a–b. *Sample answers:* take time to relax, share your feelings with others

3. Social
a–b. *Sample answers:* get involved with others at school and in your community, build strong relationships with family members

Section 1-1 Enrich

Answers to Questions 1 and 2 will vary, but may include good physical health, loving relationships, and a safe environment. Answers to Question 3 should address characteristics listed for Questions 1 and 2.

Section 1-1 Quiz

1. d **2.** a **3.** a **4.** b **5.** c

6. false **7.** false **8.** true

9. false **10.** true

Section 1-2 Practice

The role-play should show an understanding of how either heredity, environment, media, technology, healthcare, or behavior can have a positive or negative influence on health.

Section 1-2 Enrich

1. Possible risks are the temptation to drink alcohol, especially if your peers are, or accepting a ride with someone who has been drinking. Drink only non-alcoholic beverages; if necessary, call a family member for a ride.

2. A possible risk is that your cold will get worse and you will miss more days of school. Stay home, and ask a friend to bring home your assignments.

3. A possible risk is the temptation to order foods that are high in fat. Choose menu items that are lower in fat, such as a salad or a grilled chicken sandwich.

4. A possible risk is that you will end up in a physical fight. Speak to the person away from a crowd, but not in a totally isolated location. Explain how you feel, and try to find out why this person is spreading rumors about you.

Section 1-2 Quiz

1. c **2.** f **3.** b **4.** a **5.** e

6. c **7.** d **8.** c **9.** b **10.** c

Section 1-3 Practice

Give students a few days to complete this activity. Before they begin, discuss the best ways to approach people so that they will be willing to participate. Students may also want to predict which behaviors will be less common so they can ask people about those behaviors first.

Section 1-3 Enrich

1. Students should identify areas for which any person answered *sometimes* or *never.*

2. Answers will depend on the areas identified in Question 1. Possible services or programs are exercise classes, clinics that help people to stop smoking, and cooking classes that teach people to prepare healthy meals.

Section 1-3 Quiz

1. true **2.** true **3.** false

4. false **5.** true

6. d **7.** a **8.** b **9.** a **10.** d

Section 1-4 Practice

Sample answers:

Scientific studies: Tests show that people have fewer ankle sprains with this shoe.

Bandwagon approach: We can't make these fast enough to keep up with demand.

Testimonial: Joey D. did a personal best in the 100-meter race with this shoe; he threw away the rest of his shoes.

Comparison to other products: This shoe is more comfortable than all similar brands.

Emotional appeal: Treat your feet to an elite shoe.

Price appeal: This shoe has the highest quality in its price range.

Section 1-4 Enrich

Define the problem: The problem is deciding which of two bicycles to buy.

Explore the alternatives: The alternatives are a bicycle designed to be used outdoors and a stationary exercise bicycle designed to be used indoors.

Consider the consequences: Some possible negative consequences of buying an outdoor bicycle are not being able to ride every day, the risk of a crash or collision, the risk of injury from a crash, and the risk that the bicycle will be stolen. Possible positive consequences are fresh air, not depending on rides to get places, and a chance to be with friends. Possible negative consequences of the exercise bicycle are boredom, which could lead to reduced use, and the space required. Possible positive consequences are the ability to exercise daily and the chance to watch television while exercising.

Identify your values: Possible values are a love a nature, a desire to socialize, or a need for a predictable routine.

Evaluate your results: *Sample answer:* I would track the amount of time I spend exercising to see if it increases.

1. Students may say that using DECIDE made it easier to make a decision because it gave them an organized way to compare the alternatives.

2. Students should choose decisions for which DECIDE will be useful.

Section 1-4 Quiz

1. a **2.** a **3.** b **4.** d **5.** a
6. d **7.** b **8.** e **9.** a **10.** c

Chapter 1 Test

1. a **2.** d **3.** c **4.** a **5.** c
6. d **7.** a **8.** c **9.** b **10.** f
11. false **12.** false **13.** false
14. true **15.** true

16. continuum

17. advocacy

18. consumer

19. You can consider both short- and long-term consequences of the risk factors, decide whether you can control the risk factors, and analyze the possible benefits and risks of decisions.

20. To meet your personal health goals, you can gain awareness of health problems, gain knowledge about health problems, and build health skills so you can apply the knowledge.

Chapter 2

Personal Inventory

Assure students that you will not be collecting the completed Personal Inventory.

Section 2-1 Practice

The ratings will vary. The reasons should show an understanding of the traits.

Section 2-1 Enrich

Because of the personal nature of this activity, students may want to keep their responses private. If so, ask them to discuss, in general, what they learned from the activity.

Section 2-1 Quiz

1. c **2.** d **3.** a **4.** e **5.** b

6. false **7.** true **8.** true

9. true **10.** false

Section 2-2 Practice

Role-plays should clearly demonstrate how teens with different levels of self-esteem might respond to everyday challenges.

Section 2-2 Enrich

1–6. Interview results will vary.

7. *Sample answer:* positive, accepting, resilient, independent, realistic

8. *Sample answer:* the support of family and friends, and acheiving one's personal goals

Section 2-2 Quiz

1. b **2.** c **3.** d **4.** d **5.** c

6. true **7.** true **8.** false

9. true **10.** false

Section 2-3 Practice

Situation 1, Projection: You blame your sister for not seeing the radio on the floor.
Healthier Strategy: You take responsibility for leaving the radio on the floor and decide to take better care of your possessions.

Situation 2, Reaction Formation: You say that you don't care about doing well in school.
Healthier Strategy: You discuss the situation with the teacher and make an action plan to complete the assignment by a set date.

Situation 3, Rationalization: You excuse your action by claiming that everyone cheats.
Healthier Strategy: You apologize to your friend and the teacher and ask what you can do to make up for your poor behavior.

Situation 4, Regression: You sulk and refuse to talk to your parent or guardian.
Healthier Strategy: You accept the punishment and promise to pay better attention to your curfew in the future.

Section 2-3 Enrich

In ads that appeal to happiness, people are enjoying themselves. The goal is to make buyers think they will be equally happy if they buy the product. Ads that appeal to guilt might make people feel they are not good providers or are not taking care of themselves. Ads that appeal to fear imply that something bad will happen if a person doesn't buy the product.

Section 2-3 Quiz

1. a **2.** d **3.** e **4.** f **5.** c

6. b **7.** c **8.** d **9.** a **10.** a

Chapter 2 Test

1. c **2.** b **3.** b **4.** d **5.** a

6. a **7.** e **8.** d **9.** f **10.** c

11. true **12.** true **13.** false

14. false **15.** true

16. heredity **17.** self-esteem

18. learned

19. *Sample answer:* Relying on your values and looking beyond your own concerns are ways to boost self-esteem.

20. Recognizing your emotions is the first step toward dealing with your emotions in healthy ways. Name the emotion, determine the source, and think of times when you felt the same way.

1. c **2.** b **3.** d **4.** e **5.** b

1. b **2.** [illegible] **3.** d **4.** b **5.** c

6. b **7.** c **8.** e **9.** a **10.** a

Chapter 2 Test

1. c **2.** b **3.** b **4.** d **5.** a

6. a **7.** e **8.** e **9.** f **10.** c

Chapter 3

Personal Inventory

Assure students that you will not be collecting the completed Personal Inventory.

Section 3-1 Practice

Students might underline the following stressors: first big performance, hurricane, shoveling his car out of snow, couldn't find his favorite drumsticks, hall was too cold, sister is getting married.

1. major life change: sister's marriage; catastrophe: hurricane; everyday problem: first big performance, car in snow, or lost drumsticks; environmental problem: cold hall

2. *Sample answer:* Being unable to find the drumsticks might cause distress if Kenji thinks it will affect his ability to perform.

3. *Sample answer:* A first big performance might cause eustress if it improves the band's ability to concentrate.

Section 3-1 Enrich

1. Students' family charts may differ from the first chart in the rankings of particular life changes.

2. One reason family charts may differ from the first chart is the major life changes that a family has already experienced.

3. *Sample answer:* A move to a new house or apartment could be stressful because of the time required to prepare for the move, the cost of moving, or disruptions to routines until the family adjusts to the move.

Section 3-1 Quiz

1. a **2.** c **3.** a **4.** c **5.** b

6. false **7.** true **8.** false

9. false **10.** false

Section 3-2 Practice

Students should underline and record in the table any five of the following six warning signs of stress.

1. He was always too slow getting ready in the morning! (critical of others, mental)

2. There's no way I'll get to school on time. (negative thinking, mental)

3. That made Deirdre even more irritable. (irritable, emotional)

4. Deirdre had a headache. (headache, physical)

5. She wasn't sleeping very well. (sleep problems, behavioral)

6. She wasn't eating all that much, either. (hardly eating, behavioral)

Section 3-2 Enrich

Answers will vary depending on the meeting that students attend. As you evaluate students' answers look for indications that they understand the warning signs of stress and ways to reduce stress.

Section 3-2 Quiz

1. a **2.** e **3.** f **4.** b **5.** d

6. false **7.** false **8.** true

9. true **10.** false

Section 3-3 Practice

1. *Sample answer:* I know I'm going to miss this shot. (negative) I have a good chance of making this shot. (positive)

2. *Sample answer:* Everyone will laugh at me. (negative) I know I'll do a good job. (positive)

3. *Sample answer:* I'll flunk this test for sure. (negative) I studied hard, so I'll probably do well on this test. (positive)

4. *Sample answer:* I'll never see my wallet again. (negative) Maybe my wallet is still on the bench. (positive)

Section 3-3 Enrich

1. Students may take the position that teens are more resilient or the position that older adults are more resilient.
2. *Sample answer:* Students may say that older adults are better able to recognize and control their feelings. Or they may argue that teens have a larger support group of family and friends.
3. Answers should use information presented by the opposing debate team.

Section 3-3 Quiz

1. c **2.** f **3.** a **4.** b **5.** e

6. b **7.** c **8.** c **9.** b **10.** d

Section 3-4 Practice

1. *Sample answer*: having to give a class presentation
2. Students' dialogues will vary depending on the situation and coping technique they choose. For example, students' might use their dialogues to explain how to use mental rehearsal as a way to cope with the stress of having to give a class presentation.

Section 3-4 Enrich

1. *Sample answer:* The school guidance counselor could help the brother deal with his concerns about grades and graduation.
2. *Sample answer:* A psychologist could help the teammate deal with her emotional problems.
3. *Sample answer:* Family or social services could help the family deal with its financial problems.

Section 3-4 Quiz

1. false **2.** false **3.** true

4. true **5.** false

6. c **7.** b **8.** a **9.** b **10.** c

Chapter 3 Test

1. d **2.** a **3.** d **4.** c **5.** a

6. true **7.** true **8.** false **9.** true

10. e **11.** c **12.** f **13.** a **14.** b

15. stressor **16.** exhaustion

17. assess **18.** tension

19. Stress can trigger certain illnesses, reduce the body's ability to fight an illness, and make some diseases harder to control. Students may mention how prolonged stress can increase the risk of developing a cold.

20. Building resilience is important because it helps a person deal with extreme or prolonged stress. Accept any of the ways to build resilience described on page 75 of the Student Edition.

Chapter 4

Personal Inventory

Assure students that you will not be collecting the completed Personal Inventory.

Section 4-1 Practice

1. compulsion
2. personality
3. depression
4. anxiety
5. phobia
6. mood
7. schizophrenia

Section 4-1 Enrich

Students should offer carefully reasoned and well-supported arguments.

Section 4-1 Quiz

1. c **2.** d **3.** d **4.** a **5.** a
6. c **7.** d **8.** e **9.** a **10.** b

Section 4-2 Practice

Sample answers:

Define the problem: I think that my friend has bulimia, but I am not sure. I need to figure out how to help my friend.

Explore the alternatives and Consider the consequences: If I ignore the problem, my friend cannot get angry at me, but I may have left my friend with a serious problem. If I talk to a trusted adult, my friend may get the help he or she needs, but my friend may be angry. If I talk to my friend, my friend may realize that there is a serious problem, but he or she may respond by hiding the problem from me.

Identify your values: I have to balance my loyalty to my friend with my concern for my friend's well-being.

Decide and act: I have decided to talk to a trusted adult about my friend.

Evaluate the results: Although my friend was initially upset that I discussed the problem with an adult, my friend is now getting help for the eating disorder and has forgiven me.

Section 4-2 Enrich

Anorexia nervosa: extreme weight loss, has a distorted body image, growth of fine body hair, loss of menstrual periods

Bulimia: visits bathroom right after eating, has cycles of weight loss and gain, hoards or stores food, eats in private

Binge eating disorder: eats large quantities of food, eats even when full, weight gain, uses extreme diets that promise rapid weight loss

Section 4-2 Quiz

1. a **2.** c **3.** b **4.** b **5.** c
6. a **7.** b **8.** b **9.** a **10.** d

Section 4-3 Practice

Sample answers:

1. A family history of suicide; having both a mental disorder and a substance abuse disorder; a feeling of hopelessness or isolation; lack of access to mental health treatment; being influenced by the suicide of a family member, peer, or celebrity
2. Receiving treatment for mental disorders, especially depression; receiving treatment for substance abuse; feeling connected to school; having close relationships; personal beliefs that discourage suicide; knowing non-violent ways to resolve conflicts
3. I would try to convince my friend to talk with a counselor or other adult. If my friend refuses, and my instincts say to take the threat seriously, I would share my concerns with an adult.
4. I would express concern and keep my friend on the phone while I used another form of communication to notify an adult.
5. I would not leave my friend alone. I would not try to reason or argue with my friend.

Section 4-3 Enrich

Radio announcements should present some information from page 96 of the Student Edition in a way that will draw attention to the problem.

Section 4-3 Quiz

1. true **2.** true **3.** false

4. true **5.** false **6.** false

7. a **8.** a **9.** d **10.** c

Section 4-4 Practice

Role-plays should demonstrate that students understand a barrier to treatment. Depending on the barrier chosen, students might express concern about behaviors they have observed, stress the need for treatment of all disorders, both mental and physical, or provide some information about available services.

Section 4-4 Enrich

Answers will vary based on the agency. (You might want to show students a wallet card for another type of service such as the emergency roadside services offered for automobiles.)

Section 4-4 Quiz

1. c **2.** b **3.** a **4.** c

5. false **6.** true **7.** false **8.** true

9. true **10.** false

Chapter 4 Test

1. a **2.** c **3.** b **4.** c

5. b **6.** a **7.** c **8.** d

9. true **10.** false **11.** true **12.** false

13. false **14.** false

15. schizophrenia

16. panic attack

17. anorexia nervosa

18. cluster suicides

19. *Sample answer:* An individual with bipolar disorder experiences periods of deep depression followed by periods of extreme restlessness and activity. The person may start a task with enthusiasm in a manic period and abandon the task abruptly during a period of depression. The person may make poor decisions during both periods of extreme emotion.

20. *Sample answer:* Miguel has probably gained weight, which increases his risk for physical illnesses such as diabetes and disorders such as high blood pressure. Miguel's emotional health has also probably suffered; he may feel guilty, ashamed, or depressed.

Chapter 5

Personal Inventory

Assure students that you will not be collecting the completed Personal Inventory.

Section 5-1 Practice

Across

3. divorce **4.** single parent

6. blended **7.** extended

Down

1. adoption **2.** foster

4. socialization **5.** nuclear

Section 5-1 Enrich

If students live in a situation where many people are responsible for chores, suggest that they choose four people to interview. Remind students that they will not have to share any private information about their families. After students complete the activity, ask volunteers to share their proposals and explain their decisions. Ask all students what they learned in general from this activity.

Section 5-1 Quiz

1. c **2.** b **3.** d **4.** c

5. false **6.** false **7.** true **8.** false

9. true **10.** true

Section 5-2 Practice

Role-plays will vary but should reflect the advice given in Figure 5-5 of the Student Edition. For example, Student 1 should be discouraged from feeling guilty about the divorce and encouraged to continue his or her participation in activities such as drama club.

Section 5-2 Enrich

1. The number of acticles will vary.

2. Students' reactions to the number of reports will vary depending on their expectations.

3. The causes may not be explicitly stated in the articles, but students may be abe to infer factors such as drug abuse, financial problems, or jealously.

4. Articles may suggest a need for more family counseling or parenting classes. They may also call for early intervention by law enforcement and social services.

5. Many incidents occur without anyone outside of the family being aware of the violence.

6. Check that the organizations chosen are likely to offer services to victims of family violence.

Section 5-2 Quiz

1. d **2.** a **3.** b **4.** c

5. true **6.** false **7.** true **8.** false

9. true **10.** true

Section 5-3 Practice

Sample answers:

Respect and Appreciation

1. thanking your father for cooking dinner

2. congratulating your sister on getting good grades

3. praising your brother for respecting your privacy

Empathy

1. saying how sorry you are when your sister's pet dies

2. helping your mother with chores when she is stressed about her job

3. spending extra time with your grandmother when she is feeling lonely

Communication

1. offering constructive suggestions when your brother complains about his homework

2. letting a parent know when you are upset about something that happened at school

3. expressing your disagreement with a rule in a calm and respectful manner

Cooperation

1. offering to do your sister's chores when she has a school project
2. walking the dog without having to be reminded
3. helping your mother cook dinner and wash the dishes

Section 5-3 Enrich

Sample answer: Points supporting the mother's viewpoint: her responsibility as a parent to set limits, not the first violation, no phone call, and her previous verbal warnings. Points supporting Edgar's viewpoint: tried to get home on time, no chance to explain the circumstances, and a major escalation in punishment from the previous verbal warning. Edgar's mother could reduce the punishment if Edgar can explain how he will avoid similar lapses in the future.

Section 5-3 Quiz

1. c **2.** d **3.** c **4.** a **5.** d

6. c **7.** a **8.** e **9.** b **10.** d

Chapter 5 Test

1. c **2.** a **3.** d **4.** b **5.** b

6. b **7.** d **8.** a **9.** c

10. false **11.** true **12.** false

13. true **14.** true

15. siblings **16.** socialization

17. neglect **18.** runaway

19. More women have entered the workforce, which has affected the amount of time families spend together. The high divorce rate has contributed to an increased number of single-parent and blended families. Postponement of marriage has caused family size to decline.

20. *Sample answer:* Adults are stressed by financial problems because they need to provide for the basic needs of their children. Teens may be worried about being able to go to college or being able to have things that their friends have. Teens whose families are experiencing financial problems could find a part-time job to contribute to the family income. They could also reduce the stress on adults by asking for fewer things.

Chapter 6

Personal Inventory

Assure students that you will not be collecting the completed Personal Inventory.

Section 6-1 Practice

1. aggressive; insults and blames the other person; *sample rewrite*: We all need to practice more if we want to win a relay.
2. passive; too critical of oneself; *sample rewrite*: If you practice a duet with me, it would help me improve my playing.
3. assertive; acknowledges the other person's failure to participate in a respectful way and offfers the person a second chance
4. passive; giving in without expressing a preference; *sample rewrite*: I would really like to see the new movie at the mall, but I am open to other suggestions.
5. aggressive; makes fun of the other person's feelings; *sample rewrite*: I'm sorry you didn't get the part in the play. I know how much it meant to you.

Section 6-1 Enrich

1. *Sample answer:* Describe a situation that requires cooperation, such as cleaning up a shared bedroom, and one that requires compromise, such as deciding what game to play. Then ask students what they would do in each situation, to find out what they know about cooperation and compromise.
2. The activities should require the students to practice cooperation and compromise.
3. *Sample answer:* Have students explain the terms *cooperation* and *compromise* in their own words.
4. *Sample answer:* Return to the situations that were used to introduce the lesson to find out what students have learned.

Section 6-1 Quiz

1. c **2.** d **3.** a
4. false **5.** true **6.** false **7.** true
8. true **9.** false **10.** true

Section 6-2 Practice

Friendships are based on: mutual trust, acceptance, common interests or values

Qualities of close friends: loyalty, honesty, empathy, reliability

Problems in friendships: envy, jealousy, cruelty, cliques

Sample answer: Active listening can be used to solve a problem in a friendship.

Section 6-2 Enrich

Possible positive aspects include a sense of belonging, an opportunity to develop social skills, validation of one's values or interests, and the attention of people who are not in the clique. Possible negative aspects include the pressure to conform to group expectations, lack of exposure to other cultures, and not being encouraged to think independently.

Section 6-2 Quiz

1. d **2.** a **3.** b **4.** e **5.** a
6. b **7.** a **8.** d **9.** c **10.** a

Section 6-3 Practice

Accept any reasonable answers that show an understanding of the stages in the cycle of violence. Students' answers will likely mirror the examples supplied in Figure 9 on page 150 of the Student Edition, for example, threatening to break up for tension-building, destroying a favorite possession for violent episode, and promising never to do it again for calm.

Section 6-3 Enrich

1. *Sample answer:* The abused person may need emotional support or protection from an abuser.

2. *Sample answer:* If you know what resources are available, you can share this information with others if you think they need help.

3. If someone you are dating gets jealous when you talk to others, makes fun of you in front of others, is overly controlling, has a history of bad relationships, tries to isolate you from family and friends, and makes you feel less confident, these are warning signs of abuse.

Section 6-3 Quiz

1. true **2.** false **3.** false

4. true **5.** true

6. a **7.** c **8.** b **9.** c **10.** a

Section 6-4 Practice

Sample answers:

1. Setting clear limits requires teens to make decisions. The "Consider the consequences" and "Identify your values" steps of the DECIDE process are very useful in this situation.
2. Using "I" messages and active listening skills can help teens clearly communicate their limits.
3. Teens can use the "Explore the alternatives" step of the DECIDE process to help avoid high-pressure situations.
4. Besides using an assertive communication style, teens should use appropriate body language.

Section 6-4 Enrich

Assure students that they can keep their responses to this Enrich activity private. Encourage volunteers to share what they learned from the activity.

Section 6-4 Quiz

1. c **2.** b **3.** a **4.** d

5. true **6.** true **7.** false

8. true **9.** true **10.** false

Chapter 6 Test

1. c **2.** d **3.** c **4.** b **5.** c

6. d **7.** a **8.** b

9. cooperation

10. compromise

11. clique

12. dating violence

13. emotional intimacy

14. false **15.** true **16.** false

17. true **18.** true

19. *Sample answer:* I am disappointed that you didn't do your part of the group project because it will affect my grade. "I" messages are effective because they clearly state your feelings or needs without putting the listener on the defensive.

20. *Sample answer:* One advantage is that it provides a chance to get to know someone well; one disadvantage is that it can lead to pressure for sexual intimacy.

Chapter 7

Personal Inventory

Assure students that you will not be collecting the completed Personal Inventory.

After students complete the inventory, tell them that mostly **a** answers indicates a tendency to react to anger with violence, Mostly **b** answers indicates a tendency not to express anger. Mostly **c** answers indicates a tendency to respond to anger with words.

Section 7-1 Practice

Sample answers:

Poverty: Industries, community colleges, and government agencies could design and fund apprentice programs for low-income adults.

Family Violence: Provide counseling for children who are victims or observers of family violence.

Media Violence: Provide engaging afternoon and evening activities at neighborhood centers as an alternative to watching television.

Availability of Weapons: Design handguns that are unlocked by a thumb print and require gun owners to be licensed.

Drug Abuse: Reduce the time a drug abuser must wait to get into a treatment program by increasing the number of programs.

Membership in gangs: Establish partnerships between ex-gang members, police, and social workers.

Section 7-1 Enrich

Violent acts might include verbal threats, nonfatal use of physical force, homicides, sexual abuse, and suicides.

Section 7-1 Quiz

1. b **2.** d **3.** a **4.** d **5.** b
6. d **7.** c **8.** a **9.** b **10.** f

Section 7-2 Practice

1. hate violence
2. hazing
3. cyber bullying
4. prejudice
5. harassment
6. intolerance
7. bullying
8. stereotype
9. discrimination
10. vandalism: intentionally damaging or destroying another person's property

Section 7-2 Enrich

Each student should provide at least one more argument for each side of the issue. These arguments might come from their experiences, from research, or from conversations with friends and family.

Section 7-2 Quiz

1. c **2.** e **3.** f **4.** a **5.** d
6. b **7.** a **8.** c **9.** b **10.** c

Section 7-3 Practice

1. As causes, students might cite anger and embarrassment on the part of Marcus and pride and envy on the part of Brendan. To avoid a fight, Marcus could learn to ignore Brendon's comments or use humor to defuse the situation.

2. As causes, students might cite anger and peer pressure on the part of Ashante. To avoid a fight, Ashante could ignore her friends and talk with Teresa privately in a calm way.

3. As causes, students should cite anger and revenge on the part of Derek. If Derek allows himself time to calm down, he might choose to ignore the incident.

Section 7-3 Enrich

If you think students will be uncomfortable asking questions during class, provide a box where they can submit additional questions in advance.

Section 7-3 Quiz

1. true **2.** true **3.** true

4. false **5.** true

6. c **7.** b **8.** a **9.** d **10.** b

Section 7-4 Practice

Students' role-plays will vary. A good role-play will reflect an understanding of one of the two approaches for preventing a fight discussed in the text—ignoring the conflict or confronting the person wisely.

Section 7-4 Enrich

If students do not have older relatives or relatives who would provide healthful advice, allow students to interview any older adults that they trust or admire.

Section 7-4 Quiz

1. d **2.** d **3.** c **4.** b **5.** c

6. false **7.** false **8.** true

9. true **10.** false

Chapter 7 Test

1. b **2.** b **3.** d **4.** a **5.** c

6. true **7.** false **8.** true

9. false **10.** true

11. c **12.** d **13.** f **14.** e **15.** a

16. homicide

17. intolerance

18. mediation

19. poverty, family violence, exposure to media violence, availability of weapons, drug abuse, and membership in gangs

20. You can ignore the conflict or you can confront the person wisely.

Chapter 8

Personal Inventory

Assure students that you will not be collecting the completed Personal Inventory.

Section 8-1 Practice

Across

2. amino acids **4.** fat
6. carb **7.** cholesterol
8. trans **9.** protein

Down

1. saturated **3.** metabolism
4. fiber **5.** nutrient
6. calorie

Section 8-1 Enrich

1. The city dwellers have a more varied diet. Their diet includes fruits, vegetables, grains, meat, and dairy products. The fellahin eat mainly grains, beans, and legumes.

2. Sources of carbohydrates include rice, corn, chickpeas, sugarcane, and beans. These foods provide complex carbohydrates, except for sugarcane, which is a simple carbohydrate. Wealthier fellahin also get carbohydrates from milk products and fruits, which provide simple carbohydrates.

3. Sources of simple carbohydrates: fruit, laban, root beer. Sources of complex carbohydrates: beans, rice, onions, vegetables.

4. Sources of protein: rice, beans, chickpeas, corn. These protein sources are all incomplete.

5. The fellahin probably get all the essential amino acids because they combine different incomplete protein sources to form complementary protein combinations.

6. Sources of protein: sardines, eggs, beans, rice, lamb, pigeon, fish, poultry, yogurt. These protein sources are complete, except for the rice and beans.

7. The city dwellers get all the essential amino acids because they have a number of complete protein sources in their diet.

Section 8-1 Quiz

1. true **2.** true **3.** false
4. false **5.** false
6. e **7.** b **8.** f **9.** a **10.** c

Section 8-2 Practice

The seven essential minerals needed in significant amounts are calcium, phosphorus, magnesium, sodium, chlorine, potassium, and sulfur. Refer to the table in Figure 11 for the main functions and good sources of each mineral. Students should select foods from the same food categories as the sources listed for each mineral.

Section 8-2 Enrich

6. Students' completed charts will differ depending on the brands they chose to compare.

7. Students' choice of brands should be consistent with the data given in their tables.

Section 8-2 Quiz

1. c **2.** d **3.** b **4.** c **5.** a
6. false **7.** true **8.** true
9. true **10.** false

Section 8-3 Practice

Answers will vary. Students should add more high-fiber grains, vegetables, and fruits. They should eliminate or limit sugar, salt, and saturated fats.

Section 8-3 Enrich

Answers will vary depending on the type of food-service location that students investigate. To evaluate students' additional questions, look for an understanding of how nutritional needs vary with age and any health conditions.

Section 8-3 Quiz

1. true **2.** false **3.** false

4. true **5.** false

6. d **7.** c **8.** b **9.** d **10.** a

Chapter 8 Test

1. d **2.** b **3.** e **4.** a **5.** c

6. nutrients **7.** calories

8. fiber **9.** antioxidants

10. nutrient-dense

11. true **12.** false **13.** true

14. false **15.** true

16. b **17.** b **18.** a

19. Nearly all the body's chemical reactions, including those that produce energy and build new tissues, take place in a water solution. Water is also the main component of blood and tissue. Water also carries dissolved waste products out of the body and helps digest foods. Water helps regulate body temperature and contains electrolytes that regulate many cell processes.

20. You should consider age, sex, and activity level to create your own MyPyramid plan. The kind of foods you should eat most of are grains, especially whole grains. The kind of foods you should eat least of are oils.

Chapter 9

Personal Inventory

Assure students that you will not be collecting the completed Personal Inventory.

Section 9-1 Practice

Table:

Calories Cereal A: 100; Cereal B: 220

Total Fat Cereal A: 1%; Cereal B: 7%

Cholesterol Cereal A: 0%; Cereal B: 0%

Sodium Cereal A: 8%; Cereal B: 10%

Dietary Fiber Cereal A: 10%; Cereal B: 17%

Sugars Cereal A: 5 g; Cereal B: 16 g

Protein Cereal A: 2 g; Cereal B: 5 g

Vitamin A Cereal A: 10%; Cereal B: 0%

Vitamin C Cereal A: 100%; Cereal B: 10%

Calcium Cereal A: 100%; Cereal B: 2%

Iron Cereal A: 100%; Cereal B: 25%

1. Cereal A **2.** Cereal A

3. Cereal B **4.** Cereal A

5. Answers may vary. Students may choose Cereal A based on the vitamin and mineral content or the fact that it is lower in calories, fat, sodium, and sugars. Students may choose Cereal B because it contains more fiber and protein.

Section 9-1 Enrich

1. coloring agents: improves appearance

2. sodium benzoate: fruit jelly

3. calcium propionate: bread

4. sodium chloride: flavor enhancer; nearly all products

5. sucrose: nearly all products that are sweetened, plus many canned vegetables

6. aspartame: artificial sweetener

7. gelatin: thickener, stabilizer; ice cream, puddings, cream cheese, chocolate milk

8–10. Answers will vary

Section 9-1 Quiz

1. b **2.** a **3.** b **4.** c **5.** d

6. true **7.** false **8.** false **9.** true **10.** true

Section 9-2 Practice

1. *Sample answer:* Josh should eat small portions and skip the fried foods. He could eat a grilled chicken sandwich, a salad with low-calorie dressing, and a piece of fruit, for example.

2. *Sample answer:* Teresa can eat healthy snacks, such as low-fat yogurt or low-fat cheese and raw vegetables and fruits, when she is pressed for time. She should analyze her schedule to find times when she can exercise.

3. *Sample answer:* Hector should eat larger portions of nutritious foods and include some nutrient-dense snacks in his diet. He should be sure to exercise regularly, too.

4. *Sample answer:* Sophia should avoid fad diets because they exclude important nutrients and the weight loss achieved is usually temporary. Instead, Sophia should avoid high-fat and sugary foods, eat smaller portions, and increase exercise.

Section 9-2 Enrich

Answers will vary depending on students' survey results. As you evaluate students' summaries, look for indications that they understand sensible weight management strategies.

Section 9-2 Quiz

1. c **2.** f **3.** b **4.** e **5.** a

6. b **7.** d **8.** c **9.** d **10.** c

Section 9-3 Practice

1. Diabetics Health Concerns: too much glucose in blood; can be life-threatening. Diet Tips: eat balanced meals on a regular schedule; monitor carbohydrate intake; replace carbohydrates with foods high in unsaturated fats.

2. Vegetarians Health Concerns: getting enough protein and other nutrients. Diet Tips: eat a varied diet; combine foods for complete protein; eat brown rice, beans, corn, nuts, seeds, and whole grains daily; eat foods rich in vitamins and minerals.

3. **People With Food Sensitivities** Health Concerns: food allergies may require emergency treatment; food intolerances may be hard to diagnose and have many symptoms that can make a person uncomfortable. Diet Tips: if a food allergy, avoid foods that are known to cause a reaction; if a food intolerance, eliminate suspected foods until symptoms disappear.

4. **Athletes** Health Concerns: getting enough calories and fluids to sustain increased physical activity. Diet Tips: consume a balanced diet with extra calories in the form of extra complex carbohydrates instead of fat; drink plenty of water during workouts and competition.

Section 9-3 Enrich

1. *Appetizer:* fresh fruit cup or clams on the half shell
Entree: broiled swordfish
Accompaniments: vegetable and salad (with oil and vinegar dressing)
Dessert: fresh melon
Reasons for choices: Jeffrey needs to avoid foods that are high in carbohydrates because they increase the risk of diabetes. Because of his doctor's concern about weight, Jeffrey also should avoid foods that are high in calories.

2. *Appetizer:* fresh fruit cup
Entree: lentil casserole
Accompaniments: whole-wheat bread (without butter) and two of the following: any potato, vegetable, salad (with oil and vinegar dressing)
Dessert: fresh melon
Reasons for choices: Vanessa is a vegan, so she does not eat meat, fish, or dairy products. Mozzarella, ice cream, cheese sauce, and rice pudding are made with milk. The other salad dressings may contain eggs. Her protein needs are met by the lentil casserole and whole-wheat bread. Melon is the best choice for dessert, because the apple pie crust may contain butter and eggs.

3. *Appetizer:* fresh fruit cup
Entree: broiled swordfish or lentil casserole
Accompaniments: two of the following: baked potato (without butter), vegetable, salad (without dressing)
Dessert: fresh melon
Reasons for choices: Cruz should not eat clams because he is allergic to shellfish. Since Cruz wants to lose weight, his meal should be low in fat and calories. The foods chosen avoid extra calories, as they are broiled or baked rather than fried. Cruz should avoid extra salt as well as the hidden calories in salad dressings and butter.

4. Choices will vary depending on dietary needs and personal preferences. Students' reasons should reflect an understanding of nutrition and healthy food choices.

Section 9-3 Quiz

1. b **2.** f **3.** e **4.** a **5.** d
6. d **7.** b **8.** a **9.** c **10.** a

Chapter 9 Test

1. c **2.** d **3.** d **4.** a **5.** c
6. d **7.** g **8.** e **9.** b **10.** a
11. f **12.** false **13.** true **14.** true
15. false
16. nutrient claim
17. Daily Values
18. underweight
19. Any three of the following: the number of calories and how many of those calories are from fat (helps you control how many calories you consume); the amount of saturated fat, trans fat, cholesterol, sodium, carbohydrates, and protein the product contains (you can avoid the food if it is high in these nutrients); the percentage of Daily Values for different nutrients (you can determine if the food is contributing to a balanced diet); ingredients (lets you know what's in the food, including additives)
20. Any two of the following: heredity (there is a link between weight and heredity), level of activity (the more active you are, the more calories you burn), body composition (a measure of body fat compared to muscle and bone)

Chapter 10

Personal Inventory

Assure students that you will not be collecting the completed Personal Inventory.

Section 10-1 Practice

1. Mouth: mechanical digestion begins; enzymes in saliva begin chemical digestion of starch.
2. Esophagus: peristalsis moves foods to the stomach.
3. Stomach: mechanical digestion continues as layers of muscles churn the contents; chemical digestion of proteins begins when pepsin is released.
4. Small intestine: chemical digestion of carbohydrates, fats, and proteins is completed; villi absorbs nutrients into the blood.
5. Liver: produces bile. Bile is released from the gallbladder into the small intestine, where it breaks up large fat droplets.
6. Pancreas: produces enzymes that complete the chemical breakdown of carbohydrates, proteins, and fats in the small intestine.
7. Large intestine: water is reabsorbed, and feces are formed from the waste materials of digestion.

Section 10-1 Enrich

1.a. 8 cubic units

b. 24 square units

c. 3:1

d. 3

2.a. 1 cubic unit

b. 6 square units

c. 6:1

d. 6

3. The cube with 1 unit sides.

4. The chemicals have more area to work on and break down the food.

Section 10-1 Quiz

1. b **2.** c **3.** a **4.** c **5.** a

6. f **7.** d **8.** e **9.** a **10.** c

Section 10-2 Practice

Students' index cards should reflect the information in Figure 4, page 249 of the Student Edition.

Any five: eat plenty of fiber; avoid fatty foods; eat moderately; relax at mealtime; drink water; get regular exercise.

Section 10-2 Enrich

Answers will vary depending on the procedures of the health department students contacted.

Section 10-2 Quiz

1. d **2.** b **3.** d **4.** a **5.** c

6. false **7.** true **8.** true

9. false **10.** true

Section 10-3 Practice

1. excretion **2.** urea

3. kidney **4.** urine

5. nephron **6.** glomerulus

7. dialysis

W Z N A B K Y U T L E
A E E G E O I R Q F D
Y B T H X S P D Y A B
V C U D C T E I N S F
N E P H R O N A R E G
G L O M E R U L U S Y
Q H P I T O J Y R N K
L A M K I D O S E P H
B T T A O U R I A H Z
P U R I N E D S W G F

Section 10-3 Enrich

1. The results indicate that the person has a severe condition of diabetes.

2. Nitrite indicates an infection. You could also examine the urine under a microscope to look for white blood cells.

3. The doctor should check for presence of protein or red blood cells.

4. Students should define *ketones* as a byproduct of fat breakdown. When the body cannot use glucose for energy, fat may be used instead. People with uncontrolled diabetes cannot use glucose for energy. Therefore, ketones are a sign that the body is using fat as an alternative energy source.

Section 10-3 Quiz

1. c **2.** e **3.** f **4.** a **5.** b

6. c **7.** a **8.** d **9.** b **10.** a

Chapter 10 Test

1. c **2.** b **3.** a **4.** d **5.** c

6. b **7.** f **8.** a **9.** g **10.** e

11. true **12.** true **13.** false **14.** true

15. liver; kidneys

16. mechanical; chemical (either order)

17. peristalsis

18. pepsin; hydrochloric acid

19. *Sample answer:* Four simple precautions you can take are cook, separate, chill, and clean. Cook: It is important to cook all foods thoroughly. Separate: Keep uncooked foods separated. Chill: Quickly refrigerate leftovers. Keep cold foods cold. Clean: Wash hands after handling uncooked meats. Use paper towels for cleaning rather than sponges.

20. Lungs remove carbon dioxide and some water during exhalation. Sweat glands in the skin excrete water and urea in perspiration. The liver changes impurities and poisons into less harmful substances. Some of these substances become a part of bile, and are eliminated in stool.

Chapter 11

Personal Inventory

Assure students that you will not be collecting the completed Personal Inventory.

Section 11-1 Practice

1. whether or not to tell the coach about my injury
2. Answers will vary. Possible solutions and their consequences include the following: Do not tell the coach; get to play in the game; may further injure knee or not play well. Tell the coach; knee will heal, may get to play a few minutes if pain is not bad, will not let down the team because of not playing well; may not get to play at all. Call the doctor; coach may advise to wear a brace, continue icing and taking pain relievers, and play for a short time in the game; may advise to sit out for the whole game.
3. Answers will vary. Students should give valid reasons for their decisions based on the alternatives and consequences they identified in Question 2.

Section 11-1 Enrich

1. *Possible answers:* fractures, back pain, loss of height, stooped posture, spinal deformities, collapsed vertebrae
2. *Possible answers:* age, being female, family history of osteoporosis, estrogen deficiency, anorexia nervosa, low bone mass, being thin or having a small frame, abnormal menstrual periods; (the following can be controlled by patient) low calcium intake, vitamin D deficiency, inactive lifestyle, cigarette smoking, alcohol abuse
3. *Sample answer:* any eating disorder, female athlete triad
4. *Sample answer:* balanced diet, consume plenty of calcium and vitamin D, exercise regularly, do not smoke, do not abuse alcohol, get regular medical checkups

Section 11-1 Quiz

1. b **2.** e **3.** d **4.** a **5.** c

6. true **7.** true **8.** false

9. true **10.** false

Section 11-2 Practice

1. **a.** skeletal muscle
   b. voluntary because they are consciously controlled
2. **a.** smooth muscle
   b. involuntary because they are not consciously controlled
3. **a.** cardiac muscle
   b. involuntary because they are not consciously controlled
4. Skeletal muscles are used to lift the food, chew it, and swallow it. Smooth muscles help to digest food and move it through the digestive system. Cardiac muscle constantly pumps blood through the body, providing other muscles with the materials they need to function.

Section 11-2 Enrich

Answers will vary depending on the individual with whom students speak. Not all physical therapists will use the same type of treatment for various conditions.

Section 11-2 Quiz

1. false **2.** true **3.** false

4. false **5.** true

6. b **7.** c **8.** d **9.** a **10.** c

Section 11-3 Practice

1. Peripheral **2.** Brain

3. Spinal cord **4.** Sensory

5. Motor **6.** Cerebrum

7. Cerebellum **8.** Brain stem

9. Autonomic **10.** Somatic

Section 11-3 Enrich

Students should argue the side of the issue they are assigned. Answers will vary, but students should either provide facts that support laws requiring bicycle helmets or facts that oppose laws requiring bicycle helmets.

Section 11-3 Quiz

1. c **2.** f **3.** d **4.** b **5.** a

6. b **7.** a **8.** c **9.** c **10.** d

Chapter 11 Test

1. true **2.** false **3.** true

4. false **5.** false

6. c **7.** d **8.** a **9.** b **10.** b

11. d **12.** b **13.** a **14.** c

15. joint **16.** ossification

17. skeletal **18.** cerebellum

19. To maintain the health of the skeletal system you can eat well, exercise, avoid injuries, and get regular medical checkups to help detect skeletal system problems.

20. Sensory neurons pick up the sound of the buzzer and transmit the message to the brain. The brain processes the information about the sound and realizes that the microwave is done cooking. The brain sends a message through the spinal cord to the motor neurons of the somatic nervous system with instructions to walk to the microwave and take the food out.

Chapter 12

Personal Inventory

Assure students that you will not be collecting the completed Personal Inventory.

Section 12-1 Practice

1. Right atrium—The right atrium receives blood from the body that is low in oxygen and high in carbon dioxide.

2. Right ventricle—The right ventricle pumps oxygen-poor blood to the lungs.

3. Aorta—The aorta carries blood from the left ventricle to the body.

4. Left atrium—Oxygen-rich blood is carried from the lungs to the left atrium.

5. Left ventricle—The left ventricle pumps oxygen-rich blood from the heart.

Section 12-1 Enrich

Answers will vary. Students might suggest that a school nurse perform screenings at a high school event that attracts adults, such as a science fair or honors night. Or, local businesses could offer small discounts to people who can verify they recently had their blood pressure screened. Students should also mention how their event will be advertised to the public.

Section 12-1 Quiz

1. d **2.** b **3.** e **4.** a **5.** c

6. true **7.** true **8.** true

9. false **10.** false

Section 12-2 Practice

1. *Sample answer:* I could advise her to eat unprocessed foods and limit her salt intake. I could help her plan meals that are low in saturated fats. I could help her remember to take her medications as prescribed.

2. *Sample answer:* I could reinforce his attempts to stop smoking by telling him about the dangers of tobacco use. I could help him make low-calorie meals that are low in saturated fats. I could provide him with information about atherosclerosis and cholesterol.

3. *Sample answer:* I could explain to him that although he is thin and feels healthy now, his current habits influence his chances of developing cardiovascular disease later. Also, because our parents have cardiovascular disease, our risk is higher.

Section 12-2 Enrich

Family's menus will vary. Heart-healthy meals should include lots of fruits, vegetables, and whole grains. They should include more fish than meats. Any meats included should be lean meats. Beverages should be low-calorie.

Eating heart-healthy meals will reduce your risk of atherosclerosis. Reducing that risk is important because atherosclerosis can lead to a heart attack or stroke.

Section 12-2 Quiz

1. true **2.** true **3.** false

4. true **5.** true

6. c **7.** a **8.** c **9.** a **10.** b

Section 12-3 Practice

1. larger

2. decreases

3. inhale

4. smaller

5. lungs

6. Answers will vary. Students should use their own words to describe inhalation and exhalation.

Section 12-3 Enrich

Public service announcements will vary but should be persuasive, factually correct, and show that students understand the role of triggers in causing asthma attacks.

Section 12-3 Quiz

1. false **2.** false **3.** true

4. true **5.** false

6. b **7.** f **8.** a **9.** d **10.** c

Chapter 12 Test

1. c **2.** d **3.** b **4.** c **5.** d

6. true **7.** true **8.** true

9. true **10.** false

11. d **12.** b **13.** e **14.** a **15.** f

16. hypertension

17. atherosclerosis

18. asthma

19. Three functions of the cardiovascular system are delivering materials to cells, carrying wastes away, and fighting disease.

20. To maintain cardiovascular health, you should exercise regularly; eat a nutrient-rich, balanced diet; and avoid smoking.

Chapter 13

Personal Inventory

Assure students that you will not be collecting the completed Personal Inventory.

Section 13-1 Practice

Excuses for not exercising might include being embarrassed to exercise in front of others and thinking that thin people do not need to exercise. Reasons for exercising should include the physical, psychological, and social benefits of physical activity described in the Student Edition. Groups should use excuses and reasons from their charts to plan their role-plays.

Section 13-1 Enrich

Students' charts and brochures will vary depending on which facilities they included. Check that they included all the information needed to use the facilities.

Section 13-1 Quiz

1. d **2.** c **3.** c **4.** b **5.** b
6. false **7.** true **8.** false
9. false **10.** true

Section 13-2 Practice

The time of exercise for each day should not exceed 45 minutes. Make sure that the plan does not make Marcia susceptible to overtraining. Also, students should include a variety of activities that will improve flexibility and cardiorespiratory endurance.

Section 13-2 Enrich

1. *Sample answer*: Walking, canoeing, bicycling, swimming, and tennis all build cardiorespiratory endurance and muscular endurance. Canoeing, bicycling, and swimming build muscular strength and endurance. Walking, canoeing, swimming, and tennis build flexibility.

2. Students can identify any of the activities they listed for question 1 and describe the fitness components the activities help build.

3. *Sample answer*: I could ask my grandmother if I could join her when she takes walks, and I could ask my uncle to teach me how to play tennis.

Section 13-2 Quiz

1. true **2.** false **3.** true
4. false **5.** true
6. c **7.** d **8.** a **9.** d **10.** c

Section 13-3 Practice

Sample answer: Weight lifting: gloves; make sure you have enough space, don't lift heavy weights without a spotter; no weather considerations. Bicycling: helmet, gloves, reflective material, bell; ride with traffic, follow all traffic rules; don't bike in bad road conditions. Baseball/softball: batting helmet, gloves, protective cup; pay attention to the game; injury can occur on wet fields. Swimming: goggles; be aware of other swimmers and closeness to the wall, pay attention to ocean currents; don't swim during a thunderstorm. Football: helmet, padding, mouthguard, protective cup; pay attention to players around you; injuries more likely on wet fields.

Medical care should be obtained before starting an exercise program or whenever an injury occurs. Proper water intake is important to replace the water lost in sweat. A proper diet that consists of fruits, vegetables, and whole-grain products is important for any activity.

Section 13-3 Enrich

1. Answers will vary based on the ad chosen. Make sure that students understood what the product is for.

2. Answers will vary. Some ads will provide data about the product or testimonials. Some will make claims such as "results in three weeks."

3. Answers will vary. Many ads will show people with "ideal bodies" using the product. This implies, of course, that they have their body shape because they used the product.

4. Answers will vary depending on what type of product is being advertised.

5. Answers will vary. Student ads should mention the importance of physical activity, eating a well-balanced diet, and setting achievable goals.

Section 13-3 Quiz

1. false **2.** false **3.** true

4. true **5.** true

6. b **7.** c **8.** a **9.** a **10.** d

Chapter 13 Test

1. d **2.** c **3.** b **4.** b **5.** c

6. e **7.** f **8.** b **9.** c **10.** a

11. true **12.** true **13.** false

14. true **15.** false

16. mind

17. stretching

18. overtraining

19. The three steps are defining goals, developing a program, and monitoring progress. Defining goals means determining which fitness components need improvement. Developing a program involves selecting and scheduling activities to meet the goals. Monitoring progress means measuring fitness to see if you are getting closer to your goals.

20. Five safety considerations (and examples) are: medical care (getting a checkup before starting an exercise program), safety equipment (wearing a helmet for bicycling), your surroundings (bicycling in well-lit areas), weather considerations (wearing a hat in cold weather), and proper water and food intake (drinking water every 20 minutes during exercise).

Chapter 14

Personal Inventory

Assure students that you will not be collecting the completed Personal Inventory.

Section 14-1 Practice

1. crown **2.** neck

3. root **4.** root canal

5. cementum **6.** enamel

7. dentin **8.** pulp

9. gum

Section 14-1 Enrich

You can integrate a math lesson into this activity. Have the class tally their overall results for adults and teens separately. Then ask them to determine the average response for both age groups.

Section 14-1 Quiz

1. b **2.** b **3.** c **4.** a

5. true **6.** false **7.** true **8.** false

9. false **10.** true

Section 14-2 Practice

1. keratin **2.** eczema

3. dermis **4.** sebaceous gland

5. dermatologist **6.** epidermis

7. pore **8.** melanin

9. follicle **10.** melanoma

11. acne **12.** warts

13. ringworm **14.** dandruff

15. boils

Section 14-2 Enrich

Students' information about various brands of sunscreen will vary. Remind students that unit cost is the cost per fluid ounce or milliliter.

1. Students should choose which product is the best value based on cost and the amount of protection. The cheapest option is not the best value if it does not offer UVA protection.

2. Students may identify factors such as advertisements, packaging, other ingredients or friends' opinions, which influenced their decisions.

3. Answers may vary, but be sure students have a sound reason for their choice.

Section 14-2 Quiz

1. e **2.** b **3.** a **4.** f **5.** c

6. d **7.** b **8.** a **9.** b **10.** c

Section 14-3 Practice

Ear canal: Sound travels through this cavity to the middle ear.

Eardrum: The eardrum vibrates when sound strikes it.

Hammer: It vibrates when the eardrum vibrates.

Anvil: It moves the stirrup when the hammer vibrates.

Stirrup: After being struck by the anvil, the stirrup pushes on the oval window.

Auditory tube: It helps equalize pressure between the middle ear and outer ear.

Oval window: The oval window transfers vibrations from the middle ear to the outer ear.

Cochlea: The cells lining the cochlea transmit information to the brain via the auditory nerve.

Auditory nerve: It carries impulses from the inner ear to the brain.

Semicircular canals: They send information to your brain about the position of your head, which helps you to keep your balance.

Section 14-3 Enrich

Answers will vary depending upon the types of services offered at the school. Students' letters should accurately reflect the services available to students.

Section 14-3 Quiz

1. b **2.** c **3.** a **4.** d **5.** d

6. a **7.** c **8.** b **9.** e **10.** d

Section 14-4 Practice

1. Yes, maintaining a regular schedule helps you get a good night's sleep.

2. If you choose sugary foods or drinks with caffeine in the late afternoon or evening, it can be difficult to get to sleep.

3. Regular exercise can help you get a good night's sleep unless you exercise right before bed. Then it can be difficult to get to sleep.

Tips will vary. Sample tips include: avoid bright lights at night, do not sleep with the television on, avoid all-nighters.

Section 14-4 Enrich

Students should use information from the Student Edition to support their position and arguments for a debate. If desired, you could require them to do additional research to support their argument.

Section 14-4 Quiz

1. b **2.** a **3.** a **4.** d

5. true **6.** false **7.** false

8. a **9.** d **10.** c

Chapter 14 Test

1. a **2.** c **3.** a **4.** b **5.** a

6. a **7.** e **8.** c **9.** d

10. true **11.** false **12.** true

13. true **14.** false

15. orthodontist **16.** optometrist

17. audiologist **18.** dermatologist

19. *Sample answer*: Adequate sleep the night before a test can help you be focused and alert during the test. Because learning and storage of memory also happen during sleep, your brain needs rest to process everthing you studied.

20. *Sample answer:* Plaque that is not removed from teeth forms tartar. Tartar irritates the gums and causes them to pull away from the teeth. If tartar is not removed, this damage can lead to periodontal disease.

Chapter 15

Personal Inventory

Assure students that you will not be collecting the completed Personal Inventory.

Section 15-1 Practice

1. Influences on Tasha include family ("her parents are opposed to it") and peers ("she really wants to fit in and for Yolanda to like her").

2. Influences on Zach include family ("Zach has an uncle and an older brother who are problem drinkers, and Zach is determined not to end up like them") and peers ("most of Zach's friends have started to drink, and they are putting pressure on Zach to join them").

3. Influences on Bryden include the media ("Bryden thinks that the people in beer ads always look self-confident, relaxed, and outgoing").

Answers will vary. *Sample answer:* If I were Tasha in the first example, I would refuse to drink and not worry about what Yolanda thinks. I would be more influenced by my parents than by my peers. I would resist peer influence to drink by finding friends who do not drink.

Section 15-1 Enrich

1. Students may name any of the three advertisements they analyzed on the worksheet.

2. Answers will vary. *Sample answer:* I can infer that advertisements in which young adults look like they are partying and having fun influence me.

3. Answers will vary depending on the advertisements students chose. Students might say the advertisement is misleading because it does not show any risks of drinking alcohol.

4. Answers will vary. Students might say they could resist the influence by reminding themselves that the ads are misleading and by recalling the risks of drinking alcohol.

Section 15-1 Quiz

1. a **2.** d **3.** c **4.** c **5.** d

6. true **7.** false **8.** true

9. false **10.** true

Section 15-2 Practice

Nervous System: Brain activity slows down; coordination becomes impaired; sensations and perception become less clear; reflexes become sluggish.

Cardiovascular System: Heart rate and blood pressure increase; more blood flows to the skin's surface; core body temperature decreases.

Excretory System: Kidneys increase urine production; drinker loses more water from body than usual.

Digestive System: Too much alcohol in the stomach may cause vomiting.

Section 15-2 Enrich

1–3. legal penalties in their state for first through third offenses for a minor who drives under the influence of alcohol

4. insurance premium increases for first through third offenses for a minor who drives under the influence of alcohol

Students' posters should include the legal penalties listed in answers 1–3 and the insurance premium increases listed in answer 4.

Section 15-2 Quiz

1. e **2.** c **3.** f **4.** a **5.** b

6. false **7.** false **8.** true

9. true **10.** true

Section 15-3 Practice

A. 6 **B.** 1 **C.** 8 **D.** 7 **E.** 5

F. 3 **G.** 2 **H.** 9 **I.** 4

The numbers in each column, row, and diagonal should add up to 15.

Section 15-3 Enrich

Reasons why alcohol should be legal might include ease of regulating a legal substance. Reasons why alcohol should not be legal might include risk of addiction for people who use it. There are many other possible reasons on both sides of the issue.

Section 15-3 Quiz

1. e **2.** a **3.** c **4.** b **5.** d

6. b **7.** a **8.** c **9.** a **10.** b

Section 15-4 Practice

Role-plays will vary but should demonstrate how to use refusal skills to turn down alcohol or how to avoid high-pressure situations involving alcohol.

Section 15-4 Enrich

Brochures will vary but should include all the information requested in the worksheet.

Section 15-4 Quiz

1. true **2.** true **3.** false

4. false **5.** true

6. d **7.** b **8.** b **9.** a **10.** a

Chapter 15 Test

1. d **2.** a **3.** b **4.** b **5.** d

6. d **7.** f **8.** b **9.** a **10.** e

11. true **12.** false **13.** false

14. true **15.** true

16. fermentation

17. intoxication

18. dependence

19. Three major factors that influence underage drinking are peers, family, and the media. Examples will vary.

20. Two ways of abstaining from alcohol are to use refusal skills to say *no* to alcohol and to avoid situations where alcohol is present.

Chapter 16

Personal Inventory

Assure students that you will not be collecting the completed Personal Inventory.

Section 16-1 Practice

1. Tanya considered smoking to fit in (friends) but decided not to when she remembered her dad's struggle with quitting (family).
2. Reggie was influenced by tobacco ads (media) to decide to try cigarettes. Reggie has friends who offer him cigarettes, so he is also influenced by friends.
3. Elyse was influenced to quit smoking by the dangers Soledad learned about (media) and by Soledad's support (friends).
4. Farris's parents smoke. He assumed he would smoke too (family). He saw an anti-smoking television show and decided not to smoke (media). He's trying to convince his parents not to smoke (family).

Section 16-1 Enrich

1. Students may or may not have been surprised by the family member's responses. For example, a student might have been surprised by a family member's strong desire to quit using tobacco.
2. Answers may vary. For example, a family member's strong desire to quit using tobacco might influence a student to avoid tobacco.

Section 16-1 Quiz

1. a **2.** b **3.** b **4.** d **5.** d

6. false **7.** true **8.** true

9. true **10.** false

Section 16-2 Practice

Nicotine: an addictive drug in tobacco; speeds up the nervous system and heart

Tar: dark, sticky substance that forms when tobacco burns; paralyzes cilia

Carbon monoxide: colorless, odorless gas produced when things are burned; binds to hemoglobin in red blood cells in place of oxygen

Public service announcements should include definitions of the substances and some of their harmful effects.

Section 16-2 Enrich

Letters will vary but should include several of the dangers caused by the chemicals in tobacco products. Letters should also argue persuasively against tobacco use.

Section 16-2 Quiz

1. d **2.** a **3.** e **4.** f **5.** b

6. a **7.** b **8.** a **9.** c **10.** d

Section 16-3 Practice

Down: 1. chronic **3.** COPD **5.** emphysema

Across: 2. secondhand **4.** leukoplakia **6.** sidestream **7.** mainstream

Section 16-3 Enrich

Arguments in favor of smokers being denied jobs include higher healthcare costs, more illnesses leading to more sick days, smoke breaks may take away from work time, nonsmokers may have to do more work to compensate.

Arguments against smokers being denied jobs include that smoking is not an illegal activity. People have the right to smoke in their own homes. Also, it is not fair to single out smokers because smoking is not the only choice that can lead to a reduction in work productivity.

Section 16-3 Quiz

1. true **2.** false **3.** false

4. true **5.** false

6. d **7.** b **8.** c **9.** d **10.** d

Section 16-4 Practice

Sample answers:

Give a reason for your refusal: I don't want to ruin my chances to play on the basketball team.

Use body language to reinforce what you say: I would shake my head and use my hand to push away the offered cigarette.

Show your concern for others: I know you want to join the team, too, so maybe you shouldn't smoke.

Provide alternatives: Let's go get ice cream after practice.

Take a definite action: I would walk away if the person offering the cigarette would not take *no* for an answer.

Role-plays should incorporate the actions and other responses students listed in the table.

Section 16-4 Enrich

1–2. Answers will vary depending on the resources students chose. The resources are likely to vary in some or all of the factors listed in the table. For example, one resource might be more costly than another but have a better success rate and provide more follow-up support. One resource might offer support groups and counseling and another might offer hypnosis. Students may not be able to find information for all of the factors.

3. Answers will vary depending on which resource they feel will meet the needs of their friend of family member.

Section 16-4 Quiz

1. a **2.** c **3.** c **4.** d **5.** c

6. true **7.** true **8.** true

9. false **10.** true

Chapter 16 Test

1. c **2.** a **3.** b **4.** d **5.** c

6. a **7.** c **8.** b **9.** d **10.** f

11. false **12.** false **13.** true

14. true **15.** false

16. Any three: oral, esophagus, larynx, stomach, pancreas, kidney, bladder, and blood.

17. tar

18. emphysema

19. The effects of substances in tobacco such as nicotine, carbon monoxide, and tar force the cardiovascular system to work harder to deliver oxygen. Eventually the heart and blood vessels suffer damage. Substances in tobacco smoke also increase blood cholesterol, promote atherosclerosis, and increase the blood's tendency to clot. All of these factors are risks for heart attack and stroke.

20. *Any four:* Make a list of reasons why you quit and keep it handy; throw away all tobacco products, ashtrays, and anything else that reminds you of tobacco use; do little things to change your daily routine; tell your family and friends that you have quit so they can support you; avoid being around people who use tobacco; put aside the money you save and reward yourself with a present; exercise or call a friend to take your mind off smoking.

Chapter 17

Personal Inventory

Assure students that you will not be collecting the completed Personal Inventory.

Section 17-1 Practice

Students should label the drawing as in Figure 2 on page 428 of the Student Edition.

1. Brain cells naturally release the chemical dopamine when a person does pleasurable activities. Dopamine travels between brain cells and produces a pleasure signal.

2. Taking an addictive drug causes brain cells to release extra dopamine, and this produces a stronger pleasure signal.

3. Long-term drug use can cause brain cells to lose receptors for dopamine, and this produces a weaker pleasure signal.

Section 17-1 Enrich

1. Aspirin reduces inflammation in the body.

2. Aspirin is used to treat inflammation and many kinds of pain. It is also used to reduce fever and help prevent stroke and heart attack.

3. The most common side effects include gastrointestinal pain, nausea, and bleeding; ringing in the ears; rash; and vertigo.

4. *Sample answer:* Aspirin may cause increased risk of bleeding in people who also take blood-thinning drugs. Aspirin can also increase the effect of medicines used to treat diabetes mellitus, causing dangerously low blood sugar.

5. *Sample answer:* People with asthma should avoid aspirin because it makes their breathing worse. Children and teenagers should not use aspirin for flu or chickenpox because doing so puts them at risk of a serious disease called Reye's syndrome. People who are about to have surgery should not take aspirin because it can interfere with blood clotting.

6. *Sample answer:* Do not take aspirin if you are taking blood-thinning or diabetes mellitus medicine. Do not take aspirin with alcohol. Do not take aspirin if you are under age 18 and have the flu or chickenpox. Do not take aspirin if you have asthma or are pregnant or breastfeeding. Stop taking aspirin if you are going to have surgery. Stop taking aspirin if you develop side effects such as stomach pain, nausea, or ringing in the ears.

Section 17-1 Quiz

1. e **2.** c **3.** d **4.** f **5.** a

6. true **7.** false **8.** true

9. true **10.** false

Section 17-2 Practice

Students should work in small groups on this worksheet. Situations will vary but should involve a teen who has two protective factors against drug abuse, such as strong family bonds and friends who are supportive. Give groups a chance to practice and present their role-plays. Challenge the rest of the class to identify the protective factors demonstrated in the role-plays.

Section 17-2 Enrich

1. The adults interviewed may or may not have had friends or other peers who used drugs.

2. Role models might have included professional athletes, movie actors, parents, or teachers. Role models may or may not have used drugs.

3. Answers may vary. If the adults were teens during the 1960s and 1970s, their views on drug use may have been less negative than if they were teens during earlier or later decades.

4. Respondents are likely to have varied in their attitudes toward drug use as teens. Some may have been strongly opposed to drug use, whereas others may have had less negative attitudes toward drug use.

5. Factors will vary but might have included peer pressure to use drugs, role models that used drugs, or parents who discouraged use of drugs.

6. *Sample answer:* The cultural value of showing respect for elders, including parents, helped to protect me from drug use as a teen. Students' ideas about how factors have changed will depend on the interview responses. Sample answer: There is less peer pressure to use drugs today, and drug use is seen more negatively now than it was when my relative was a teen.

Section 17-2 Quiz

1. a **2.** c **3.** a **4.** b **5.** a

6. true **7.** true **8.** false

9. false **10.** true

Section 17-3 Practice

1. Depressants **2–4.** (*any order*) Barbiturates, CNS depressants, Opiates

5. Stimulants **6–8.** (*any order*) Amphetamines, Methamphetamine, Cocaine

9. Hallucinogens **10–12.** (*any order*) LSD, Psilocybin, PCP

13. Marijuana **14.** Club drugs

15–17. (*any order*) Rohypnol, GHB, Ketamine

18. Inhalants **19.** Anabolic steroids

Section 17-3 Enrich

Students can find the address for editorial correspondence in their local newspaper. For dangers of commonly abused drugs, students can rely only on information in the Student Edition or use additional information from other reliable sources. Letters should be accurate, well organized, and persuasive.

Section 17-3 Quiz

1. d **2.** b **3.** f **4.** a **5.** c

6. c **7.** d **8.** d **9.** b **10.** c

Section 17-4 Practice

1. Corinne used to be fun but has been acting very grouchy; her grades are slipping and she doesn't care; she is neglecting her appearance; she denies there is a problem.

2. Corinne could become addicted to drugs, suffer from dangerous side effects or drug interactions, become involved in other risky activities, or even have a drug overdose, which could be fatal.

3. *Sample answer:* Stacia should tell a trusted adult—such as a parent, teacher, or guidance counselor—about Corinne's problem.

Section 17-4 Enrich

Students' charts will vary depending on the insurance plans they compared. For example, a plan might cover 50 percent of hospitalization costs for a maximum of 50 days, and it might cover 50 percent of the costs of physician visits for a maximum of 30 visits.

1. Students may choose any of the three plans they compared.

2. Criteria may vary but should be reasonable and consistent with students' choices. For example, a student might choose a particular plan because it covers a greater percentage of the cost of treatment. Another student might choose a plan because it pays for longer-term treatment.

Section 17-4 Quiz

1. true **2.** false **3.** true

4. false **5.** false

6. c **7.** a **8.** b **9.** c **10.** a

Chapter 17 Test

1. b **2.** a **3.** c **4.** a **5.** a

6. c **7.** d **8.** e **9.** a **10.** f

11. true **12.** true **13.** false

14. true **15.** false

16. personal **17.** psilocybin **18.** heroin

19. Depressants, such as heroin, slow body functions. They decrease heart and breathing rates and lower blood pressure. Stimulants, such as cocaine, speed up activities of the central nervous system. They increase heart and breathing rates, blood pressure, and alertness.

20. *Sample answer:* You can stay drug free by practicing refusal skills, seeking help when you need it, and getting involved in drug-free activities.

Chapter 18

Personal Inventory

Assure students that you will not be collecting the completed Personal Inventory.

Section 18-1 Practice

Role-plays will vary but should show the following sequence of events: the hypothalamus produces a releasing hormone, which signals the pituitary gland; as a result, the pituitary gland releases a pituitary hormone that stimulates the thyroid gland; in response, the thyroid gland produces thyroid hormone.

Section 18-1 Enrich

1. Hormone replacement is a way of treating endocrine hormone deficiencies. In hormone replacement, patients are given synthetic versions of the hormones to replace the hormones they lack.
2. Children with growth hormone deficiency are injected with synthetic growth hormone during childhood. This results in nearly normal growth rates and adult heights.
3. Predictions may vary but should reflect the knowledge that thyroid hormone regulates the body's overall metabolic rate and calcium levels in the bloodstream. For example, students might predict that not having enough thyroid hormone would slow down your metabolism and make you feel tired.
4. Web sites may vary but should be reliable. Possible symptoms of hypothyroidism include tiredness, weight gain, and cold intolerance, among other possible symptoms.
5. People with thyroid hormone deficiency take synthetic thyroid hormone, usually in the form of a once-daily pill. This reduces or eliminates the symptoms of hypothyroidism.

Section 18-1 Quiz

1. d **2.** d **3.** b **4.** c **5.** b
6. true **7.** true **8.** false
9. true **10.** false

Section 18-2 Practice

1. seminal vesicle, adds fluid that gives sperm energy
2. prostate gland, adds fluid that protects sperm
3. bulbourethral gland, adds fluid that helps protect sperm from acidity
4. epididymis, stores sperm while they mature
5. testis, produces testosterone and sperm
6. vas deferens, transports sperm from epididymis to seminal vesicle
7. penis, delivers sperm to female reproductive tract
8. urethra, transports sperm to outside of body
9. scrotum, holds the testes

Section 18-2 Enrich

Allow students to keep their answers to this activity private if they wish.

1. Students are likely to find that male and female relatives have different attitudes and behaviors relating to health care. *Sample answer*: My male relative goes to the doctor only when he is too sick to go to work. He does not think he needs to get regular medical checkups as long as he feels fine. He does not know anything about testicular self-exams. My female relative goes to the doctor whenever she is sick. She also gets annual Pap smears and mammograms. She knows how to do breast self-exams and does a breast self-exam "most" months.
2. Differences and similarities will vary depending on the interviews.
3. Answers will vary but should show an awareness that getting regular medical checkups and doing self-exams is likely to have a positive effect on one's health.

Section 18-2 Quiz

1. c **2.** a **3.** f **4.** e **5.** b
6. false **7.** false **8.** false
9. true **10.** false

Section 18-3 Practice

Letters will vary but should be persuasive, factually correct, and show that students understand the role of mammograms in detecting cancer early when it is more likely to be curable.

Section 18-3 Enrich

1. Students may name any culture, including African, European, Native American, Middle Eastern, or Asian cultures.

2. Rituals might include the Jewish *bar mitzvah* or *bat mitzvah,* Roman Catholic communion, or Hispanic *quinceañera.*

3. Some rituals, such as the Christian communion, are for both boys and girls. Other rituals, such as the Hispanic *quinceañera* are gender-specific.

4. Answers will vary depending on the rituals, but should include at least some descriptive details about them.

5. Most puberty rituals confer (or mark the age at which people can assume) some of the rights and responsibilities of adulthood. For example, they may be able to participate more fully in certain religious ceremonies after they come of age.

6. Rituals may have changed. For example, the Hispanic ritual of *quinceañera* has become less religious and more social.

Section 18-3 Quiz

1. c **2.** e **3.** f **4.** a **5.** d

6. d **7.** d **8.** b **9.** d **10.** b

Section 18-4 Practice

Traits: dominant trait (widow's peak), two colored squares or one colored square and one white square; recessive trait (smooth hairline), two white squares

Family Tree: Both people with a smooth hairline have two white squares; both people with a widow's peak have one white square and one colored square.

Explanation: The child with a widow's peak had to inherit a recessive gene from the father, and the parent with a widow's peak (the mother) had to pass on a recessive gene to the other child. This is how you know both family members with a widow's peak must have one dominant and one recessive gene.

Section 18-4 Enrich

Letters will vary but should be polite, well-written, and addressed to the nearest chapter of the March of Dimes Birth Defects Foundation. If students select other foundations, make sure the foundations are involved with genetic disorders.

Section 18-4 Quiz

1. false **2.** false **3.** true

4. true **5.** false

6. a **7.** a **8.** a **9.** b **10.** d

Chapter 18 Test

1. c **2.** a **3.** d **4.** b **5.** b

6. c **7.** a **8.** f **9.** b **10.** d

11. true **12.** false **13.** true

14. true **15.** false

16. hypothalamus

17. abstinence

18. mammogram

19. The functions of the male reproductive system are to produce sex hormones, to produce and store sperm, and to deliver sperm to the female reproductive system.

20. On days 1–4, the uterine lining is shed during menstruation. On days 5–13, an egg matures in an ovary, and the uterine lining starts to thicken. On days 14–15, the ovary releases the mature egg during ovulation. On days 16–22, the egg travels through the fallopian tube to the uterus, and the uterine lining continues to thicken. On days 23–28, the egg enters the uterus.

Answer Key

Chapter 19

Personal Inventory

Assure students that you will not be collecting the completed Personal Inventory.

Section 19-1 Practice

1. placenta **2.** wall of uterus

3. amniotic fluid **4.** amniotic sac

5. cervix **6.** umbilical cord

7. vagina

8. The placenta lines part of the wall of the uterus during pregnancy and nourishes the embryo with substances from the mother's blood.

9. The amniotic sac is a fluid-filled bag of thin tissue that develops around the embryo. The fluid inside helps cushion the embryo.

10. The umbilical cord carries nutrients and oxygen from the placenta to the embryo and carries wastes away.

Section 19-1 Enrich

1. Some students may feel that if all parties agree, couples should have the right to hire a surrogate mother. Others may feel that couples should not have the right.

2. Some students will feel that a contract is a legal document that must be honored. Others may feel that because of a unique relationship between the natural mother and her newborn child, the natural mother should be able to change her mind.

3. Responses should include mention of such factors as the circumstances under which the contract was signed, the feelings of all the parties, and the welfare of the child.

4. Some students may feel that surrogate motherhood should be legal because people have the right to make their own decisions in these matters. Others may feel that it should not be legal because of ethical, moral, or religious reasons.

Section 19-1 Quiz

1. a **2.** c **3.** d **4.** b **5.** c

6. true **7.** false **8.** false

9. false **10.** true

Section 19-2 Practice

Role-plays will vary but should advocate for healthful behaviors during pregnancy, using the points discussed in Section 2.

Section 19-2 Enrich

Table

Ultrasound: usually at 16 to 20 weeks; almost routine—more frequent in high-risk pregnancies; depends on the experience of the person reading it, can identify congenital abnormalities; none

Alpha-fetoprotein screen: at 16 to 18 weeks; all women are offered this screen; false positives are common and some abnormalities can go undetected; none

Amniocentesis: at 14 to 16 weeks; women older than 35 years, family history of genetic disorder, previous child has a birth defect; almost 100% accuracy; between 0.5% and 1% risk of miscarriage, uterine infection

Chorionic villus sampling: at 8 to 14 weeks; women older than 35 years, family history of genetic disorder, previous child with a birth defect, earlier screening test indicates a concern; 100% accuracy; between 0.5% and 1% risk of miscarriage, premature birth, early labor, infection, spotting or bleeding

1–2. Answers will vary.

3. Answers will vary. Students might explain that the woman needs none of the tests described in the table because she has no medical or genetic concerns and the results of the alpha-fetoprotein screen are not accurate enough. Others might explain that she needs both an ultrasound and the alpha-fetoprotein screen.

Section 19-2 Quiz

1. b **2.** d **3.** c **4.** a **5.** f
6. b **7.** d **8.** c **9.** a **10.** b

Section 19-3 Practice

Answers should be in this general order:

First stage of birth: 6, 8, 4, 3; Second stage of birth: 10, 1, 9, 7, 2; Third stage of birth: 5

Section 19-3 Enrich

Answers for all questions will vary depending on the individual experiences of the couples during the birth process.

Section 19-3 Quiz

1. b **2.** e **3.** f **4.** a **5.** c
6. c **7.** d **8.** b **9.** c **10.** a

Section 19-4 Practice

Answers will vary, but should include important milestones of mental and physical development for each stage as described in the Student Edition. They should be placed on the time line in chronological order. *Sample answers:*

Birth to 18 months: by 3 or 4 months—baby recognizes parents and siblings, still cries to get what it needs; by 18 months—learns to walk and has baby teeth

18 months to 3 years: child learns to talk, physical coordination improves, plays alongside others

3 years to 6 years: energy is high, communication skills advance, learns to play with others and makes friends

6 years to 12 years: permanent teeth appear, muscles and bones grow, learns higher-level thinking skills; by 10 years—approval of friends is important

Section 19-4 Enrich

1. Answers may include keeping the child safe, following the directions of the parents, telling the parents what happened while they were gone.

2. Skills include first aid and understanding the needs of children. Babysitters can obtain these skills from special training courses or from their parents.

3. Answers may include how long the parents will be gone, telephone numbers where the parents can be reached, emergency numbers, any special needs of the children.

4. *Sample answer:* read the child a book

5. *Sample answer:* Elevate the finger and apply light pressure directly to the injury, apply a pressure bandage, call the parents.

6. Questions and answers will vary.

Many schools offer babysitting courses. The Red Cross offers a babysitting course.

Section 19-4 Quiz

1. false **2.** true **3.** true **4.** false **5.** true
6. c **7.** b **8.** a **9.** a **10.** d

Chapter 19 Test

1. b **2.** d **3.** c **4.** a **5.** b
6. c **7.** a **8.** b **9.** c **10.** d
11. a **12.** a **13.** d
14. pre-adolescence **15.** postpartum
16. trimesters **17.** implantation
18. fraternal

19. Regular checkups throughout pregnancy greatly increase the chances of having a healthy baby.

20. A cesarean section may be necessary if the fetus is too large or is in the wrong position. Premature birth occurs when the baby is born before it has fully developed. Low birthweight babies didn't grow enough before birth. A multiple birth carries greater risk to the mother and babies.

Chapter 20

Personal Inventory

Assure students that you will not be collecting the completed Personal Inventory.

Section 20-1 Practice

1. *Sample answer:* Increased skin oil production is a secondary sex characteristic that occurs in adolescent boys and girls. Oily hair and skin can be managed with good hygiene and health-care products designed for oily skin and hair.
2. *Sample answer:* Not everyone experiences the growth spurt of adolescence at the same time. With time, you will probably be just as tall as your parents. If your height is really a concern to you, maybe you should check with your doctor.
3. *Sample answer:* Clumsiness and growing pains happen during the adolescent growth spurt. Physical activity can help you feel less clumsy. Give yourself some time, and you will find that both of these problems diminish.
4. *Sample answer:* Increased appetite is an effect that growth has on our body. It is normal during adolescence to need extra food to supply energy to fuel your growing body. Be sure, though, to eat nutritious meals and snacks.

Section 20-1 Enrich

1. Answers will vary.
2. Answers will vary.
3. *Sample answer:* The claim that an acne product will improve skin over a 3-week period seems reasonable. The claim that a shampoo will help control oily hair also seems reasonable.
4. *Sample answer:* The claim that a pill can reduce body fat seems fraudulent. A pimple cream that guarantees overnight results is also probably misleading.
5. *Sample answer:* Most of the products were marketed to make teens feel insecure about the physical changes they are experiencing, so they will buy a product in response to this insecurity. For example, an advertisement for a product that claims to increase muscle mass makes late bloomers feel inadequate.

Section 20-1 Quiz

1. adolescence
2. reproductive maturity
3. secondary sex characteristics

4. false **5.** false **6.** true

7. true **8.** false **9.** true

10. false

Section 20-2 Practice

Role-plays will vary, but should portray an adolescent demonstrating responsibility.

Section 20-2 Enrich

Letters to the editor will vary, but should list examples of specific opportunities for teens to demonstrate responsibility in their community.

Section 20-2 Quiz

1. b **2.** d **3.** c **4.** a

5. d **6.** a

7. true **8.** true

9. false **10.** true

Section 20-3 Practice

Students' goals will vary. Responses to the "Steps I can take now" portion of each question should reflect short-term actions that can contribute to the stated long-term goal.

Section 20-3 Enrich

Stories will vary.

1. *Sample answer:* Both my grandfather and I excel at math, but struggle with athletics.
2. *Sample answer:* My grandmother did not have the option to go to college; attending college is one of my goals.

Section 20-3 Quiz

1. false **2.** true **3.** false
4. true **5.** false

6. c **7.** a **8.** a **9.** d **10.** d

Section 20-4 Practice

1. *Sample answers:* What did you enjoy doing with your grandmother? What were some of your grandmother's hobbies? What is your favorite memory of your grandmother?

2. *Sample answers:* What can I do to help? Would you like me to watch your children as you prepare for the funeral? Could I run to the grocery store for you?

3. *Sample answers:* Can I help you keep up with your school work? If I take notes in lab, would you like to meet to discuss them? Could I drop by to see if you need any help?

4. *Sample answers:* You seem so sad, do you want to talk? Could I go with you to the guidance counselor? Do you want to come over to study with me?

Section 20-4 Enrich

1. Paragraphs will vary, but should note that all the quotes express the idea that a healthy way to manage grief is to discuss your thoughts and feelings. Applications may include strategies for managing personal grief or helping grieving friends to talk about their loss.

2. Answers will vary.

Section 20-4 Quiz

1. d **2.** b **3.** a **4.** c **5.** e
6. false **7.** true **8.** true
9. false **10.** true

Chapter 20 Test

1. c **2.** d **3.** a **4.** b **5.** c
6. e **7.** b **8.** c **9.** f **10.** d
11. false **12.** true **13.** true
14. false **15.** true

16. autonomy

17. compatibility

18. hospice

19. During adolescence, the ability to think abstractly, or consider ideas that are not concrete, increases. The ability to reason, or to weigh the pros and cons of a situation, increases. Many adolescents have trouble with the ability to control impulses, which are quick reactions to emotions. Impulse control improves over time.

20. Establishing healthy habits as a young person can reduce or delay some of the physical signs of aging. For example, consuming sufficient quantities of calcium as a teen can help reduce the likelihood of developing osteoporosis later in life.

Chapter 21

Personal Inventory

Assure students that you will not be collecting the completed Personal Inventory.

Section 21-1 Practice

1. 16
2. People with a cold should avoid direct contact with others. They should cover their mouths when coughing or sneezing.

Section 21-1 Enrich

Assure students that you will not be collecting the completed worksheet. This activity will help students and their families consider whether to change practices to make the kitchen a safer place.

Section 21-1 Quiz

1. d **2.** e **3.** b **4.** a **5.** f
6. true **7.** false **8.** true
9. true **10.** false

Section 21-2 Practice

Answers may vary somewhat. The following are possible answers, in the order of the listing in the chart.

P & C—mucus traps and attacks pathogens; saliva and tears wash away and attack pathogens

P & C—chemicals kill many pathogens; normal motions move pathogens out of the body

INF—phagocytes engulf and kill pathogens; inflammation process heals the damage

IMM—T cells destroy infected body cells; B cells produce antibodies that keep the pathogen or toxin from harming the body

IMM—active immunity: B cells and T cells remember the virus; quick attack prevents disease

IMM—active immunity as a result of immunization: antibodies attack the pathogen and prevent disease

IMM—passive immunity: injections of rabies antibodies prevent disease

Section 21-2 Enrich

Benefits and risks of required immunizations will vary. The following are some sample answers.

Benefits of required immunizations:

1. Immunizations prevent children from becoming ill, becoming disabled, or even dying with a serious disease.
2. Immunizations prevent the whole student population at school from being exposed to a child who becomes infected with a serious disease.

Risks of required immunizations:

1. Immunizations may not always be effective in protecting against disease.
2. Some people believe there is evidence that some vaccines can cause serious problems in children, such as autism.

Risk-benefit analysis:
Sample answer: The benefits far outweigh the risks.

Section 21-2 Quiz

1. c **2.** f **3.** a **4.** d **5.** b
6. c **7.** d **8.** a **9.** a **10.** b

Section 21-3 Practice

1. *Sample answer:* She should stay home from school so that she does not become more ill or spread the disease to others.
2. He can suggest that his grandmother receive an influenza vaccine.
3. He can get the hepatitis A vaccine, drink bottled water, and eat only well-cooked foods.
4. He should prevent spreading strep throat by avoiding contact with other people and by covering his mouth when he coughs. He can treat the problem by taking an antibiotic prescribed by his doctor.
5. Tuberculosis is a highly contagious bacterial infection of the lungs. It is transmitted when droplets from an infected person's cough or sneeze are inhaled.

6. You could avoid close contact with people who are ill. You could also wash your hands several times a day. In addition, you could make sure you eat well-balanced meals and get plenty of sleep at night.

Section 21-3 Enrich

Answers will vary according to the disease that a student chooses to research. Students should cite the names of reliable books or Web sites and be able to provide a source for any fact recorded about a disease.

Section 21-3 Quiz

1. a **2.** a **3.** d **4.** d **5.** b

6. true **7.** true **8.** false

9. true **10.** false

Section 21-4 Practice

Students should circle the sentence that describes close contact between humans and infected animals and the sentence about international travel.

1. Symptoms include a high fever, headache, body aches, a dry cough, and pneumonia.
2. SARS is spread by close person-to-person contact. When an infected person coughs or sneezes, infected droplets spread through the air and can be breathed in by others or can also contaminate objects.
3. The first contributing factor was close contact between humans and infected animals. Investigators discovered that the virus is widespread both in a wild mammal called a civet as well as in a type of bat. Both of these animals were sold for food at markets in China.
4. The second contributing factor was international travel. International travel spread the disease from China to other countries.

Section 21-4 Enrich

Plans will vary. The following are sample answers.

1. Groups of people should be given vaccines in this order of priority: the elderly, children, people with weakened immune systems, medical professionals, police officers, and fire fighters.
2. The major hospitals of the community can be designated as places where people can go to get treatment.
3. The mayor of the largest city should be in charge.
4. If the disease is very contagious, people may have to be quarantined to protect people in the community who have not contracted the disease.
5. There is probably no practical way of keeping people from traveling to the community.
6. Answers may vary. Students might suggest controlling animals that spread certain diseases.

Section 21-4 Quiz

1. false **2.** true **3.** true

4. true **5.** false

6. b **7.** a **8.** c **9.** b **10.** d

Chapter 21 Test

1. c **2.** b **3.** a **4.** c **5.** b

6. true **7.** false **8.** true

9. true **10.** false

11. c **12.** f **13.** a **14.** d **15.** b

16. infectious

17. toxins

18. emerging

19. A vaccine causes a person's immune system to produce antibodies against the pathogen, as if the person had actually been infected.

20. You can avoid contact with pathogens, make sure that your immunizations are current, and choose healthful behaviors.

Chapter 22

Personal Inventory

Assure students that you will not be collecting the completed Personal Inventory. Statements 2, 3, 4, 6, 7, 8, and 9 are false.

Section 22-1 Practice

Step 1. Answers will vary. They may include any questions about STIs and topics based on the questions.

Step 2. Answers will vary but should be relevant to the topic listed in Step 1.

Step 3. Answers will vary but should be relevant to the topic listed in Step 1.

Step 4. Answers will vary but should be relevant to the topic and also reliable and recent (published within the last year or two).

Students may or may not be able to answer their question based on the source listed in Step 4. If they cannot, they might revise their topic or look at different books or magazine articles.

Section 22-1 Enrich

Answers will vary depending on which example students choose to learn about. Their information should be based on reliable sources. Answers should reveal an understanding of the role of education, testing, abstinence, or other healthful behaviors in controlling the spread of STIs. Students should explain how the cultural beliefs and behaviors interfere with one or more of these healthful behaviors.

Section 22-1 Quiz

1. d **2.** a **3.** c **4.** a **5.** b

6. true **7.** true **8.** false

9. false **10.** false

Section 22-2 Practice

1. gonorrhea **2.** herpes

3. chlamydia **4.** papilloma

5. trichomoniasis **6.** syphilis

7. hepatitis

Section 22-2 Enrich

1. Answers will vary depending on the advertisements students select. Sample answers: prevent genital herpes blisters; kill the bacteria that cause chlamydia

2. Side effects might include upset stomach or allergic reactions; or no side effects may be listed in the advertisement.

3. The advertisement may say the product has been tested and shown to be effective; or it may say nothing about testing and make unfounded claims about effectiveness.

4. Costs and availability will vary depending on the products students select.

5–6. Students may or may not recommend the products, depending on their responses to questions 1–4.

7. *Sample answer:* The products might do more harm than good because they might be used instead of medicines with proven effectiveness. If a person thinks he or she might have an STI, a doctor should be consulted before taking any medicine.

Section 22-2 Quiz

1. c **2.** f **3.** a **4.** e **5.** d

6. false **7.** true **8.** false

9. false **10.** false

Section 22-3 Practice

1. AIDS, or acquired immunodeficiency syndrome, is a disease of the immune system that is often fatal.

2. AIDS is caused by HIV, or human immunodeficiency virus. HIV attacks specific cells of the immune system, disabling the body's defenses against other pathogens. When the immune system becomes severely disabled, the infected person has AIDS.

3. HIV is transmitted when infected individuals pass the virus on to someone else through the exchange of blood, semen, vaginal secretions, or breast milk. There are four main ways this can happen: sexual contact, shared needles, contact with blood or other body secretions, and mother to baby.

4. People at greatest risk of HIV infection are people who share needles to inject drugs and people who engage in high-risk sexual behaviors.

5. You can protect yourself from HIV by practicing abstinence, avoiding drugs, and avoiding contact with others' blood and body fluids.

Section 22-3 Enrich

Students should identify as areas of misunderstanding any "agree" statements, because all of the statements are false. Any "undecided" statements are areas where information is lacking. Ways to clear up the misunderstandings and deliver information might include running public service announcements on radio and television and distributing educational pamphlets through doctors' offices and clinics.

Section 22-3 Quiz

1. b **2.** c **3.** a **4.** f **5.** d
6. b **7.** a **8.** c **9.** c **10.** c

Section 22-4 Practice

Situation 1: *Sample answers:* I would question whether Tanya was the right girlfriend for me because she does not seem to respect my decision to remain abstinent. I would tell Tanya to get tested for HIV before I would even consider a sexual relationship.

Situation 2: *Sample answers:* I would seek medical attention right away. I would tell Manuel to get tested for STIs. If he tested positive, I would get tested too because I would also be at risk.

Situation 3: *Sample answers:* I would leave the party because it is safer and more fun to hang out with people who share my decision to avoid drugs. I would refuse the drugs because it wouldn't be worth the risk.

Section 22-4 Enrich

Students can summarize and use in their debate any additional reasonable arguments in favor of mandatory HIV testing (e.g., infected people could be quarantined or otherwise prevented from transmitting the infection) and against mandatory HIV testing (e.g., the information could be used to discriminate against HIV-infected individuals by insurance companies, employers, and others).

Section 22-4 Quiz

1. true **2.** true **3.** false
4. false **5.** false
6. c **7.** c **8.** a **9.** a **10.** c

Chapter 22 Test

1. b **2.** d **3.** d **4.** c **5.** b
6. b **7.** c **8.** a **9.** f **10.** e
11. true **12.** false **13.** false
14. true **15.** false

16. sexually transmitted infection, or STI

17. urethritis **18.** sexual abstinence

19. Risky behaviors that contribute to the spread of STIs include ignoring the risks of sexual activity, having sexual contact with multiple partners, and not getting proper treatment for STIs when necessary.

20. You can protect yourself from HIV infection by practicing sexual abstinence, avoiding drugs, and avoiding contact with others' blood and body fluids.

Chapter 23

Personal Inventory

Assure students that you will not be collecting the completed Personal Inventory.

Section 23-1 Practice

1. hypertension, stress, former cigarette smoker

2. diabetes, stress

3. stress, cigarette smoking, hypertension, being overweight, lack of exercise

4. Answers should reflect students' own risk factors as well as healthy behaviors.

Section 23-1 Enrich

The saturated fat content of products will vary. For each type of product, students should record the grams per serving as well as the percent of recommended daily value for both the regular product and the low-fat product.

1. *Sample answer:* In general, the low-fat foods have less saturated fat than the regular foods. For example, there was little difference in the packages of meat, but there was a big difference in the packages of snack crackers.

2. *Sample answer:* My experience is that the low-fat foods do not taste as good as the regular foods.

Section 23-1 Quiz

1. b **2.** d **3.** a **4.** c **5.** e

6. false **7.** true **8.** true

9. true **10.** false

Section 23-2 Practice

1. oncogene **2.** carcinogen

3. tumor **4.** malignant

5. metastasis **6.** biopsy

7. cancer

Section 23-2 Enrich

1. medical oncologist

2. urologist

3. surgical oncologist

4. pathologist

5. personal physician

6. dermatologist

7. radiation oncologist

8. proctologist

Section 23-2 Quiz

1. true **2.** true **3.** false

4. true **5.** false

6. b **7.** a **8.** b **9.** d **10.** c

Section 23-3 Practice

Students' letters will vary. An excellent letter will describe what type 2 diabetes is, explain what causes the disease, and describe a diet and exercise plan that will help prevent development of the disease. The diet should be low in saturated fats and sugars. The exercise plan should recommend regular, vigorous exercise.

Section 23-3 Enrich

1. Typical symptoms of osteoarthritis include pain in one or several joints. Some people with osteoarthritis have back pain as well.

2. People with osteoarthritis may face any number of problems, from not being able to open cans and bottles to having difficulty walking.

3. Most people with osteoarthritis take painkillers or anti-inflammatory drugs daily.

4. Answers will vary. Swimming or water aerobics might be mentioned. Some people eat foods recommended for arthritis sufferers, including fish such as salmon.

Section 23-3 Quiz

1. false **2.** true **3.** false

4. true **5.** true

6. d **7.** f **8.** b **9.** a **10.** e

Section 23-4 Practice

Role-plays will vary. A typical role-play might involve a "helpful" person who grabs a person's wheelchair without asking. The dialogue may involve the disabled person explaining to the "helper" to wait until asked before helping a person with a disability.

Section 23-4 Enrich

1. A typical business might be a grocery store or a department store.

2. Entrances need to be a certain width to allow people with wheelchairs to enter. There also must be a ramp in place of stairs to at least one entrance.

3. Accommodations might include larger bathroom stalls for people with disabilities.

4. Answers will vary depending on the size of the business and the number of changes that might have been made to an older building.

5. Answers will vary depending on whether the business is in a new or old building.

6. A typical question might be whether the business owner, manager, or head of human resources has noticed people with disabilities using the required accommodations.

Section 23-4 Quiz

1. b **2.** c **3.** a **4.** b **5.** c

6. false **7.** true **8.** true

9. true **10.** false

Chapter 23 Test

1. c **2.** c **3.** a **4.** d **5.** b

6. d **7.** e **8.** a **9.** c **10.** b

11. true **12.** false **13.** true **14.** false **15.** true

16. chronic **17.** metastasis **18.** insulin

19. Managing stress can help keep your blood pressure at a healthy level, which may reduce your risk of developing hypertension and other cardiovascular diseases.

20. They are similar in that both result in a high level of glucose in the blood. They are different in that a person with type 1 diabetes produces little or no insulin, while a person with type 2 diabetes produces sufficient insulin but the person's body cells do not respond normally to insulin.

Chapter 24

Personal Inventory

Assure students that you will not be collecting the completed Personal Inventory.

Section 24-1 Practice

A. 6 **B.** 1 **C.** 8 **D.** 7 **E.** 5

F. 3 **G.** 2 **H.** 9 **I.** 4

The sum is 15.

Section 24-1 Enrich

1. Answers will vary, but should be a legitimate place or agency in the community.
2. Answers will vary, but most nurses complete either a 2-year program or a 4-year program with additional retraining to remain certified in techniques such as CPR.
3. Answers will vary depending on the types of patients the nurse sees.
4. Answers will vary, but should include a brief explanation of the incident or injury.
5. Answers will vary depending on where the nurse works and existing state laws.
6. Answers will vary, but nurses may find it easier to keep track of records and communicate with a doctor and their patients.
7. Answers will vary depending on the opinion of the nurse being interviewed.
8. Answers will vary and will be based on questions that students pose themselves.

Section 24-1 Quiz

1. f **2.** d **3.** c **4.** b **5.** e

6. d **7.** c **8.** a **9.** c **10.** b

Section 24-2 Practice

Role-plays will vary but should include questions that a person might ask to determine whether a doctor is best suited to his or her needs.

Section 24-2 Enrich

1–6. Answers will vary based on the insurance plans students are comparing.

7. Students may decide to choose the higher cost plan because they do not want to change doctors, or because it provides better coverage. Other students may decide to choose the less costly plan.

Section 24-2 Quiz

1. b **2.** d **3.** c **4.** a **5.** c

6. true **7.** false **8.** true

9. false **10.** false

Section 24-3 Practice

1. Food and Drug Administration
2. Occupational Safety and Health Administration
3. Administration for Children and Families
4. Environmental Protection Agency
5. Department of Agriculture
6. Health Resources and Services Administration
7. Substance Abuse and Mental Health Services Administration
8. National Institutes of Health
9. Agency for Healthcare Research and Quality
10. Administration on Aging

Section 24-3 Enrich

1. Answers will vary.
2. Common childhood diseases of people over 60 years old include polio, measles, diphtheria, and pertussis (whooping cough). Common childhood diseases of people 30 to 60 years of age include measles, mumps, rubella (German measles), and chickenpox.
3. Answers will vary.
4. chickenpox, influenza, common cold

5. Most students will have been immunized against measles, mumps, rubella, polio, diphtheria, tetanus, pertussis (whooping cough), varicella (chickenpox), hepatitis B, and *Haemophilus influenzae* type b. Some students may also have been immunized against hepatitis A and meningitis.
6. The immunization program has reduced the occurrence of, and in some cases completely eradicated, infectious childhood diseases.
7. Answers will vary. In many cases, outbreaks occurred because immunity provided by vaccinations decreases over time, leaving individuals more susceptible to the disease. Highly contagious bacteria and viruses cause the risk of infection to increase as greater numbers of people get the disease.

Section 24-3 Quiz

1. f **2.** a **3.** e **4.** b **5.** d
6. d **7.** c **8.** a **9.** c **10.** b

Section 24-4 Practice

United Nations:
World Health Organization—boosts food production, prevents diseases through education and immunization, and collects health statistics; United Nations Children's Fund (UNICEF)—aids children by immunization, day-care, healthcare, school food programs, nurse and teacher training

United States:
The Agency for International Development (USAID)—provides food in famines, funds healthcare programs; Peace Corps—trains volunteers to help improve agriculture, provide healthcare, construct shelters, and improve sanitation and water supplies

Private sponsors:
International Committee of the Red Cross—provides aid to victims on the battlefield and of natural disasters; Oxfam International—provides clean water and sanitation services in disaster areas; the Cooperative for Assistance and Relief Everywhere (CARE) aids refugees and disaster victims

Section 24-4 Enrich

Answers will vary depending on the organization that students choose to research.

Section 24-4 Quiz

1. true **2.** false **3.** false
4. true **5.** false
6. a **7.** c **8.** d **9.** a **10.** c

Chapter 24 Test

1. d **2.** b **3.** c **4.** c **5.** d
6. a **7.** b **8.** f **9.** a **10.** e
11. d **12.** b **13.** c
14. quarantine **15.** diagnosis
16. health codes **17.** inpatient
18. medical history

19. You should consider whether the doctor is in a clinic or in private practice; ask for recommendations from family and friends, as well as the opinion of other healthcare providers; research the doctor's education, areas of specialization, and board certifications; consider your own personal preferences; and consider the doctor's personality and ability to listen to questions and clearly explain medical procedures and diagnoses.

20. International health organizations work in developing nations to overcome public health problems. Developing nations do not have the resources to make their own public health programs succeed. Often, these countries are unable to provide the basic needs for food, water, and medical care.

Chapter 25

Personal Inventory

Assure students that you will not be collecting the completed Personal Inventory.

Section 25-1 Practice

1. Students should write the city name, estimate a total population, and briefly note the main governmental bodies and positions, such as mayor and city council.
2. Students should give a brief description of the main neighborhoods from which students come. They might describe a suburban neighborhood, a section of the city, or various different developments within the city.
3. Students should list aspects they find important, such as friends, after-school clubs, and basketball courts for pick-up games.
4. Students should list important cultural communities within the larger community, such as communities based on heritage and ethnicity.
5. Students might list organizations such as 4-H clubs, Boys and Girls Clubs of America, Boy Scouts, Girl Scouts, and SADD.

Section 25-1 Enrich

1. Students should name two adult members of the cultural community.
2. Students might describe the community in terms of race, ethnicity, or country of origin.
3. Students might mention such values as honesty, respect for elders, and sexual abstinence before marriage.
4. Students might mention special ways of celebrating holidays or coming-of-age rituals.
5. Students might name a religious organization or an organization that advocates for the community, such as the NAACP.
6. Students should describe a dish or two that is traditional in the cultural community, such as tamales in a Mexican American cultural community or fried rice in an Asian cultural community.

Section 25-1 Quiz

1. d **2.** b **3.** c **4.** a **5.** c

6. true **7.** true **8.** true

9. false **10.** true

Section 25-2 Practice

1. When fossil fuels are burned, particles and harmful waste gases are produced and released into the air.
2. *Sample answer:* I could walk, ride a bicycle, or use public transportation instead of riding in an automobile. I could make sure lights and appliances are turned off when they are not being used.
3. *Any five:* fumes from carpets and paint, pesticides, plywood glues, foam insulation, gas stoves, fuel-burning indoor heaters, air fresheners, mold, dust mites, asbestos, radon, tobacco smoke
4. have adequate ventilation; have asbestos removed

Section 25-2 Enrich

1. ground-level ozone, particle pollution, carbon monoxide, sulfur dioxide, nitrogen dioxide
2. Good, green; Moderate, yellow; Unhealthy for Sensitive Groups, orange; Unhealthy, red; Very Unhealthy, purple; Hazardous, maroon
3. The AQI, primary pollutant, and health message for cities will vary from city to city and from day to day. Often, three days in a row will have the same data, though changes in weather can greatly affect these determinations. Students should write a summary of what they have recorded for the three days.

Section 25-2 Quiz

1. c **2.** e **3.** d **4.** a **5.** b

6. b **7.** c **8.** d **9.** a **10.** c

Section 25-3 Practice

1. Conservation

2. Biodegradable

3. landfills

4. Recycling

5. Hazardous

6. sewage

7. runoff

Section 25-3 Enrich

1. Products may include various kinds of paper products, clothing, shoes, construction materials, containers, bags, carpet, and so on.

2. Students should clearly explain why they would buy one product over the other. Most students will choose to buy the product that contains recycled material, because these products are usually as good as other products, may cost less, and help protect the environment.

Section 25-3 Quiz

1. c **2.** a **3.** c **4.** b **5.** d

6. c **7.** a **8.** e **9.** b **10.** d

Section 25-4 Practice

Students' letters will vary. A good letter will be firm but respectful, state the issue clearly, and provide persuasive reasons for a point of view.

Section 25-4 Enrich

1. Items recycled often include various kinds of paper, certain kinds of plastics, glass, and metals.

2. Students might describe residents placing recyclables into a bin that is picked up by a collection company or residents taking recyclables to a recycling center.

3. Answers will vary depending on a location's system. Often, recyclables are taken to a collection center, where they are separated to be sold or sent to companies that use recycled materials.

4. Answers will vary. Cities may make money, despite the collection costs, by selling the recycled materials.

5. Flowcharts will vary depending on the process used in a community. A typical flowchart will begin with residents placing recyclables into a bin, the bin being picked up by a collection company, the recyclables sorted at a collection center, and the materials sold to companies that process recyclables into new products.

Section 25-4 Quiz

1. true **2.** true **3.** false

4. true **5.** true

6. b **7.** d **8.** a **9.** d **10.** a

Chapter 25 Test

1. b **2.** a **3.** c **4.** a **5.** c

6. true **7.** true **8.** false

9. true **10.** false

11. e **12.** d **13.** a **14.** f **15.** c

16. pollution

17. recycling

18. conservation

19. Three solutions are cleaning up waste sites, improving waste management, and conserving natural resources.

20. Three steps are to become informed, to volunteer your time, and to be an advocate.

Chapter 26

Personal Inventory

Assure students that you will not be collecting the completed Personal Inventory.

Section 26-1 Practice

Sample answers:

1. I will not unlock the door or let the stranger into the house. I'll use a phone to call for help.
2. Before getting into the car, I check to make sure no one is hiding in the back seat or on the floor.
3. I do not unlock my car door. I ask the person to call the police for assistance.
4. I step into the nearest business.
5. I don't stop and try to intervene. I use a phone to call the police immediately.
6. I call a friend to walk into the park with me.

Section 26-1 Enrich

Answers will be specific to the local office of the American Red Cross. You might suggest that students learn about the American Red Cross online before they call the local office.

Section 26-1 Quiz

1. b **2.** a **3.** d **4.** b **5.** c

6. c **7.** f **8.** b **9.** a **10.** d

Section 26-2 Practice

Letters will vary but should be persuasive and show that students understand how to apply the four basic guidelines for recreational safety to a specific sport.

Section 26-2 Enrich

1. Students' data will vary.
2. Which helmet students think is the best buy will vary, though safety should be the primary factor in making a choice.

Section 26-2 Quiz

1. c **2.** c **3.** a **4.** b **5.** d

6. true **7.** false **8.** true

9. true **10.** false

Section 26-3 Practice

Role-plays will vary. Some role-plays may demonstrate how unsafe behavior causes the bus to crash. All role-plays should reflect an understanding of the rules that should be followed on a school bus to ensure everyone's safety.

Section 26-3 Enrich

Arguments for and against seat belt laws will vary, though most students will use arguments similar to those given. During the debate, a good presentation on either side will be logical and persuasive.

Section 26-3 Quiz

1. true **2.** true **3.** false

4. false **5.** true

6. c **7.** b **8.** b **9.** a **10.** c

Chapter 26 Test

1. d **2.** a **3.** d **4.** b **5.** c

6. true **7.** false **8.** true

9. false **10.** true

11. e **12.** f **13.** a **14.** b **15.** c

16. rape

17. occupational

18. defensive

19. Answers should include awareness, knowledge, ability, state of mind, and environmental conditions.

20. Learn and apply the proper skills. Have appropriate, well-maintained equipment. Know the safety rules specific to the activity. Prepare adequately for the activity.